The
Lost Gardens of
Glasgow University

A. D. Boney

CHRISTOPHER HELM
London

© 1988 A.D. Boney
Christopher Helm (Publishers) Ltd, Imperial House
21-25 North Street, Bromley, Kent BR1 1SD

ISBN 0-7470-0220-7

A CIP catalogue record for this book
is available from the British library

The publisher acknowledges subsidy from the Scottish Arts
Council towards the publication of this volume.

Typeset by Leaper & Gard Ltd, Bristol, England
Printed and bound in Great Britain by Biddles Ltd, Guildford, Surrey

CONTENTS

For Rosemary

Frontispiece: Slezer's drawing of the College and its Gardens, published in 1693 but probably drawn earlier

PREFACE

On joining the Department of Botany at Glasgow University some 18 years ago I began to find reminders of its history — as only to be expected in an institute which had just commenced its 265th session of teaching botany. The sense of continuity is a real one, especially now (in the 283rd teaching session) when pertinent reminders of our predecessors can be seen in a building housing the modern, sophisticated equipment necessary today for the study of plants. There seemed, however, to be many gaps in our knowledge of Departmental history. One name from the early years of the eighteenth century came to symbolise this lack of information: that of John Marshall, the first Botanist appointed to the staff of the University. Virtually nothing was known of this man, and my starting point was to find out more about the Kilsyth-born 'chirurgeon'. Marshall's particular responsibility was to manage the Physic Garden laid out in the University grounds in 1705–6. It was soon apparent that little was known about this small garden, and in turn that its story could not be separated from that of the University gardens as a whole, especially during the late seventeenth, eighteenth and early nineteenth centuries. Hence this book, which is offered as a further contribution to the history of a great University.

Acknowledgements

My sincere thanks go to Michael Moss, University Archivist, for placing the resources of his Department at my disposal and for his continuing interest and advice; to Dr Derek Dow, Archivist to the Greater Glasgow Health Board, for his help at all times. I thank my colleagues in the Department of Botany for their patience with my occasional historical ramblings. I am especially grateful to Dr J.H.

Dickson for much helpful discussion and, at a time when his paper was in manuscript form, supplying me with information on Mark Jameson's Physic Garden. Mr N. Tait's professional expertise in producing excellent photographs from old prints and manuscripts earns my profound gratitude. My thanks also to Mr E. Curtis, Curator of the Glasgow Botanic Garden, for his help with some of the old Scots horticultural terms. Permission to utilise previously published illustrations is gratefully acknowledged: to Dr J. Durkan for his plan of the medieval University; to Mr Keith Thomas and Allen Lane (Penguin Books) Ltd for the illustration of a 'tree-transplanting machine' from *Man and the Natural World*; and to Professor A.G. Morton and Mr I.C. Hedge, Hon. Secretary of the Edinburgh Botanic Garden (Sibbald) Trust, for the portrait of Professor John Hope and his Principal Gardener. In fairness to the several colleagues who have given me help, I must stress that any errors or misconceptions in this book are mine alone.

My wife Rosemary has patiently borne with the incursion of the Old University gardens into our lives for some three years now, and yet was still willing to cope with the difficult task of typing the manuscript from my much-corrected drafts. Her constant support has made this book possible.

INTRODUCTION

The 29 July 1870: a significant date in the long history of Glasgow University. The day on which the Principal and 25 professors constituting the Senate assembled on the 1690 Lion and Unicorn Stair for a group photograph headed by the Bedellus carrying the silver gilt and enamelled fifteenth-century mace. That same evening, the Senate, the University Court, representatives of the General Council and friends of the University dined in the Fore Hall for the last time. Professor John Caird took the chair in the absence of the Principal and proposed the toast 'The Memory of the Old College'. More toasts followed, ending with the circulation of the Loving Cup, each recipient as he drank reciting '*Resurgat in Gloria, Alma Mater*'. Finally all present joined in singing 'For Auld Lang Syne'. The next day the Senate vacated the 'Old College' and handed over the buildings and grounds to the purchasers, the City of Glasgow Union Railway Company. Thereby took place a final severing of the principal link with the medieval University, a link extending over some 400 years. More of ancient Glasgow had to give way to Victorian progress.

The students had left at the end of the teaching session in the previous April. They marked the occasion the following 7 November, at the commencement of the next academic session, by organising a torchlight procession from the Old College to the new University buildings on Gilmorehill in the west of the city. As the city boundary ended a few hundred yards from the Gilmorehill site, the police escort to the procession here withdrew. The continuing procession and subsequent events around a ceremonial bonfire on the site of the new buildings became the scene of a violent confrontation between the students and what one University historian has called the 'town roughs'[1] — a town-and-gown affair which seems to have been a bruising event for both sides. The celebratory bonfire started by the students with their torches was supplemented by the 'roughs' with

1

wood from the buildings and with student hats; the battle raged until the bonfire died down.

Whilst the move to new buildings on open land in the west of the city was no doubt made with some element of sorrow, it seems to have been inevitable. The city's environment, and especially that of the University (or 'Glasgow College'), was vastly different from that of the small but attractive town with its wide streets and gardens which were so much admired by travellers from England in the seventeenth and eighteenth centuries. The eighteenth-century University possessed attractive buildings with extensive and beautiful gardens to the rear, including a small physic garden, which were then at their best. With the passage of time the surroundings became increasingly less salubrious. In 1846, the Royal Assent was given to an Act enabling the University to exchange buildings for a new College on more open land in the west of the city, to be built in exchange for the medieval site by the Glasgow, Airdrie and Monklands Railway Company. This plan came to nothing. The state of affairs in the mid-nineteenth century was ably summarised in an appendix to the Scottish Universities Commission Report of 1858, dealing with the condition of the buildings at Glasgow:

'... the localities around the College have been filled up by a dense mass of the lowest class of labouring population, with a considerable admixture of much more unsuitable neighbours, and a large proportion of chemical and other nuisance creating manufactories of the city. The College is, in consequence, surrounded with an atmosphere impregnated with the effluvia and filth occasioned by such a population, in a town in which the sewerage is far from being in a satisfactory condition, and with fumes and vapours of the aforesaid chemical and other manufactories, than which it is hardly possible to conceive a combination of circumstances less favourable to the bodily and mental well being of the youth attending the University, or less suitable for conducting the business of a public seminary of instruction.'

The Commission's Report gave a brief word picture of the College's environment in which the houses were dilapidated and overcrowded and the wynds (narrow streets or lanes) filthy. Close to the north wall of the University grounds were the Havannah and Vennel slums, the haunts of rag-dealers, thieves, receivers of stolen goods and prostitutes. This Dickensian state of affairs and the moral temptations placed before the students were key features of the Report and no doubt hastened the decisions taken by the Senate. Whilst the hygienic and other problems surrounding the mid-nineteenth century College are undeniable, a present-day author has rightfully described the ultimate destruction of the College buildings as Glasgow's most grievous architectural loss.[2] All that remains at the present day are the Lion and

Unicorn stair, translocated and re-erected during the construction of the new buildings; and Pearce Lodge, now standing at the northeastern gate of the University campus and rebuilt from the main gateway and adjoining buildings of the Old College in 1888, the costs of the latter borne by Mr (later Sir) William Pearce, who rescued this small part of the Old College when the railway company demolished the remainder in 1887.

With the proceeds from the sale of buildings and remaining land to the railway company, and with money from public subscriptions, from Government sources and from realisation of assets, the land at Gilmorehill had been purchased and the new buildings erected to the design of George Gilbert Scott. The apparent philistinism of the Senate in agreeing to the deal which at the same time led to the destruction of their heritage must in fairness be judged in the context of the times. There was no official mechanism to ensure the preservation of ancient buildings for which there was no further practical usage. To overcome its environmental problems and to increase its living space were entirely the responsibility of the University, which had both to raise the money from its own resources and to supplement this by appeals to its members past and present, and to outside benefactors, including the Government. Individual regrets there would have been, but in general the Senate was sure it was doing the right thing and looked to the future with confidence. The medieval foundation in the High Street, the Old College, had been described from its beginnings both as the College and as the University, the two terms interchangeable and referring to one and the same place.

The gardens were very much a part of the University's history. Previous historians have given brief references,[3,4] and a more anecdotal account has described some aspects.[5] A history of the University (up to 1577) recently published[6] includes valuable information on the buildings and grounds, but the seventeenth- and eighteenth-century gardens have not been described in detail. A paper on eighteenth-century botany in the University[7] was based largely on data collected for a larger history,[3] and a short account of the Physic Garden has been published recently.[8] The *Munimenta* of the Maitland Club, based on University records, is another source of University history if it is remembered that the four volumes were 'edited well though not impeccably'.[4] The Faculty, the governing body of the University over most of the time covered by the present book, met at regular intervals and the minutes of its meetings have been valuable sources of information on the gardens, much of which seems to have been missed by previous historians. The various College Accounts have also been useful, although often lacking the necessary details about a purchase or other forms of expenditure. Most of the information presented in the following pages, however, has come from archival documents — letters, draft notes, memoranda, scrolls (the rough notes from which the more elegant official records were prepared), accounts and precepts — the

3

last being receipted bills issued on behalf of the Faculty and authorised by the Principal with his signature. All College business, large or small, for most of the time with which this book is concerned came under the close scrutiny of the Faculty. It was only by its authority that payments could be made by the College Factor — the individual with responsibility for cash payments. The historical value of a precept lies in its itemising of the materials purchased, whilst the Faculty records and the College Accounts would usually list the overall sum with an associated general description. The Faculty would have already considered the expenditure in detail, and the Factor would have retained the receipted precept as the legal proof that the payment made had been authorised by the Faculty via the Principal and received by the payee. For example, whilst the Faculty records or the Accounts would list the overall cost of 'fine flowers for the Physick Garden', the precept gave the quantities and costings of the individual plants.

Many of the precepts are on small pieces of paper of varying size, rarely more than 15 × 20 cm. Some are appended to an invoice or account as presented. Their format changed little over the seventeenth and eighteenth centuries, and they were usually stored in mixed bundles classified according to the particular revenue with which they were associated. As an example, one of the most unusual of the many examined will be quoted, although it has nothing to do with gardens or gardeners:

C. Glasg. 13 Decr. 1722

Mr. A. Carmichaell pay to Ro^{t} Ker Barber two guineas for the horns cut out of the woman's head and this wi. his receipt shall be your warrant.

Jo. Stirling

Receibed the contents of the above by me Robt Kerr[9]

Leaving aside the curious implications of the precept and concentrating on its form, which is typical, 'C. Glasg.' refers to 'Glasgow College', Andrew Carmichaell (also Carmichael) was the Factor, and John Stirling the Principal (1701–27). The written and signed receipt of the payee was required before any payment was made — usually on the same day. A striking feature of the many precepts examined is the large number of payees who themselves wrote down and signed the receipts. Whilst the spelling was often individualistic (as was also that of the Principal), the humblest gardeners and tradesmen (less so the women) were usually literate enough to write legibly; the witnessed 'mark' was very much an exception. Such manifestations are probably a tribute to some successful parish schools of the time. The sum involved was usually given in Scots money, unless stated to be in sterling. Hence a sum would be described as 'pounds Scots' or 'sterling money'. One pound Scots was equal to one-twelfth of a pound sterling. After the 1707 Act of Union, many of the tradespeople preferred to deal in sterling, so that a precept could bear reference to both sorts of money since in the College Accounts up to 1765 all entries were in Scots money. Any sums of money mentioned in the following pages will be designated 'Scots' or 'sterling' as on the accounts or precepts described.

In passing, we return briefly to the unique precept quoted above. It should be remembered that witchcraft was still a capital offence in Scotland up to 1727 — one of the then remaining 'black spots' of Scottish law. Horn-like growths, whether of bone or enlarged sebaceous cysts, would have had obvious connotations for the ignorant, as well as being disfiguring. The precept is somewhat ambiguous but suggests the purchase of the 'horns' after they had been removed by the barber. The University at that time was building up its facilities for medical education and the 'horns' may have been required as part of an anatomical collection. On the other hand we may be witnessing the recording of an act of kindness by the Faculty to ease the lot of an unfortunately disfigured serving woman. Whatever the reason, we can only hope that the operation was not too painful in those pre-anaesthesia days and that there were no secondary infections in an age ignorant of microbial causes of disease.

It might well be considered a somewhat inward-looking approach to restrict sources of information on the gardens largely to archival documents; this has been done purposely. The history of the University Gardens in the seventeenth, eighteenth and early nineteenth centuries is that of a small community bounded by its enclosing walls, jealous of its amenities, not brooking any outside interference and quick to ensure that there were no unwelcome invasions of its privacy. The University was a dynamic community with daily activities involving all facets of its membership, and nowhere is this overall involvement better illustrated than in the management and day-to-day running of the gardens. Inevitably the documentary records, though numerous, are incomplete, bringing to mind Darwin's comment on the imperfections of the geological record: '... Of this volume, only here and there a short chapter has been preserved'. Nevertheless, the available documents have enabled a fairly comprehensive picture to be built up of the management and those managed. The management, the Principals and Professors, are known to us from many other sources. Some rightfully achieved lasting international fame, and some were locally infamous and soon forgotten. They form a colourful pageant of individual personalities who, despite their internal wranglings on occasions, and in a few cases downright underhand dealings, on the whole kept the well-being of the University as their foremost aim. These are the men of whom the Call to Commemoration speaks when read out at the annual University Service of Commemoration: '... For all who by their goodwill in times past have enriched the University, and for all who by their devotion to true learning have increased her fame and usefulness'. The history of the University's lost gardens, however, is very much an account of another stratum of its society — the men who did the manual work — the gardeners ('gardiners', 'gardners', 'gairdners') together with the 'workmen' who, as we shall see, were regarded as being of lower rank. From the many documents examined it is possible to name these artisans and to determine their rates of pay, the hours they worked, the implements used and their cost, and the plants and seeds cultivated. Their continuing care of the soil — their heritage — will also be described.

Direct quotations abound in the following pages, for these encapsulate the spirit and attitudes of the times and are much more worthy of space than any present-day interpretations and summaries. In all of these quotations the original Scots words and abbreviations are reproduced exactly, although on occasions some interpretations will be necessary. Readers are asked to accept that the quotations are exact copies and that the many variants of spelling and mathematical inaccuracies are not typographical errors.

Notes

Here, and in all subsequent chapters, the archival sources will be suitably designated:

GUAA = Glasgow University Archives Accessions. These are the sources of all documents examined and will be individually listed with their reference numbers as in The Archives.

FM = Minutes of Faculty Meetings. These will all be dated and will bear a reference number for the relevant volume in The Archives and the page reference.

SM = Minutes of Senate Meetings. Dated and with reference numbers to volumes and page numbers, as with the Faculty Minutes.

CA = College Accounts Books. The reference numbers are for the volumes in The Archives.

Munimenta = *Munimenta Alme Universitatis Glasguensis* of the Maitland Club, vols. I–IV. The volume number and page will be quoted.

1. David Murray, 1927. *Memories of the Old College of Glasgow* (Jackson, Wylie & Co., Glasgow), pp. 597–8.

2. Maurice Lindsay, 1987. *Victorian and Edwardian Glasgow from Old Photographs* (B.T. Batsford, London), p. 28.

3. J. Coutts, 1909. *History of the University of Glasgow, 1451–1909* (James Maclehose & Sons, Glasgow).

4. J.D. Mackie, 1954. *The University of Glasgow 1451–1951* (Jackson, Son & Co., Glasgow).

5. D. Murray, 1927. *Memories of the Old College of Glasgow*, pp. 247–54, 414–21.

6. J. Durkan and J. Kirk, 1977. *The University of Glasgow 1451–1577* (University of Glasgow Press).

7. F.O. Bower, 1903. Notes on botany in the University of Glasgow in the 18th century. *Transactions of the Natural History Society of Glasgow*, vol. 7, pp. 121–36.

8. A.D. Boney, 1986. A history of the Glasgow University Physic

Garden. *Transactions of the Botanical*   pp. 43–62.
Society of Edinburgh, vol. 45,   9. GUAA 42554.

The many old Scots terms in the documents have been interpreted with the
assistance of the following:
W.M. Metcalfe, 1927. *Jamieson's Dictionary of the Scottish Language* (Alexander
Gardner, Paisley).
M. Robinson (editor in chief) 1985. *The Concise Scots Dictionary* (Aberdeen
University Press).

'REGULAR AND PROFITABLE FOR THE UNIVERSITIE...'

In the beginning there was a public announcement on Trinity Sunday, 30 June 1451, from the Mercat Cross at the foot of the High Street — the main street running from the Cathedral in the north to the Cross. The assembled and perhaps puzzled townspeople were told that Pope Nicholas V had issued a Bull of Foundation for a 'Studium generale' in Glasgow.[1] The Bull was issued on 7 January 1451 at the request of King James II and following the instigation of William Turnbull, Bishop of Glasgow 1447–54, the true founder of the University. The papal charter decreed that this new public place of study should be modelled on the University of Bologna, and envisaged the formation of a typical medieval university, having a basic Arts faculty through which all students were to progress before entering one of the higher faculties (Divinity, Law, Medicine) for professional training. The new institution did not reach this medieval ideal for some considerable time. The first meeting on an unknown date in 1451 was held in the Chapter House of the Black Friars in the High Street, when 37 members of the 'general chapter' met.[2] The masters and students were to be governed by a Rector, who in turn was the representative of the Chancellor, the Bishop of Glasgow. The first Rector was David Cadzow, precentor and sub-dean of the Church of Glasgow; his successors over some 30 years were to be Canons of Glasgow.[3] The term 'master' was to remain in general use until well into the eighteenth century, by which time the title professor was often used alongside the older one. The system of 'regenting' was soon introduced, in which one master took his students through the whole of the Arts course: the *trivium* of verbal Arts (grammar, rhetoric, logic) and the *quadrivium* of numerate Arts (mathematics, geometry, astronomy, music). For the first 100 years of its existence the University remained so small that the Arts Faculty, with a Dean at its head, was Glasgow College and until the nineteenth century the 'College' and 'Faculty' were to be the same.

After its first meeting the general chapter of the infant University continued to meet in the Cathedral Chapter House. The earliest teaching was carried out in the crypt of the Cathedral or in the Black Friars Chapter House, and in the 'Auld Pedagogy' — a small tenement building providing 'teaching, lodging and a common table'[4] and situated in the Rotten Row (Ratoun Raw), a street lying to the southwest of the Cathedral.[5] In 1453 the schools moved to a more spacious but rented tenement on the east side of the High Street. In 1460 James, first Lord Hamilton, gave the Faculty a tenement, also fronting onto the High Street, with four acres of land at the rear extending back to the Molendinar Burn; and to this was added, in 1467, an adjacent tenement and croft, the gift of Thomas Arthurlie.[6] Later, Queen Mary was to give some 13 acres of land on the Dow Hill east of the Molendinar Burn; the main site for the future development of the College was established.

The struggling College remained small and short of funds until the arrival in 1574 of Andrew Melville, a dynamic personality and brilliant academic. He obtained from James Douglas, fourth Earl of Morton and Regent, a new constitution, the *Nova Erectio* of 1577. Set against a background of great change in the nation, with the reformed Confession of Faith authorised in 1560 the most significant outcome of the Reformation, this new constitution was a renaissance in the administration, funding and teaching of the University, and with new endowments placed the establishment on a much surer foundation. The property now became invested in the Principal and Masters, excluding the Chancellor and Rector. This control of funds and endowments by the Principals and Masters (later Professors) of the Faculty was to continue until 1858.

The medieval College fronting the High Street was not devoid of yards or gardens. A recent reconstruction of the medieval College and its surroundings shows a Little Meadow, an Old Pedagogy Yard, Paradise Yards, West Yard, a small Coalhouse Yard and the Great Orchard to the east (Figure 1.1).[7] The Old Pedagogy Yard (or Kitchen Yard) was for growing vegetables and supplying fowls for the kitchen and the common table, and there is mention of a mudwall dyke being built in it in 1490. The Little Meadow was in due course taken over by the Principal. The Blackfriars Kirk was to remain associated with the College after the Reformation. Between it and the College buildings lay the Paradise Yards, of which the larger one on the north side was leased by the friars to tenants (the tackholders) in 1558. This land was in time taken over by the University. The friars grew mustard and fruit trees ('pipanis' or pippin apples) and 'ympis'.[8] Most monastic institutions of any size possessed a small physic garden or plot for growing plants of medicinal value.

Evidence for the existence of a small physic garden, not in the University grounds but close by, has been obtained recently from examination of an annotated copy of Leonhart Fuchs's (1549) *De*

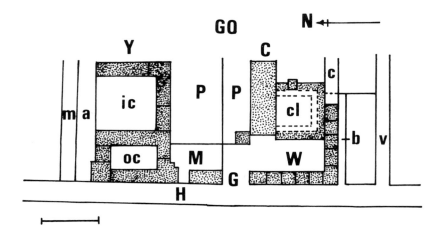

Figure 1.1. The medieval University buildings, adjacent buildings and yards (buildings stippled). Redrawn from Durkan and Kirk[7]

GO	= Great Orchard	ic	= Inner Close
P	= Paradise Yards	oc	= Outer Close of College of Glasgow
W	= West Yard	m	= St Michael's Chaplain Lands
Y	= Old Pedagogy Yard	a	= Arthurlie Lands
H	= High Street	cl	= Cloisters
C	= Church	c	= Coalhouse Yard
G	= Outer Gate	b	= Blackfriars Wynd
M	= Little Meadow	v	= Vennel (later the Old Vennel)

Scale line: 100 feet

Historia Stirpium Commentarii Insignes (Significant Notes on the History of Plants) belonging to Mark Jameson, Deputy Rector of the University in 1555 and later Vicar-Choral of the Cathedral.[9] Of particular interest is his handwritten list of 22 plants 'To be set and sawin in ye garding'. The annotations indicate the hand of a physician interested in medicinal botany, and Jameson was known to be a benefactor of St Nicholas's Hospital and of St Ninian's Leper Hospital. Jameson's list of plants, however, is a specialised one, seemingly excluding a number of common plants of medicinal value well known at the time. Of the 22 plants listed as those to be sown in the garden, twelve had recognised properties of a gynaecological nature according to Fuchs (Table 1.1). Of these twelve, nine possessed emmenagogic properties (promoting menstruation) with four also having ecbolic properties (stimulating parturition), and one also being galactogogive (promoting milk production). Three other plants listed had well-known ecbolic properties, including the Savin, *Juniperus sabinus*, a notorious abortifacient of the time. Four other plants were noted by Jameson in

Table 1.1. Plants noted by Jameson in back fly-leaf of his copy of Fuchs's (1549) *De Historia Stirpium Commentarii Insignes* (see Table 2 in Dickson and Gauld[9])

Plants to be sown in the garden

Name noted down	Identification	Modern vernacular	Properties (Fuchs 1549)
Petroselinum	*Petroselinum crispum*	Parsley	D, K, M
Peusedamus	*Peucedamum officinale*	Hog's Fennel	B, headaches, nerves, kidneys
Milium folis	*Achillea millefolium*	Milfoil	V, ulcers
Apium	*Apium graveulens*	Celery	D, K, M
Asparagus	*Asparagus officinalis*	Asparagus	D, K, kidney stones, liver
Betonica	*Stachys officinalis*	Betony	D, M, liver, kidneys
Verbena	*Verbena officinalis*	Vervain	F, V, lungs
Philopendula	*Filipendula vulgaris*	Dropwort	B, C, D, kidneys, coughs
Valeriana	*Valeriana officinalis*	Valerian	D, M
Saxifragia	*Asplenium adiantum-nigrum*	Black Spleenwort	B, M
Coriandrum	*Coriandrum sativum*	Coriander	K, skin
Cumenum	*Cuminum sativum*	Cumin	Skin, eyes, kidneys
Anetum	*Anethum graveolens*	Dill	D, K, colic, gripe, skin troubles
Anisum	*Pimpinella anisum*	Anise	C, D, G, K, heachaches
Daucus	*Daucus corota*	Carrot	
Pastinaca	*Pastinaca sativa*	Parsnip	B, D, K, M, liver, spleen
Fenum Grecum	*Trigonella foenum-grecum*	Fenugreek	K, liver, spleen, scabs
Feniculus	*Foeniculum vulgare*	Fennel	D, G, K, M, lungs
Lingua cervina	*Phyllitis scolofendrium*	Hart's Tongue	Spleen
Saturegia	*Satureja montana*	Savory	B, D, K, M, chest
Calendula	*Calendula officinalis*	Pot Marigold	B, K, M, teeth
Savina	*Juniperus sabinus*	Savin	B

Other plants noted

Consolida regalis	*Delphinium consolida*	Forking Larkspur	B, M
Pulegium	*Mentha pulegium*	Penny Royal	B, M, V

Other plants noted

Name noted down	Identification	Modern vernacular	Properties (Fuchs 1549)
Aristolochia	*Aristolochia clematitis*	Birthwort	B, M
Fumaria	*Fumaria officinalis*	Fumitory	Eye ointment

Key:
B = ecbolic (stimulating parturition)
C = carminative (curing flatulence and colic)
D = diuretic (stimulating urine discharge)
F = febrifugal (reducing fever)
G = galactogogive (stimulating milk secretion)
K = culinary
M = emmenagogic (promoting menstruation)
V = vulnerary (wound-healing)

his copy of Fuchs (but not to be grown in the garden), and of these three possessed ecbolic and emmenagogic properties. The 22 plants to be sown also had other medicinal virtues — diuretic, wound-healing (vulnerary), for fever (febrifugal), for flatulence and colic (carminative) — as well as being of culinary value in some instances. The annotations suggest that Mark Jameson intended growing a somewhat specialised physic garden with a high proportion of plants having known ecbolic properties. The question remains open whether he was a practising abortionist. Nor can it be certain that his physic garden played any role in the teaching of the University; his residence would have had a sizeable walled garden suitable for his requirements and if any such instruction did take place it would have been of an informal nature. Formalised teaching of medicine lay many years in the future. Notably, some of the plants which Jameson especially noted down for their ecbolic properties are today regarded as being highly dangerous.

The medieval College was to remain on the lines shown in Figure 1.1 until the early years of the seventeenth century, having undergone a number of repairs and rebuilding, becoming a mixture of old and new. In 1630, Principal Strang opened up a subscription list with a view to a complete rebuilding. Money came in or was promised from royalty, nobility, gentry, clergy and merchants, and, whilst not all promises were fulfilled (notably the £200 sterling promised by Charles I, which was eventually paid by Oliver Cromwell in 1654), a sizeable sum was accumulated for those times. Work on rebuilding commenced towards the end of 1631 and some progress was made, so that by September 1633 the new 'house' was being roofed.[10] The Civil War and other disturbances interrupted building, which was resumed in 1653 under Principal Gillespie, with the completion of the Inner Quadrangle in 1656. The north and south sides of the front quadrangle were completed by 1658 and the buildings fronting onto the High Street in

1661. Slezer's view of the College, published in 1693 (Frontispiece), shows the completed buildings; the drawing was probably executed during his visit in 1669, since the old Blackfriars Kirk was damaged by lightning and fire in 1670 and not rebuilt until the close of the century.[11] Slezer's drawing, however, shows a spacious and well-planted garden (the Great Yard or Garden) to the rear (east) of the College, with smaller gardens north and south of the main College buildings, and to the south of the kirk. This last garden, of which only a corner is visible in Slezer's drawing (indicated by the shadow of the kirk spire), was to be known as the Little Yard or Blackfriars Yard, its southern border being the Blackfriars Wynd (see Figure 1.1). The Principal's garden in the drawing lies to the left (north) of the kirkyard and a further garden area lies to the north of the main College building. As indicated earlier, the Great Garden extended eastwards to the banks of the Molendinar Burn, tending to slope down to the burn, whilst the Dowhill on the east of the burn was raised ground. In the seventeenth century this College land on the Dowhill was mainly kept in pasture, but was to be further developed in the eighteenth century.

Information on garden management in the seventeenth century is rather sparse. Principal Strang is credited with laying out a 'large and stately orchard' — presumably in the Great Garden — and with laying out a new walled garden and building a gardener's lodge. This latter building would have been under construction in 1633–4, as indicated by an account for work done between 14 June and August 1634. 'Givine for timbering the roof of the Gardners hous, laying the loft thereof, making of dores and ledders xlvj l'.[12] A later account, dated 15 June 1639, is 'To John Boyd for compleating the whole stone work of the East Quarter of the Colledge Building (except the riggin stones), building of the Garden gate, another gate upon the dyke of the College Yairde, and dyke from the Gardners house to David Jacks house ... ljc l'.[13] The new walled garden created by Principal Strang, associated as it was with the gardener's house, was the one to be known as the Little Yard or Blackfriars Yard, with its south boundary facing onto the Blackfriars Wynd. A renunciation (a surrender of lease) of one William Leitch, dated 18 March 1633, is 'of his tack of a fourth part of the Blackfriars Yard'.[14] This gardener's house enters the story in some detail at a later date (p. 34). It is uncertain whether the gardener was a College servant or whether the house was included in the tack of the Great Yard, as was to be the case later in the century.

Records of actual plantings are sparse. In 1614–15 John Govane, 'gairdner', was paid £5 Scots 'for vij hunder and hald hunder thornis to ally hedge in the College' (allay = garden path). The precept was issued over the signature of Robert Boyd of Trochrig, Principal 1615–22.[15] This was followed by a payment of £7 Scots 'To W. Seller and his man vij dayis setting and building the hedge'. According to Boyd's precept for this work, Seller was paid 12/- Scots per day and his man 8/-.[16] An undated precept signed by Robert Boyd refers to a labourer building up a hedge and building a 'fale dyke' in the yard (fale dyke = wall coped with turf).[17] Robert Hutchisone received £10 Scots in the year 1637–8 'for binding and dressing of the Garden hedges'.[18] In 1656 the accounts included reference to £1/14/- being paid for 'parcells of Flowers for the Gardene, tulips, anemonies and ranunculus'.[19] 'Hewing the rolling stones for the Gairdene' cost £2 Scots in October 1656.[20] Two payments to John Govane, gairdner, of £20 Scots for 1627–8 and £13/6/8d for 1628–9, both for 'kaill and herbs', most probably represent sales made from outside the College if this is the same John Govane who supplied the thorns in 1614–15.[21] 'Kaille' seems to be the only vegetable mentioned in a victualling contract for the common table drawn up between the Faculty and one John Stirling on 26 December 1649, although the varied meat and fish courses are described in detail.[22] An earlier (1630) victuals list similarly details requirements for meat, fish, eggs, butter and milk; for vegetables 'kaille' is the only one mentioned, apart from a single reference to 'neeps'. Fruit included 'beries', 'cheries' and figs.[23] Many of the rarer fruits came from merchants in the town, as seen in an account of John Anderson, merchant, dated 10 August 1672:[24]

	Scots		
	£	s	d
7 lb cordy cedroune [citron?]	14.	0.	0
3 lb conff oranges	07.	4.	0
3 lb lymonds [lemons]	07.	4.	0
4 lb sott [soft?] pears	10.	4.	0
2 lb best Soutt chieres	07.	4.	0
3 quarters lb off an Lattuce	02.	0.	0

The earlier reference to a 'large and stately orchard' having been laid out by Principal Strang rather suggests that for fruit the College was self-sufficient. Fruit sales from the Great Yard in 1643 and 1644 raised £26/13/4d Scots.[25] A sizeable order for fruit trees with accompanying planting instructions is available. Whilst not dated, its style of writing is placed as late seventeenth century (Table 1.2).[26] The distinction between the free-standing standards and those 'for the wall' (espaliers), with branches trained horizontally right and left, is clearly shown. The varied spellings include names of varieties well known in the seventeenth century.[27] The pears include 'borgamoett' and 'borgoamet' for Bergamot; 'winser' for Windsor; 'bogentan' and 'boncritan', probably Bon Chretien: all with winter and summer varieties. The 'Kathern' pear is most likely the Catherine. The apples listed included the 'pearmanes', 'pearmens' or Pearmains. The Winter Permain mentioned, or Old English Pearmain, is reputedly the first apple recorded in England, in 1204,[28] and a popular dessert variety. The pippins ('pipenes', 'peapenes') include the Golden, the Russeting ('Russat'), Kentish and Black, of which the Golden Pippin was much

Table 1.2. A late seventeenth-century account for fruit trees for the College Garden[26]

Pear tris	£ s d
It. 1 summer borgamoett standard	00 - 01 - 8
It. 1 winter bogentan pear for the wall	00 - 01 - 8
It. 1 winter winser pear standard	00 - 01 - 8
It. 2 sumer winser pear standard	00 - 01 - 8
It. 1 Early winser pear standard	00 - 01 - 8
It. 2 winter winser pear wall	00 - 01 - 6
It. 1 sumer boncritan pear standard	00 - 01 - 8
It. 1 winter borgoamet pear wall	00 - 01 - 6
It. 1 King Kathern pear standard	00 - 01 - 8
It. 1 quein Kathern pear standard	00 - 01 - 8
It. 1 grein felds pear	00 - 01 - 8

Aple Treis	
It. 2 sumer pearmanes	00 - 02 - 4
It. 2 winter pearmens	00 - 02 - 4
It. 2 golden pipenes	00 - 02 - 4
It. 2 Russat peapenes	00 - 02 - 4
It. 1 Kentish pipen	00 - 01 - 2
It. 1 black pipen	00 - 01 - 2
It. 2 sumer Arbe apell	00 - 01 - 2
It. 1 winter Arbe apell	00 - 01 - 2
It. 1 queen Apell	00 - 01 - 2
It. 1 gellieflour apell	00 - 01 - 2
It. 2 early aprikoaks	00 - 06 - 0
It. 2 ordinarie aprikoaks	00 - 04 - 0
It. 2 may cheris for the wall	00 - 02 - 8
It. 2 corrum cheris wall	00 - 02 - 8
It. 2 duke cheres for the wall	00 - 02 - 8
It. 1 Red 1 black harts chere	00 - 02 - 8
It. 3 duke Cheres standard	00 - 04 - 0
It. 2 Carnation Cherres standards	00 - 02 - 8
It. 1 red harte chere	00 - 01 - 4
It. 2 White harte chere standards	00 - 02 - 8
It. 2 greatt baring Cheres standards	00 - 02 - 8
It. 8 Earllie flanders Cherrie standards	00 - 10 - 8
It. 2 great flanders Cherie standards	00 - 08 - 0

prized. The 'Arbe' listed is probably a Harvey, the 'gellieflour' is obviously Gillyflower and the 'Queen' is probably Quinning. For the most part these varieties are named in some of the earliest gardening books with information on fruit-growing, e.g. Gerard's *The Herball or Generall Historie of Plants* (1597), Parkinson's *Paradisi in Sole* (1629) and Tradescant's *Plantarium in Horto* (1634).

The inclusion of 'aprikoaks' (apricots) and cherries in the list is of interest, since John Gibson, writing in *The Fruit Gardener* of 1768, was less than enthusiastic about cherry-growing in Scotland with the problems of frost damage, bird damage (which could be prevented, he suggested, by spreading nets over the trees) and the perishable nature of the fruit.[29] Most of the varieties in the list are recognisable also in contemporary records, e.g. the May cherry, or acid red cherry; the Duke cherry, first mentioned by John Rea in 1665; the heavy-bearing Black heart, popular for wine-making, or for its unfermented juice; the Great-bearing cherry, with its juice then popular for colouring drinks (cider, perry, white wine); the Carnation cherry, a good quality light-cropping variety; and the Flanders cherry — the most planted according to Ralph Austin's *A Treatise on Fruit Trees* (1635, 1657, 1665).[30] 'Corrum' might represent Caroon or Crown. The prices listed are probably in sterling. Some prices given in Sir Thomas Hanmer's *The Garden Book* (1659) list cherries and apples at 8d per tree and pears at 12d.[31]

Some notes on the account show that the 'caredg of the tries' (caredg = carriage) cost 1/-, and '5 matts for to mak wi the tries' cost 5/- (the 'matts' being used to wrap around the roots). 'Freight and chairdges' were included; these show that the trees came to Leith by ship, and were then transferred to Edinburgh before carriage to Glasgow, these operations costing 14/-. The planting notes included are of special interest:

Concerning the apricoaks hark as follows be carefull to sett them wher the morning sune shynes and lett them grew a yier beffoir you aether prunae ym or naill ym to the wall

As for your winter pears be carefull to sett them under the shadow of the wall

As for your sumer pears be carefull to sett them wher the morning sune may shyn upon them

Another fruit-trees account is from about the same time and is headed 'Accompt of the London Trees: Accompt of tres shiped for Georg Nickolson his shop 20 Dec. 1685'.[32] There are, as expected, many similarities between this account (Table 1.3) and the preceding one. Possibly the 'corrowne' or 'crownne' of Nickolson's list may well be the 'corrum' of the previous one. The spelling of apricot in both lists is the same as that of Parkinson in 1629. The 'early aprikoaks' of the earlier list are probably the same as the 'Mascaline apricook trees' of

Table 1.3. An account dated 20 December 1685 for fruit trees[32]

	£ s d
It. for 4 May Cheres for the wall	000 : 04 : 08
It. for 2 Corrowne Chere standards	000 : 02 : 08
It. for 2 Crowne Chere walle	000 : 02 : 04
It. for 1 Black heart Chere wall	000 : 01 : 02
It. for 1 Red heart Chere wall	000 : 01 : 02
It. for 1 Red heart Chere standarde	000 : 01 : 04
It. for 2 whitt heart Chere standarde	000 : 01 : 04
It. for 2 Maskaline apricook trees	000 : 06 : 00
It. for 2 ordinary apricook trees	000 : 04 : 00
It. for 2 Rugott pipens	000 : 02 : 04
It. for 2 sumer Borgamoat pears	000 : 03 : 04
It. for 2 mattes to pack them up	000 : 02 : 04
It. for a porter to carrie them	000 : 00 : 06

Nickolson's account, and the 'ordinaire' and 'ordinary' names on the two lists were probably the Lesser apricot (*Armeniaca malus minor*), although a variety called Ordinary was sold from 1688 by Leonard Meager of Brompton Park Nursery.[33] Sir Thomas Hanmer in his 1659 *Garden Book* stated that apricots needed to be protected by high walls facing south or east and receiving shelter from winds and excessive rain:[34] summer months in the west of Scotland are not known to lack either of the latter on occasions. Fruit trees were to be one of the major attractions of the Great Garden, and these purchases show that the Faculty was prepared to invest in some of the rarer varieties.

Little mention is ever made of the Principal's garden at any time in the history of the gardens. Principal Gillespie's investment is, however, on record: 'dressing the Principal's garden, gravelling and making the walks, laying a green walk with turf, cutting out the south west quarter in a plot, furnishing stones and timber to border the plot and walks, planting all the west wall with plumes, apricoks, amonds, figs, laurels etc the planting and making of the close walk, all which were done at his own chairges, besides all the floures that he planted and left in and on the housetops'.[35] Gillespie was also following Hanmer's advice about the protection afforded by east-facing high walls for the more sensitive fruit trees. The 'amond' or almond probably refers to the Almond peach, described among 21 varieties by Parkinson in his *Paradisi in Sole* (1629).[36]

The Great Yard or Garden was a restricted area. Only the Principal and Masters were allowed to walk within its bounds, as is evident in a memorial of 14 May 1649:[37]

We the undersubscrybing having receaved every one of us a key to the Bak Hall doore for our entrie to the College Yeard doe promise to use our best endeavour to keep the said key, that neither it be lost not communicat to any students within the Colleg, nor (without approbation of the rest) to any other. And at our departure out of the Colleg to render it back to the Principall or in his absence to the Eldest Regent

John Strang
John Young
Hugh Binning   Nigellus Campbell
Joa Kilpatrick   Alexr. Gordoun
Wil. Strang
Pat. Young

There would seem to have been one door leading from the back of the College to the garden and students were definitely excluded.

Purchases and exchanges of adjoining land are occasionally reported. A precept issued by Principal Wright on 22 January 1676 was for £29 Scots to be paid to John Rob, mealmaker, for 'quitting his interest of the bakland & yard adjacent to the College and the north side which the Masters bought from the Laird of Torrance'.[38] This purchasing of land and improvement of the Great Garden was especially carried on by Principal James Fall, as he has recorded in his own hand:[39]

October 20th 1685 The Colledge entered into Contract with Rot Boyd and Alexr Tam Massons for building the College Yeard Dyke with good ston and lyme, they furnishing all materials and workmanship were to have 80 merks for every 36 Elles at Elle high. November 1st Being to inclose the Colledge Yeard with so good a wall it was thought fit to take in as much ground as possible to make it Regular and profitable for the Universitie. Therefore the Masters transacted and bought in three yeards on the North side of the Colledge Yeards that which lay nixt it belonged to the Laird of Torrance which was bought for 28 years purchase, the second belonged to Robert Boyd Masson for the same Rate, the third belonged to Robert Barton for the same rate the three yeards together amounted to — merks by having of which ground the Colledge yeard goes now from the South to the East Vennal freae from all houses These two Vennals being the march on the South and North and the Burne towards the East. It is to be remembered that the barren trees are upon the ground tho without the dyke

The last point about the 'trees without' probably refers to the College land — about one yard in width — which lay outside the wall. If this was the first full enclosure of the Great Yard then the earlier careful arrangements regarding access only from the one door would seem unnecessary, unless there was some wood-paling fencing (of 'stobs', or stakes, and rafters). Some walls did exist before Fall's time. A precept issued by Principal Wright on 12 March 1673 was 'to Andrew Nemo & John Wilson for lagging the Colledge yard dyke five days att four shillings per day in all two Pounds Scots'.[40] One of Fall's dealings is recorded in an excambion (exchange of land) of 16 August 1690 between the College and John King merlman (= mealman), in which King was to receive from the College a piece of land 'of twenty four elnes of length and seaven elnes of breadeth' on the north side of the College in exchange for 'fiftein elnes in lenth and nyne elnes in breader' of King's land, which was to be enclosed within the College bounds.[41] In modern measure the elne or elle was 37.2 inches; the College enclosed 144 square yards of King's land in exchange for 179.4 square yards of its own. Whilst King gained in terms of area, the College presumably benefited by the achievement of a regular boundary. The excambion expressly states that the land exchanged would belong to the College 'in all tyme coming'. A contract was also drawn up between 'James Stewart of Torrance and Alexander Stewart his son whereby the former dispone the latter part of their yeard possessed by John Allan'.[42]

The contract with the masons for building the wall was for a payment of '80 merks' for 'every 36 elles at Elle high'. The height of the wall was missing from Fall's notes but a later source tells us it was 4 Elles. One merk is equal to 13/4d Scots; therefore 80 merks was £53/6/8d Scots or £4/8/10¾d Sterling, and this was paid for every 37 yards of wall of height just over 4 yards. A series of precepts signed by Fall cover these payments for wall-building. The first is for 'three hundred merks Scots' to Robert Boyd for the 'south wall of the College yeard';[43] at the rate agreed, this would have been about 139.5 yards of wall. A second payment to Boyd of 400 merks was made on 4 March 1686 (186 yards of wall),[44] and in November 1686 he received another 800 merks 'in part of what is owing to him for building the College wall'.[45] As the wording suggests, this payment may have been for other mason work carried out by Boyd. The contract also included a second mason, Alexander Tam. Tam died early in 1686 and two precepts for wall-building, each of 300 merks, were paid to his relict (widow) Jennet Gilchrist in June 1686.[46,47] Since Tam was paid separately, this suggests that he erected some 270 yards of wall. From what measurements are available of the College grounds of the time — and these are not entirely reliable — both the south wall bordering the lower vennel and the longer north wall would have been well within the limits of the building so far accounted for. It is possible, however, that other walls within the College precincts were included in the precepts. The lines of the two main enclosing walls are shown in Figure 1.2. From some later information it seems that the south wall incorporated an elm tree, and this ancient elm became an object of much care and attention in the latter half of the eighteenth century. Its approximate position is shown in Figure 1.2.

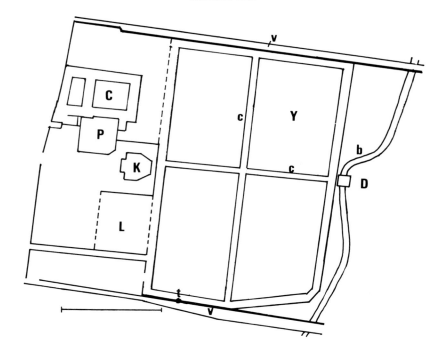

Figure 1.2. Enclosure and subdivision of the Great Yard from 1685 according to Principal James Fall's notes. The thickened lines represent the main walls inside the two vennels (V); t = elm tree built into the wall. The walks 'round about' were 20 feet wide, the 'cross walks' (c) 15 feet

C = College building **P** = Principal's garden **K** = Blackfriars Kirk **Y** = Great Yard or Great Garden **b** = Molendinar Burn **D** = Dowhill (later Dovehill) **L** = Little Yard (The broken lines indicate approximate boundaries: that of the Little Yard is uncertain, since a bowling green was in close proximity. The Little Yard stood in part on the site of the Blackfriars Cloisters)

Scale line: 300 feet

Fall's delineation of the bounds of the Great Garden, with the two vennels north and south and the Molendinar Burn to the east, set the shape of the garden for the future. Again, applying such measurements as are available, the Great Garden was of area about 9 Imperial acres (= 7.2 Scots acres). This Great Garden was to remain a source of income for the College, as had been the practice with its lands from the earliest times. Various references to tackholders are available: for example, renunciations in the names of James Stirling (5 June 1654) for some parcel of College land, and for Margaret Wilkie (some time in 1668) 'for the ground called the Nurserie'.[48] A tack for the 'yeard' was held by Thomas Finniw in 1578 (the bond was signed by Andrew

Melville), and other tacks dated 1610 and 1630 are available, although the names of the tackholders are indecipherable.[49] These last two indicate the time scale of the tacks, which were fixed at 19 years assuming that the tackholder survived that time or that financial conditions did not cause him or her to renunciate early, for which there was a penalty clause. Survival became a matter of concern for all citizens of the town in 1645, when a severe plague developed and continued with varying intensity for some three years. The University moved its classes to Irvine on the coast for the two sessions 1645–7. The tack issued for the Great Garden in 1666 to Margaret Miller was due to expire in 1685.[50] As the next tackholder, George Dron, entered on his lease at Candlemas 1673, however, Margaret Miller must have either renounced or died before its termination. (All College business of this nature was formally timed to begin or end on Quarter Days, and these are listed in Table 1.4.) George Dron similarly did not see out his tack the full 19 years. A precept issued on 12 September 1685 for 35 merks was in the name of 'Elspith forsyth, Relict to George Dron ... for all she can pretend to a tack granted to her husband of date 1673 years'.[51] This was a refund of rent. Who followed Dron is not known, but the new tackholder seems not to have been satisfactory, as Principal Fall recorded for 20 June 1690:[52]

> The Colledge Yeards being so well inclosed with a stone wall and all finished for two years it was let for three hundred Merks; but finding these men to whom it was then let neither able nor capable to put things therein in such order as was meet, or for improvement of that ground. An agreement was made with Robert Robertsone to plant the walls with all sorts of fruit trees as also all the borders of the great plott cast into four quarters with new trees of all good kinds rooting out the old, and laying out the walks at twenty foot broad round about and the crosses walk fifteen foot broad. To entertaine these walks and to keep all things in good repair as the contract at more length beares. And all this he is to perform at his own expence and

Table 1.4. Quarter Days in Scotland

Candlemas	2 February
Whitsunday[a]	15 May
Lammas	1 August
Martinmas	11 November

Note: a. *Not* the sabbath

(The three main terms at the University of Glasgow are still named Martinmas, Candlemas and Whitsun, with the extra Lammas term in the summer for medical students)

charges for which the College granted him a tack for Nineteen years
he is to pay yearly at the rent of the year four hundred merks, but in
consideration of the great expence he will necessarily be at in the
first planting, he is to have an abatement of fiftie merks for the first
nine yeares. So by the Improvement of the College Yeard then is
two hundred merks augmentation our Rentall it having payd
formerly but 200 Merks before the walls were built

As shown in Fall's notes, the tackholders besides paying their annual
rental were expected to keep the garden in good order. The unknown
tacksmen who followed George Dron were evidently incapable of doing
this. Tackholders were expected to make their profits from the sale of
grass cuttings and fruit in the town. By this means the Faculty ensured
proper upkeep of the garden by the regular mowing of the grass of the
large plots and by the care of the fruit trees and other trees, shrubs and
flowers in the borders. With an annual rental of 350 merks (£233/6/8d
Scots or £19/8/10³/₄d sterling), Robert Robertsone (his name is
variously spelt in different documents) had to be sure of a fair profit
from his sales each year, and there was always an element of risk as
with all crop-growing. Rainfall in the Glasgow area would probably
have ensured some good grass crops.

Robert Robertsone's tack contract (a document 78.5 cm × 31 cm) is
of particular interest, since his 19-year term carries us into the early
years of the eighteenth century, when a number of changes were taking
place in the gardens.[53] Some of the main points of the tack have been
outlined in Fall's notes, especially the financial arrangements, which
will not be considered further. The tack was for 'all and haille the grate
yeard or orchyeard of the samen is now inclosed with the new stone
dyke with the bak walk on the fortheast syd yrof nixt to the burn and
the yard house high and laigh with pertines of the samen in blackfriars
wynd with the Little yaird at the back yrof belonging thereto ...'. The
back walk lay on the east side of the garden near the Molendinar Burn
(Figure 1.2); the house 'high and laigh' (the latter the 'low' house,
probably for privy or for storage of tools) with the Little Yard was to
play an important role some 14 years later in the establishment of the
Physic Garden. The tack conditions also laid down rules about access
to the garden with which Robertsone was expected to comply and
which he was to enforce where necessary, the benefit of possessing
'kyes or libertie to walk in sd yeard' being limited to the Masters and
'Primarii', e.g. sons of noblemen (the latter a change from the 1649
ruling). This item will be further discussed in a later chapter.

The plantings briefly referred to in Fall's letter are given in greater
detail in the tack contract where, regarding Robertsone's duties, the
Faculty '... chairges him to plant the whole walls round the said yeard
with aple, pear, plum, Cherie, Peach, Apricock ... and trees and
shrubs proper to the walls'. Since these trees and shrubs would have
been bought by Robertsone no lists or accounts are available, but there

are obvious similarities between the tack requirements and the fruit trees listed in the orders of 1685 (Tables 1.2, 1.3). Plums and peaches are not listed in these earlier accounts, but numerous varieties of each were available at the time.[54] Robertsone was also required to plant 'the borders within the sd. yeard and cross walk therein the samen with aple, plum and cheries standerds all of fyftein feet and of Good and sufficient kind and at Regular and Competent distance according to the height of the walls which are four elns and breadth of walks, which walks are fifteen feet in breadth ... And where any of the trees of the said yeard alreadie planted are become barren thorow age or any other acidents ... he is to remove them and put new are of good kyndes in there Roumes'. Evidently the fruit trees to line the walks were to be of similar heights, and the wall trees (espaliers) would be presumably less than 12 feet. Proper cultivation of the fruit trees and grounds were written into the tack. Robertsone was to leave 'the whole yeard, dykes, borders and walks and plots sufficiently planted with good and sufficient kynds of trees and in sufficient rare and repaire by nailling and pruning'. A further condition was that at no time were horses or cows to be pastured in the garden. Whilst the Masters agreed to maintain the gardener's house in a habitable condition, they required that Robertsone would build them a stone summer house in the north corner of the garden. The costs of this were to be allowed from his annual tack payments in addition to the allowance over the first nine years to cover the costs of trees and shrubs. Two receipts are available for Robertsone's rent payments. One dated 23 March 1694 is for £255/6/8d Scots for 'ye Rent of the Coladj yeard' from 'Rot. Robisoun'[55] and the other for £293/19/4d Scots from 'Rob. Robisone', each payment somewhat in excess of the sums in the tack contract.[56]

With the conditions imposed and outlays required, we can only assume that Robertsone cleared sufficient profit over the years to keep the tack full term. The Little Yard mentioned may have been used for growing vegetables. Its shape and area cannot be decided, since somewhere in close proximity there was a bowling green, separate from the Great Garden. From all available evidence it would seem that the College obtained a satisfactory maintenance of the Great Garden, which was essentially all that the Faculty required. From the Masters' point of view, the garden as an amenity was of first importance; the fruit trees for them were decorative, while for the tackholder who had to cultivate them the trees were sources of income from their produce, together with the grass sales from the plots and walks of the Great Garden.

Principal Fall's intention that the Great Garden was to be made 'regular and profitable for the Universitie' was to follow its enclosure within a 12-foot-high wall — emphasising the closed society which was the University. As described elsewhere,[57] the post-Reformation University was a distinct, elitist, competitive society ... separated from the rest of society by the College gate and walls — a true physical barrier. The students of the time were completely under the authority of the Masters, unable to move beyond the walls without permission and excluded from the gardens, except for the favoured few who were sons of noblemen — a state of affairs which was to continue for many years into the future. Under Fall's management the garden assumed the form it was to retain for the remainder of its existence. For the Masters the garden was for pleasurable recreation, with its tree-lined and grassed walks (later to be sown with clover) and the trim plots, with their borders of flowers and shrubs, something akin to the paradise gardens of the old monastic institutions. Repairs to the gardener's house, as required in the tack, were set in train by Fall,[58] with the bill amounting to £76 Scots.[59]

In the available records of the College for the late 1600s there are no real indications of whether gardeners were employed as servants of the College, as distinct from tackholders who were self-employed. A precept of 14 September 1685 is for payment of £24 Scots to Adam Wilson for 'rooting up the garden hedge',[60] and one for 17 October 1685 was to pay — Gilbert 4/- Scots for 'sawing the trees which grew on the north walk'.[61] There is a later Faculty record (4 September 1692), also concerning Adam Wilson:[62]

> The whilk-day the Faculty considering the complaint against Adam Wilson one of the gardeners of the College, and he being compeared and acknowledged that he had cutt three elm trees and one ash tree of the planting belonging to the Colledge in and about the Great Orchyeard and that without the knowledge and allowance of the Masters The Rector and the remanent members of Faculty his assessors discerns Adam Wilson their Gardener in the sum of twenty pounds Scots conforme to the Act of Parliament for each of the four trees cut within and about the College Yeards, without the knowledge or allowance of the Masters thereof, in regaird he judicially compeared in their presence and confessed the samen, and ordains him to be sent and lye in the Tolbooth till he repay the same

The fate of the unfortunate Adam Wilson who had been 'compeared', i.e. called before a higher authority, is not known. To repay £80 Scots from earnings of about 8/- per day would seem an impossible task, unless he sold the trees in which case the College were determined to get the money from him. The employment of gardeners and their emoluments became a much better documented matter in the years of the following century. From the account of a traveller, in the 1670s the Great Garden contained a large number of fruit trees, many of them considered to be rare at the time.[63] From the various sources it is possible to build up a picture of the walled garden with its fruit trees, flowering shrubs, tree-lined walks and trim grassed area divided into four plots by the cross walks. The walks and plots would have required regular cutting by means of scythes: probably more than one man alone could do at a time. To the east of the Molendinar Burn lay the ground of the Dowhill (also Dovehill), for the most part let out in pasture. Another garden area lay to the north of the main building; no mention is made of this, but from Slezer's drawing it was probably a grassed area with bordering trees and shrubs. The Principal's garden is mentioned only rarely, but from information available it was walled, with grass, walks and fruit trees and flowering shrubs in its borders. Similarly, from what can be seen in Slezer's drawing, the Little Yard south of the Blackfriars Kirk was planted with trees and shrubs in its borders. This Little Yard became the object of the Faculty's attention in the early years of the following century.

Notes

1. Anon. 1951. *The University of Glasgow through Five Centuries* (University of Glasgow), p. 9.

2. J. Durkan and J. Kirk, 1977. *The University of Glasgow 1451–1577* (University of Glasgow Press), p. 9.

3. J.D. Mackie, 1954. *The University of Glasgow 1451–1951* (Jackson, Son & Co., Glasgow), p. 19.

4. Anon. 1951. *The University of Glasgow through Five Centuries*, p. 11.

5. J.D. Marwick, 1911. *Early Glasgow* (James Maclehose & Sons, Glasgow), p. 328. (Sketch Plan of sites of Principal Buildings and Places in the vicinity of Glasgow Cathedral in the 16th century.)

6. Anon. 1951. *The University of Glasgow through Five Centuries*, p. 13.

7. J. Durkan and J. Kirk, 1977. *The University of Glasgow*, pp. 31–6.

8. Ibid., p. 170.

9. J.H. Dickson and W.W. Gauld, 1987. Mark Jameson's Physic Plants, A Sixteenth Century Garden for Gynaecology in Glasgow? *Scottish Medical Journal*, 32, pp. 60–2.

10. J.D. Mackie, 1954. *The University of Glasgow*, pp. 91–118.

11. Anon. 1951. *The University of Glasgow through Five Centuries*, p. 18.

12. Munimenta 3, p. 485.

13. Munimenta 3, p. 487.

14. GUAA 58040.

15. GUAA 1618.

16. GUAA 1618.

17. GUAA 1618.

18. Munimenta 3, p. 572.

19. Munimenta 3, p. 579.

20. Munimenta 3, p. 500.

21. Munimenta 3, p. 570.

22. Munimenta 3, pp. 540–3.

23. GUAA 22000.

24. GUAA 58269.

25. Munimenta 3, p. 574.

26. GUAA 21198.

27. F.A. Roach, 1985. *Cultivated Fruits of Britain: Their Origin and History* (Basil Blackwell), pp. 124–30.

28. Ibid., pp. 85–97.

29. Ibid., p. 170.

30. Ibid., pp. 166–7.

31. Ibid., p. 126.

32. GUAA 9229.

33. F.A. Roach, 1985. *Cultivated Fruits of Britain*, pp. 190–3.

34. Ibid., p. 192.

35. Munimenta 2, p. 329.

36. F.A. Roach, 1985. *Cultivated Fruits of Britain*, p. 182.

37. Munimenta 3, p. 539.

38. GUAA 58269.

39. GUAA 26630: 'Affaires relating to the Coledge of Glasgow from my entry thereto to be principall writne with my own hand as they occurred to me. Ja. Fall.' p. 2.

40. GUAA 9257.

41. GUAA 1628.
42. GUAA 1629.
43. GUAA 39565.
44. GUAA 32566.
45. GUAA 39567.
46. GUAA 39563.
47. GUAA 39546.
48. GUAA 58040.
49. GUAA 58023.
50. GUAA 58023.
51. GUAA 29582.
52. GUAA 26630: 'Affaires relating to the Coledge of Glasgow ... writne with my own hand as they occurred to me. Ja. Fall.' p. 9.

53. GUAA 58023.
54. F.A. Roach, 1985. *Cultivated Fruits of Britain*, pp. 147–53, 181–4.
55. GUAA 47661.
56. GUAA 47657.
57. J. Durkan and J. Kirk, 1977. *The University of Glasgow*, p. 347.
58. GUAA 47665.
59. GUAA 47687.
60. GUAA 39572.
61. GUAA 39573.
62. Munimenta 3, p. 510.
63. D. Murray, 1927. *Memories of the Old College of Glasgow* (Jackson, Wylie & Co., Glasgow), p. 415.

'FOR THE STUDENTS IMPROVEMENT IN THE SKILL OF BOTTANY...'

At their meeting on 4 July 1704,[1] the members of Faculty took a significant decision regarding the future of the gardens and the teaching of medicine in the University. As stated in the relevant minute:

> The Faculty, considering how suitable it is for the College That their Great Yard together with that behind the Gardiner's house be better improved for the ornament of the College and for the students improvement in the skill of Bottany Doe Resolve and Enact that some part be set apart for that use as soon as may be, and in order this, and that it may be more regularly and to the best advantage done, That Mr Sutherland be brought West, that he may view the ground and give his advice what parts may be proper for this design.

Whilst general improvements were envisaged for the Great Garden, the main thrust of the minute concerned that part of the grounds to be set aside for teaching purposes. Whilst not named as such, a physic garden was to be established, and with its inception the University was entering on the first phase of instituting the teaching of medicine.

The sentiment expressed in the minute, and taken as the heading for this chapter, recognised the essential role that the study of plants then played in medicine. As stated by William Hamilton, one-time Professor of Botany and Anatomy in the University (1781–90), '... the history of Botany & medicine is nearly the same. Botany in this sense is as old as medicine' (p. 197). The study of plants was to include that of the 'simples', the 'medicamentum simplex', or simple drugs, of the herbalists and apothecaries. It was essential that budding physicians should be able to recognise those plants, or the parts of them, with medicinal properties, to be used either directly or more often as the sources of decoctions. This medical association is reflected in the term

'Physic' for the garden, although such gardens were as often described as 'Botanic'. (As originally conceived, the adjectival 'botanic' comes from the Latin *botanicus*, in turn derived from the Greek *botane*, and was used by Theophrastus to describe weeds or herbs, and by Dioscorides to mean anything pertaining to herbs.[2]) Whilst this was the first physic garden to be founded in the University, it was not the first one in the town. Reference has already been made to Mark Jameson's garden in mid-sixteenth-century Glasgow. Knowing Jameson's associations with the University it may be that his garden had a teaching function, although this would probably have been unofficial. Herbalists and apothecaries often had gardens of their own, and Glasgow in the seventeenth and eighteenth centuries was a small town with many large and spacious gardens. This is not the place to review in detail the history of physic gardens in general; a number of recent books supply the necessary information.[3,4,5] A brief digression is required, however, to place the Glasgow Physic Garden in its historical context as a necessary adjunct to the teaching of medicine, and also to explain the significance of the reference in the Faculty minute of 4 July 1704 that 'Mr Sutherland be brought West'. In two earlier contributions to aspects of the University's history, this minute is quoted without this last sentence.[6,7]

The first University Physic Garden to be established in Britain was at Oxford in 1621.[8] With financial backing from the Earl of Danby, a garden was laid out on the presumably fertile soil of the medieval Jewish cemetery on the banks of the River Cherwell below Magdalen Bridge. Robert Morison, a native of Dundee, was appointed the first Professor of Botany at Oxford in 1669. The Physic Garden belonging to the Society of Apothecaries was initiated in 1673 on 3½ acres of land by the Thames at Chelsea, and a hothouse (greenhouse) was erected there in 1686. This was a 'teaching garden' for the instruction of apprentices. The freehold of the ground was purchased for the Society by Sir Hans Sloane in 1722. At Cambridge University two abortive attempts to found a physic garden were made in 1588 and in 1665–6, the second time with the help of 'Mr Loudon, the King's Gardiner', from London. Richard Bradley was appointed first Professor of Botany there in 1724, but Cambridge did not get its physic garden until 1762.[9]

In seventeenth-century Scotland, the most significant developments in the teaching of Botany as allied to medicine were taking place in Edinburgh. Two physicians, Andrew Balfour and Robert Sibbald, played key roles.[10,11] Balfour was born in Fife in 1630. After graduating as an MA at St Andrews University, an awakening interest in botany led him to study medicine in London, Paris and Caen, taking his doctorate at the latter University in 1661. After graduation, his travels in Europe continued for a number of years. On these expeditions he built up extensive collections of books on medicine and natural history, mathematical and surgical instruments, medals, arms, plants, animals, fossils and 'simples'. His botanical studies had been further encouraged by meeting Robert Morison, then living in exile in France in charge of the gardens of the Duke of Orléans. Morison had been on the losing side in the Civil War and was to be made King's Botanist by Charles II after the Restoration, before appointment to the Chair at Oxford. When Balfour set up practice in Edinburgh in 1677–8 he established a small physic garden adjoining his house and carried on an extensive general correspondence, exchanging plants and seeds. A 'herb garden' had been laid out in the town in 1656 for the instruction of apprentices to surgeons and apothecaries.[12]

Edinburgh-born Robert Sibbald, younger by eleven years than Balfour, had pursued his medical studies at Leiden, Paris and Angers, obtaining his doctorate at the latter in 1661. He set up practice in Edinburgh in 1662. He was of like mind with Balfour in deploring the appalling state of much of the so-called medical practice then existing in the town, and together they were instrumental in founding the College of Physicians in 1681, with Balfour playing the major role. Sibbald's botanical interests were centred mainly on the indigenous plants of Scotland as sources of 'simples', and he also established a small garden to cultivate these native plants. In 1670 Balfour and Sibbald rented a piece of ground, 1600 square feet, in St Anne's Yard near Holyrood Abbey. This ground they stocked with plants from their own gardens and from the extensive collection of Patrick Murray, Laird of Livingston in West Lothian, who was a mutual friend. An able young gardener of unknown origins, James Sutherland, was appointed to take charge of the garden, in which some 900 plants were eventually assembled. Sutherland's successful management led to the search for more extensive facilities. In 1675, with the support of Balfour and other leading physicians in the town, Sutherland was given the lease of some land by the Town Council. This ground, an area 300 by 190 feet, adjoined the Trinity Hospital at the mouth of what was then the Nor' Loch (land now occupied in part by Waverley Station). This new venture was to be known as both the 'Physick' and the 'Botanic' garden, where some 2,000 plants were to be grown with Sutherland installed as 'Intendant'.

Having established the identity of the 'Mr Sutherland' of the Glasgow Faculty's minute of 4 July 1704, there is need to explore further how his standing was achieved.[13] In 1683 Sutherland published his *Hortus Medicus Edinburgensis*, a list of plants in the Physic Garden. In 1676 he became associated with the 'Towns College' or University in Edinburgh (the Town Council being its governing body), but was not given the title of Professor until 1695. Meanwhile he also planted out and managed the College Physic Garden, and in 1695 took over the running of a third garden in part of the Royal Garden at Holyrood. Sutherland was appointed King's Botanist in Scotland by Royal Warrant in 1699. His rise to prominence was entirely due to his own abilities as a gardener and botanist. His career had its setbacks. The financial arrangements for his salary and the expenses for the gardens were not always straightforward. The garden by Trinity Hospital was flooded in 1689 when the Nor' Loch was drained during the siege of Edinburgh Castle. A large number of valuable plants were lost, as was also the mainstay of Sutherland's livelihood for one to two years. His pre-eminence in botany at Edinburgh, and probably in Scotland, was clearly appreciated at the time by Principal Stirling and the Glasgow Faculty. Sutherland was 66 years old in 1704. In 1706 he resigned his University Chair and turned to his numismatic interests. In 1710 he was made Regius Professor of Botany by Royal Warrant issued by Queen Anne, but this became void on her death in 1714. Sutherland died in 1719.

In sixteenth- and seventeenth-century Glasgow, the major developments in medicine lay outside the University. Whilst Andrew de Garleis, a doctor of medicine, was received into the University in 1469, there is no evidence that he engaged in any teaching. Andrew Boorde, a physician who was also an agent of Thomas Cromwell, came to study and practice medicine in Glasgow in 1536 and may have been an early example of an 'extra-mural' teacher, but he was not officially a member of the University.[14] The history of medical practice in the town in the sixteenth century is one of a small number of physicians and midwives paid by the Town Council, and a large number of quacks, regarding whom the Kirk Session made representations to the Council in 1598.[15] In 1599 King James VI granted letters patent to Peter Lowe describing him as 'professoure of medecine', but having no connection with the University.[16] Lowe took the lead in founding the Faculty of Physicians and Surgeons in 1599 with control of all medical activities in Glasgow and over a large area of west-central Scotland. In later years the members of this Faculty were to oppose the development of medical education in the University, claiming that they had this function. In 1637, as a result of a Crown visitation, a professor of Physic was instituted at the University, to which Robert Mayne, one of the Regents, was appointed on 26 October in that year. Five years later a Kirk inspection abolished the Chair, allowing Mayne to retain the title until his death in 1646. Hence, the teaching of medicine in Glasgow made a somewhat abortive start in the first half of the seventeeth century.

By the time we arrive at the decision of Glasgow University to found a Physic Garden there were already six such gardens in existence in Edinburgh.[17] Of all the physic gardens known in Europe in the early years of the eighteenth century, the one at the University of Leiden had the most influence on the teaching of medicine in Scotland. Founded in 1587, it was to attain international prominence under the supervision of Hermann Boerhaave, appointed Professor of Botany and Medicine in 1709. Boerhaave was a distinguished scholar who undertook a more serious study of Botany on his appointment to the joint Chair, and who developed a lifelong enthusiasm for the subject. Between 1709 and 1719 he added some 2,000 species to the garden.[18]

His prowess in teaching Botany was balanced by his excellence in other branches of medicine, and medical students were drawn to Leiden from all over Europe, including a number from Scotland who were later to occupy Chairs in Scottish Universities. Boerhaave's enthusiasm for Botany left its mark on many of his students, who became protagonists of his methods of teaching and garden organisation. His outstanding abilities as a teacher and communicator remain his lasting scientific memorial. His reputation was such that a letter from Asia addressed simply 'To the Greatest Physician in the World' was said to have been delivered safely to him.[19]

We return to the deliberations of the Glasgow University Faculty regarding the institution of their Physic Garden. Following the meeting of 4 July 1704, Principal Stirling set in train a number of consultations. There is no positive record of James Sutherland having visited Glasgow as proposed in the July minute. In the next chapter a letter from him, sent with some plants, will be quoted in full and its contents suggest that he was familiar with the layout of the Glasgow garden. The outcome of Stirling's consultations was minuted at the 3 October 1704 Faculty meeting:[20]

The faculty considering it is now a fit time to set apart some piece of ground for the Bottanik Garden designed, and being informed that the physicians and surgeons in the Town having viewed the College Great Yard and the Little one behind the Gardiners house were unanimously of the opinion that the said little yard with the addition of John Bowman and James Allan their yards contiguous thereto, both holding of the University, were the proper place for the said Design: Severall of the Faculty having also seen the ground themselves, and being of the same sentiment. Therefore the Faculty orders the said Little Yard with as much of John Bowman's as may make the wall of the said Bottanik Garden, joyn with the west corner of the College Kirkyard Dyke, and as much of the said John Allan's yard as shall be found necessary by those who are best skilled in these matters, to be set aside for a Physick and Bottanik garden, and inclosed within a suitable and sufficient wall for that purpose, and hereto impower the Principal to treat with the forenamed persons concerned in the ground to be added to the said Little Yard, that after the Faculty is acquainted with the Terms on which they will part with the same ground, the same may be inclosed as soon as can be: as also to do what is necessary for getting the said Little Yard from Mr Robertsone and the Gardiners. As Likewise the faculty recommends it to the Principal to see that a wall for inclosing the whole ground of the said Bottanik Garden be built with all expedition, and to cause move the Gardiners house if same shall be needfull: and to find a place for it, and cause rebuild the same ...

Following these directives, Principal Stirling wasted no time, and on 6 October was able to report back to Faculty:[21]

> This day the Principal reported the terms upon which John Bowman, Francis Stevensone and James Millar are willing to part with the ground which is to be included for a physick Garden, wherewith the Faculty declare themselves satisfied.

There seems to be some confusion in the Faculty's concept of the garden, calling it 'Physick' and 'Bottanik' in the same sentence. Both terms were interchangeable as far as contemporary attitudes were concerned: a similar confusion of terms was afforded the garden alongside Trinity Hospital in Edinburgh. The name 'Physic' subsequently came into common usage in all associated documents and official records at Glasgow; 'Botanic' or 'Botany' Garden were descriptions not used until near the end of the century. It is evident that some consultations went on with the Faculty of Physicians and Surgeons regarding the siting of the garden.

There is a need to establish the exact site chosen for the Physic Garden in order to correct an error which first arose in an earlier history of the University;[22] an error which has been perpetuated in two subsequent publications, both of which commemorate the fifth centenary of the University's foundation.[23,24] To quote from the last of these:

> Immediately to the south of the Church was the Physic, or Botanic, Garden laid out in 1754 in place of an earlier one in the east grounds dating from the beginning of the century ...

This statement gives the impression that there were two sites for the garden in the first half of the eighteenth century. The Faculty minute of 3 October 1704 contains most of the relevant information. It refers to the suitability of the Little Yard 'behind the Gardiners House', together with additions from neighbouring ground leased to others but belonging to the College. Robert Robertsone's tack of 1691 (p. 22) states that he was to have possession of the 'house high and Laigh with pertines of the samen in blackfriars wynd with ye Little yaird att ye back yrof'. In some earlier tacks the Little Yard is described as the Blackfriars Yard. The gardener's house opened onto the Blackfriars Wynd, a narrow alley lying south of the Blackfriars Kirk and its Yard and the College Buildings. The wynd was known when the earliest buildings of the College were erected (Figure 1.1, p. 10). The minute of 3 October states that some of John Bowman's land contiguous with the proposed garden was to be taken to construct a wall which would join with the 'west corner of the College Kirkyard Dyke'. Part of this kirkyard wall can be seen in Slezer's panoramic drawing of the College and its grounds published in 1693 (Frontispiece), with the corner of the

Little Yard just showing (and conveniently indicated by the shadow of the kirk spire). This places the Physic Garden on the south side of the kirkyard, and situated on the *west* side of the College grounds.

Verification that this was the first site of the garden is to be found in documents associated with some protracted litigation (1729–32) between the University and William Bowman, son of the John Bowman named in the minute of 3 October 1704. The fine particulars of this lengthy affair, with the papers prepared in elaborate detail on both sides, are not relevant. In outline, John Bowman was a Cautioner (one who stood security) for a loan of £484/10/- Scots made by the University to two merchants. The merchants defaulted, and when John Bowman died in 1728 the University claimed against his son William for the sum plus accrued interest. William Bowman's reply was based on the concept that the best method of defence is attack. After preliminary skirmishing, he presented a petition to the Lords of Council and Session on 21 July 1731. In this he counterclaimed from the University for money allegedly owed to his father over land purchases which he stated had not been paid for fully. The Petition includes the following:[25]

> ... and that the Pursuers were otherwise Debitors to me for the value of a Parcel of Ground which had belonged to my Father, which the University has taken at their own hand without any Right, for the Conveniency of making a Physic Garden ... I condescend upon a Claim that the University knows my Father has against them, and that was for the Ground taken into their Physick-Garden in the Year 1704, and the Fruit-trees then cut down ...

The Faculty's reply to the above petition was dated 23 December 1731,[26] and includes a passing reference to the ground taken for the Physic Garden. Regarding the counterclaim made by John Bowman before he died, the Faculty's reply ('Answers') referred to his statement that they should 'also give him satisfaction for some pretended Damage done by a Dike of the Universities Physick Garden, which he alledged was built upon his Ground, tho' in Truth in the straightening of that Dike, which was done by Consent, the Provost got more Ground from the College than they had from him'. John Bowman at one time held the post of Provost, and the implication of the Faculty's explanation was that he got more out of the deal than they did! The parcel of land incorporated was further described by William Bowman as 'which Ground is bounded on the East and South by that part of the Physick Garden which is properly their own, by the Blackfriars Church Yard & the yard now belonging to me on the North, and my said yard on the West'. Whilst the lawsuit confirms the position of the Physic Garden as first laid out, it is not clear whether the exchange of ground with Bowman was finalised in written form. The implications are that the mutual consent on the exchange of land was a verbal one between

Principal Stirling, John Bowman and the others involved. Such a verbal agreement may explain the rapidity with which Stirling accomplished the transactions as required of him by the meeting of Faculty of 3 October 1704. He was able to report satisfactory arrangements having been made three days later. John Allan, another leaseholder from whom land was taken, was to make a claim for losses incurred some seven years after the event (p. 54).

John McArthur's map of the town prepared in 1778 includes the University and its grounds (Figure 2.1) and shows the Physic Garden south of the Blackfriars Kirkyard. This is exactly the site chosen for it in 1704, and, as will be shown in a later chapter, there was no laying out of a second garden in 1754. The reason for the error in location in earlier historical accounts probably arose through an incomplete reference to the relevant Faculty minutes. The key sentence lies in the first of the historical studies quoted above regarding the Faculty's initial moves in establishing the garden:[22]

> In 1704 they resolved to set aside part of their Great Yard or Garden for the purpose

A footnote on the same page points out that the Great Garden lay to the east of the inner quadrangle of the College. Hence the confusion and the subsequent erroneous statements in which the Physic Garden was said to have been laid out on the east side of the Great Garden.

The College Accounts for the years 1704–6 contain numerous references to the expenses involved in the founding of the Physic Garden. The largest outlay was for dismantling and re-erecting the gardener's house, the necessity for which had been pointed out in the Faculty minute of 3 October. A noticeable feature of these accounts is the involvement of a certain Thomas Young, who was paid for 'severall things to the Gardiner's new house' to the value of £132/13/- Scots in 1704–5. Young continued to be associated with the building of the new house and with developments in the Physic Garden over a number of years. Whilst the College Accounts books record the total sums paid out, as was usual, Young kept meticulous accounts of all the sums of money involved, for examination by Principal Stirling; those for 1705–6 have survived intact. On each the first entry is prefixed 'Impr' for 'Imprimis', and subsequently 'Itt', although on occasions 'Item' is written in full. Thomas Young was the College Bedellus, with an annual salary of £52 Scots — £40 for his duties as Bedellus and £12 for watching over the College buildings during vacations. The handwriting and signatures on precepts for his salary and on precepts for expenses concerning the Physic Garden and other College business are identical. Young was the agent for all manner of small purchases and payments, the largest and very much an exception being for £7 Scots and the smallest for 2/-. Whilst the individual amounts were small, over the course of a year of a year they could reach totals far in excess of his

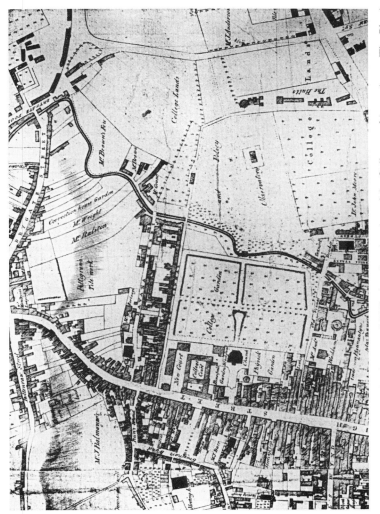

Figure 2.1. From McArthur's map of 1778, showing the plan of the College and its environs. The Physic Garden site south of the Blackfriars Kirkyard is that on which it was established in 1704-5

salary. There was, however, a definite pattern in his presentation of the accounts and the repayments made on the precepts. The 'summa' was usually in the region of £30 Scots and mostly the timing of the presentation was every three months, unless the expenditure was close to the maximum after a short time interval. It might be assumed that Young was an enterprising individual who, with the approval of the Principal and Faculty, acted as a 'middleman' to expedite the minor works and payments to merchants, craftsmen and labourers. If this was so, then he ran up bills far in excess of his salary, even allowing for any small commissions he may have earned. A close scrutiny of Young's accounts shows that most of the payments were made expressly 'By orders of Principall', the latter evidently keeping a close watch on all the cash outlays. It seems more likely that Young was the holder of a cash 'float' of about £30 Scots and that the payments made to him via precepts were intended to maintain this float. This is indicated on one such precept for £31/1/4d, dated 18 November 1706, on which the Principal's authorisation states: 'Mungo Cochrane Pay to Thomas Young the above threttie pounds ane shilling four pennies Scots to be again deburs'd for the use of the Colledge, and this wi his receipt shall be y^{or} warrand'.[27] To be 'again deburs'd' means to be paid out and underlines the fluid nature of the moneys held by Young. The extent and variable nature of the expenditure show that Young was deeply involved in routine College affairs in addition to his duties as Bedellus. These additional duties on the part of the Bedellus were to be formalised in later years. John Bryce, Bedellus at some time between 1740 and 1760, was still paid £40 Scots for his duties as such but also received £66/13/6d for his services as 'Master of Works'. Bryce's accounts for sundry payments in the years 1758–60 are similar to those kept 50 years earlier by Thomas Young — but Young received no extra salary.

Among the recommendations made by Faculty regarding the Physic Garden was one stating that the Principal should '. . . see that a wall for inclosing the whole ground of the said Bottanik Garden be built with all expedition' and 'to cause move the Gardiner's house if same shall be needfull . . .'. To clear the ground for the garden, the house on the north side of Blackfriars Wynd[28] was to be moved further along the wynd. No records are available for the costs of dismantling the house but, since its stones would have been used to build the new one, the dismantling costs were probably included in the overall charges made by the masons. Building the 'inclosing wall' would not have been straightforward. In the 1704–5 College Accounts there is mention of £12 Scots paid to 'John Bartoun, for the loss he sustained in quitting the Bowling Green, now included in the Physic Garden'. The relevant precept, dated 9 March 1705, is more explicit: 'Mungo Cochran Pay to John Barton Gardiner twelve pounds Scots for the loss sustained by him in quitting the Boulin green (now to be included in the physick garden) by dung laid by him the former year and otherwise and this with this his receipt shall be yor warrant'.[29] Barton (or Bartoun) was a gardener with responsibility for the Bowling Green and would have dressed the ground the preceding winter. A John Bartoun was admitted to membership of the Incorporation of Gardeners of Glasgow on 26 January 1700.[30] (The principle of paying for previous manuring of the land is maintained to the present day in the purchase of cultivated ground.) Barton would also have been responsible for mowing the sward throughout the playing season, and it is likely that the grass cuttings would have been his, for sale in the town. The precept shows that the incorporation of the bowling green took place after 5 March 1705. The bowling green was also enclosed by a wall. An account submitted by Walter Corbet, Hammerman, on 17 July 1690 includes two items: 'For ane pair of bands to the bowlling grein gate weight 1 ston — lib 02/13/4d', and '... for ane new key and mending ane old Lock thereto 00/12/0d'.[31] A gate which could be locked would have been part of a wall around the bowling green. The dismantling of this wall would have been necessary, although the stonework could have been re-used for the Physic Garden wall. Nowhere are there any references to the purchase of stones for the Physic Garden wall.

Over the two years the Thomas Young accounts include entries which state either 'to drink money ... by the orders of the Principall' or 'to morning drinks ... etc'. All such entries emphasise the prior authorisation by the Principal. The entries are primarily for the craftsmen engaged in building the walls of the Physic Garden and the gardener's house: masons, wrights (carpenters), 'sklaitters' or 'sclaitters' (slaters) and on one occasion a 'plummer'. The first such entry (2 January 1705)[32] reads '... given in drink money to ye Gardners of ye sd Garden by the princlls orders — £01=09=00' (the 'sd Garden' being the Physic Garden). For the following 9 March, the entry states '... given to ye Masons in drink money at ye working at ye Dyk of ye fsd garden — £01=09=00'. Entries for 'drink money' implying the handing over of a small cash bonus were distinct from those for 'morning drinks', when pints of ale were supplied to the workmen from a nearby inn. These, however, were Scots pints, or Stirling jugs (jougs), equal in volume to 3 Imperial pints. Some later precepts reveal that one (Scots) pint cost 2/- Scots. The sums involved in these drink bonuses were usually 14/6d–£1/9/- Scots. Usually one pint at a time per workman was regarded as an adequate (or safe enough) reward. Over the two years 1704–6 these drink allowances came to about £27 Scots, equivalent to 270 Scots pints or 810 Imperial pints. In authorising these 'drink money' bonuses Principal Stirling was keeping up a long-established tradition. A note written in 1619 by Principal Robert Boyd of Trochrig states: 'John Craig ye sall paye le laboure for yair 4 dayes work in sawing ye Colledge dailles together with yair drink accordinge ye custome'.[33] A closer scrutiny of the Thomas Young accounts shows that these 'drink money' entries occur at various intervals, and usually indicate a particular job having been completed, or a phase of the house construction having ended. The drink money entries offer some insight into the timing of the various construction phases of the garden walls and the gardener's house.

According to the precept quoted earlier, incorporation of the Bowling Green into the Physic Garden was to take place after 9 March 1705. On the same day, drink money was paid to the masons engaged in building the 'Dyk' (= wall) of the Physic Garden and possibly for dismantling the wall of the Bowling Green. Also, on 3 March, 'a lyn to the Masons building the above Dyk' cost 14/- and a 'brick stand to them' was 12/-. If the 'lyn' was a length of cord for aligning the stones of the wall it would seem somewhat expensive, since later in the year 'a Lyne to the Wrights for taking a measure of the roof of the fsd house' cost 2/- (the 'fsd house' was the gardener's new house under construction). In present-day Glasgow, to 'have a line' means possession of a directive in note form, or an order for purchase. The 1705 'lyn' for the masons may have been of a similar nature. The building of the garden wall continued through April and into May 1705.[34] A doorway to the garden having been constructed, three hundred 'plenshur' (= plensher) nails were purchased for 'dressing the door' and 7/6d was paid 'for sawing 5 dealls for lyneing the Door of the sd Gardine'. The 'dealls' (also 'dailles' or 'daills' at various times in the accounts) were planks and would have been affixed with the plensher nails. 'Oak nailes' for fixing 'bands' to the garden door cost 10/-, these bands being the hinge fastenings.

The rebuilding of the gardener's house was in progress at the same time as the garden walls were under construction. This house-dismantling and rebuilding was a sizeable financial commitment on the part of the Faculty in 1705–6 and in its own way is closely linked with the history of the Physic Garden. The Thomas Young accounts refer to the inclusion of stairs at a later stage in the building process, revealing that the house was two-storeyed. In the early summer of 1705 some of the 'Oak nailes' purchased for fixing the bands of the Physic Garden door, together with some of the 'plenshur' nails, were used for the door of the 'Gardiners house'. Construction of the house door would imply that the walls of the house had reached first-storey level. At the same time, 1,000 'single flooring nails' were purchased for 'nailling the scaffolding of the Gardiners house', which would in turn suggest that the walls were reaching up to the second storey. This rate of progress is underlined by a bill for £800 Scots presented by Samuel Carruth in the late summer of 1705 (eventually paid in September 1706) in 'part payment of the pryce of the building of the physicke gardine Dyke and for the Gardiners house and pertinents'. This payment was made on a separate precept,[35] being too large a sum for the Thomas Young accounts. Samuel Carruth signed himself 'Measone in Glasgow', but we may assume that he was a master mason who employed the others working on the walls of the garden and house. Work on the upper storey of the house continued into autumn, as shown by the purchase on 6 October 1705[36] of '2 hodgheads for the use of the masons that are working on the Gardiners House' costing, together with 'girths and nails for the sd hodgheads', £3/6/- Scots. As recorded in the accounts, once the walls were of sufficient height much of the emphasis on the building work in the summer months moved to the work of the wrights. Once again, there are few indications of costings regarding the timber used other than payments for cartage. The accounts show that planks were frequently brought to the College and were stored in a 'daill-house' somewhere in the grounds.[37] Timber was constantly being used for repairs or rebuilding somewhere in the College. Rarely are any timber costings listed solely as being concerned with the gardener's house. In addition to the daill house (sometimes called a 'timber house'), there was a 'work-house' in the grounds where tree trunks or 'cabers' were sawn into 'daills' by 'sawers'. On occasions workmen would be paid small sums (4/- or 6/- Scots) for carrying planks from the daill house to the building site, or timber from the daill house to the work-house or vice versa. There was also a 'weigh-house' somewhere in the grounds.

All evidence points to the College keeping a sizeable quantity of timber of various forms in storage. The planks, tree trunks and cabers came via the 'Broomy Law' (the Broomielaw of the present day: then, and within living memory, a busy quayside but now no longer so). Other timber loads came from 'The Grein' (Glasgow Green). Thus, 'for loading up 100 Dealls from the Grein to the Colledge' cost 14/-, or 'To a Carter for loading up a Duzon of Great Planks for the Gardiners house from ye old grein 12/-'. Carriage of materials to the College and within the grounds is often described as 'hurling' in the accounts, and to this day in Glasgow two-wheeled hand barrows are called 'hurlies'. Another relevant entry reads 'to ye Boatman for bringing up a hundred planks from Greenock, — £1/10/0'. A similar transportation of 200 planks cost £2/8/- Scots. The shallow channel of the River Clyde meant that large vessels could not navigate nearer the town than the mouth of the estuary, 14 miles downriver. Cargo was offloaded onto small boats of shallow draught; the timber so transported came mainly from Scandinavia.

The Thomas Young accounts give a detailed listing of the nails bought for the rebuilding of the house. Over two years £41/6/8d Scots was expended on a variety of nails, of which 'single flooring nails' formed the bulk. Other entries record purchases of 'double flooring naills; door nailles; plenshur naills; big nailles' and 'Great Carron nailles'. The latter were large spikes used for fixing large beams. In the late summer the wrights were involved in laying the 'jests' (= joists) of the house and £1/15/- Scots was paid for '6 Oak Cabers for supporting the jests of the fsd house'. A carter was paid £1/15/- Scots for 'loading up 4 Duzon of Oak planks for ye roof of ye Gardiners house', and it was at this time that the aforementioned 'lyne to the wrights for measuring the roof of fsd house' was purchased. Throughout October and

November 1705[38,39] there were frequent purchases of 'single flooring nailles', which suggests the laying of floor planking. 'Glew to the windows of fsd house' was bought in September. Drink-money payments to the wrights at intervals are recorded through the autumn and winter. Frequent purchases of candles 'for the wrights' were also made during the late autumn and winter, suggesting that work on the internal construction was continued during those short days. A hearth stone was laid in early November and a lock and key to the house was bought on 5 December at a cost of 18/-. An entry in the accounts for 19 October 1705 is for 'drink money to ye masons and ye sclatters working at ye house'. This is the first mention of the employment of slaters; on the same day a payment of £2/14/- Scots was made for 'loading up 2000 sclaitts from ye Broomy Law to ye sd house', and on 4 November £4/-/- Scots was paid for 'sklaitt nailles'. A further load of slates was brought in on November 29, and £1/8/- Scots was paid for 'sawing 14 Daills for the Gutterboards and tabletts for use of ye Sklatters'. Drink money (14/6d) was paid 'to the sklaitters men ... at finishing of ye work' on 7 January 1706. The 'gutterboards' were presumably for roof drainage and the 'tabletts' were flat pieces of wood used for roofing. A bill for the slate work was presented by 'George Thomsone slaiter':[40]

Moving and rebuilding the Gardners House George Thomsone Slaiter

Itt. for 8 rude of sclait work at 7 pound per rude   £56=0=0
Itt. for 4 days of 2 men per rude for helping up the
roof of the Gardiners house at 13 shill 4
pennes per day   5=6=8
Itt. for 4 days of 2 men recaaving ye sclaitts at
ye Briimelaw and for hurling ym in at 10 shill p day   4=0=0

Summa   65=6=8

Pay George Thomson Sclater fiftie pounds half ane merk Scots wi thwelve
punds formerly pd him compleat ye above accompt
Jo Stirling P.

George Thomson receipted the precept without argument, his receipt being dated 7 January 1706. A precept in the name of Thomas Young, dated 1 March 1706, allowed payment of £10/10/- for 'sclaites to the Gardiners house'.[41] Whether this represents a belated payment for slates received earlier — as part of the Thomson work-phase — is not known.

It is to be noted that Thomson's account was for 'moving and rebuilding' the gardener's house. The '8 rude of sclait work' would probably have involved removal of the original roof as well as covering the new one. One 'rude' (= ruid or rood) in old Scots was equal to 36 square ells and an ell was about 36 inches (to be precise 37.2 inches).

Therefore 1 square ell was about equal in area to 1 square yard, making 8 rudes equal to an area of 288 square ells (or square yards). If, however, this measure is for roof removal as well as rebuilding, perhaps half of it represented the area of the roof. The payment to men for 'helping up the roof' was probably for labourers assisting the slaters.

Internal construction continued whilst the roof was making progress. On 28 December 1705, £2/5/- was paid to 'the Sawers for sawing up 30 daills for the parpall walls and windows of the gardiners house'.[42] The 'parpall' walls were the inner partition walls, and on 29 December payment was made to a workman 'for carrying daills from the daill house to the Gardiners house' for the same purpose. On 9 January 1706, 'snecks and bands' were fitted to the 'parpall doors' ('snecks' = locks). Whilst the 'parpall' walls were being constructed some 'ffogg' was also purchased. Fogg was an unnamed filler material — it may have been mossy turf — and was probably for the cavities of the partition walls.[43] Work was still in progress well into 1706; 'Fir deallls' for the house were carried from the daill house on 29 April. Later in the year (September) quantities of 'Redd' (= rubble) were carted from various parts of the College to the house, together with '10 cairts of sand', all to be used for 'the midle walls of the Gardeners house'. On 7 October 1706, Samuel Carruth was paid £300 as a further instalment for 'work wroght at ye Gardiners house' by the masons.[44]

A necessary additional building attached to the house was constructed in the summer and autumn of 1706. In June a workman was paid £1/8/- for 'helping up the Roof of the Gardners Office houses for 4 days at 7p p. day'.[45] Here we see an entry in which the daily payment is given in sterling and the overall sum in Scots money — a frequent occurrence now and later on in accounts and precepts. It should also be noted that 'p' was in those days sometimes used as an abbreviation for 'pence'. 'Helping up the Roof' suggests work with the rafters and there is probably a connection here with a payment of 6/- to a workman for 'carreeing dealls to the New House'. The 'Office houses' or privies were to be thatched. An entry for 20 June gives a payment of 6/- '. . . of Expences at buying the strae to thatk the new house', and 7/- went to 'a workman for Carrying the sd. strae to the new houses'. A precept to Young (not listed in his accounts) for 5 July states:[46]

> pay to Thomas Young fourteen pounds fyve shillings Scots for threttie thrive of straw for thacking the office houses of the gardiners house at 9/6d ye thrive — £14/05/0

'Thrive' was a local spelling for threave. A threave consisted of two stooks of straw, each stook containing twelve sheaves; the roof would have been covered by 720 individual sheaves. On 3 July the accounts record payment of £2/16/- for '400 fir tethers for sewing on the thatk on the sd houses', and '200 temple wands for that same house' cost £1/6/-.

41

The fir tethers and the temple wands (of hazel) were used to anchor the thatch. On 4 July '300 Divats for Rigin the sd houses' cost £2. The divots were pieces of turf used to line the edges of a thatched roof and to form a ridge coping on the top. 'Half Garon Nailes for Nailling the baak and geigts of the sd house' cost £1 on the same day. The 'baak' probably refers to a beam, and the 'geigts' were probably some sort of wood border (below the line of the thatched roof?). Four locks for the office houses cost £4/-/- Scots on 3 August, and later in the month £2/5/- Scots was paid for '9 Carts of stones to cassa the Gardners office houses'.[47] 'Cassa' is an abbreviation of 'cassaying' or 'causeying', i.e. laying a paved or stone floor. The stone was followed by 14 carts of sand (£2/16/- Scots) 'for the foresd use of cassaying' and an additional '12 carts of causay stone' (£3/-/- Scots) on 4 October. On 10 October, £4 was paid to a 'causier for causaying the sd house'[48] and 'a workman to serve the sd causier for the space of 6 days at 7p per day' received £2/2/- Scots. This last work suggests the paving of the ground floor of the gardener's house.

Hence, it would seem that by the autumn of 1706 all the necessary attributes of the gardener's residence were completed. Re-use of stone from the dismantled 'office houses' must have taken place, since nowhere in the accounts is there any reference to stone being purchased for the use of the masons. Dismantling the thatched roof required a new one on the rebuilt privies. No reference can be found to building a chimney or 'lum' in the house, but this would probably have been included in the masons' work. None of the College records gives any clear indication of the siting of the moved house. Nor is there any indication over the years that it was used other than by the gardeners who were appointed with responsibility for the Physic Garden; in those days, such a possession must have been a major incentive to obtain the position. In later years, a letter addressed to a gardener bore his name and the street name — Blackfriars Wynd. The house therefore stood on the north side of the wynd and was probably moved westwards a short distance. In 1755, one George Garden was paid 1/- for a key to the lock 'for the Gardiners hous door in the blackfreer wynd'.

Accounts in the name of Young are not available for 1707. The 1708 accounts include the puzzling information that work was continuing on the 'gardiners house'. On 2 September 1708, 20 pounds' weight of lead was bought for the masons 'for fastening the stenchels in the windows of the gardiners laigh houses'[49] and the masons were paid 14/- 'for carrying the said stenchels from the smith to the sd house and for morning drinks'. 'Stenchels' were iron gratings to be fitted over window spaces; 'laigh houses' were small huts, possibly for storage of tools. Samuel Carruth, the master mason, presented another bill on 8 March 1709 which included work on the 'new house' and on some aspects of the Physic Garden:[50]

Accompt of Masson work wroght to the Colledge about the new
house and new Dyck Be Samuel Carruth Measson

Impr. for putting up 2 stairs to the new house at 22 lib p pair	£44/0/0
It. For a new door in the Dyck between the two yeards	10/0/0
It. for eight new hearth stanes in the new house at 3 lib per pair	24/0/0
It. for 24 Storm Reebitts and 12 Lintells and 12 topping stones and hewing and felling them above ye walls heads in the new house	36/0/0
It. for mounting the geat head of the Physick Garden with Bassis and Pirimides according to order	2/8/0
It. for 2 stairs to the Physic Garden	15/0/0
It. for 80 foots of rigging stones to the new house	16/0/0
It. for building partition walls in the office houses belonging to the Gardiner being 12 days of work of ye massons at a merk p. day and 6 days of workmen at 8 s per day	10/8/0
It. of hewen stones furnished to the said partition wall being 20 pieces at 7s per piece	7/0/0
It. for 6 draught of wall stones to boamfill the Gardiners house at 12p per draught	3/12/0
It. to 2 massons half a day and a workman half a day filling a window at ye Gardiners house	17/4
	169/5/4

The final stages of wall-building for the Physic Garden included
some decorative stonework over the entrance (the 'geat [= gate] head'),
steps to it, and a door in the wall between the Physic and the Great
Garden. Reference in Carruth's account to work continuing on the
'gardiners house' needs some explanation. Partition walls being
installed in 'office houses' supposedly completed in 1706 raises a
question; and why would the house now require eight new hearth
stones and two stairs? 'Storn Reebitts' (= Rabbets: pieces of masonry
grooved to join with other structures?), lintels and coping stones imply
some final wall embellishments; 'boamfill' probably meant to infill
with stones the wood frames ('boams') for the inner walls. Samuel
Carruth's account also shows the pay differential between a craftsman
— the mason — at 13/4d per day and a workman at 8/- Scots.

These references to th building of a new 'Gardiners' house are
confusing. What is not cla.ified in Young's accounts is that this was
new construction work and that it refers to another house built by
orders of Faculty which took the form of a tenement together with
accompanying 'offices' and 'laigh houses': hence the two sets of stairs,
several hearth stones and 'partition walls in the office houses'. This new
building was on the south side of the Blackfriars Wynd and part of it
was to be let to the tacksmen of the Great Garden (as will be described

in a later chapter), thus explaining its description as a 'gardiners house'.

As stated earlier, the rebuilding of the gardener's house and the construction of enclosing walls around the Physic Garden were financial commitments taken on without argument by the Faculty and were clear signs of the determination of its members to initiate the teaching of medicine in the University. It is difficult to get an accurate picture of the overall expenditure, since much remains hidden in general expenses and many bills and precepts were probably lost. Totalling as much of the outlay as can be judged relevant over the two years 1705–6, however, gives a sum of about £1400 Scots, not an insignificant expenditure at that time.

Whilst particular attention has been focused on the payments for the Physic Garden and the gardener's house, the Thomas Young accounts also yield some interesting insights into the functional day-to-day life of the University in its infrastructure well below the levels of formal academic work. For 1705–6 there is a series of entries, always 'by ye Principalls orders', of payments to a 'poor man' or 'poor woman' — in most cases amounting to 14/6d Scots. On one occasion 'a poor woman with six shildren' received £1. Payments to needy students were recorded at times: 'a Colledger who was sick', 'Dickson a Colledger', and 'Wm Dunlop a student' each received £1, whilst 'Donald Crawford a student' was paid £2/18/-. Robert Brown who 'had his house burned in the Vennill' received £3/14/- and 'Mr David Robertsone, distempered' was given £1/9/-. 'A poor seaman' and 'a blind woman' each received 14/6d, whilst 'a lame man' was given only 3/-. We are left pondering on the identity of 'Highland Mary', who on two occasions received 14/6d from Thomas Young, and also that of John Dunn's daughter Sarah, who on four occasions was paid the same sum and was still in receipt of similar financial help in 1708. 'A poor lad from Ireland' was given 14/- and a 'poor man from Ireland' was paid £2/18/-. This charitable service by the University was a function recognised both within and outside the College and was still a service listed in the accounts of John Bryce, the Bedellus in the 1760s.

Walter Langmuir's name appears frequently in the 1704–6 accounts. He was the College labourer or odd-job man. On one occasion he was paid 8/- for one day's work on the gardener's house; on another 'a shovell to Walter Langmuire' cost 10/6d. He was paid small sums at various times for carrying letters to Nether Pollock, south of Glasgow — probably a good day's journey; this was the residence of the then Rector, Sir John Maxwell. Langmuir was also the beneficiary of the College's charity at times, being given 14/6d 'by the princlls orders qu his wife was sick', and some payments were made towards the repair of his wife's roof.

More than anything else, the Thomas Young accounts offer a constant reminder of the expenses involved in the running repairs of the College fabric. This is seen in the purchases of planks, tree trunks (for the 'sawers'), slates, slate nails, 'flooring' and 'plenshur' nails — these always bought in large quantities. Sand, stones and lime were regularly bought by the College, and the accounts record both the sums involved and the payments for 'hurling them in'. The many craftsmen employed — masons, wrights, slaters, sawyers, causeyers, as well as many 'workmen' — had to be paid the 'going rates' for their crafts. For all of these there were the regular awards either of 'drink money' or of 'morning drinks'. Among the more mundane outgoings at regular intervals are 'ane pound of candles for faculty' at 4/- per pound. To 'sweep a lumb' (= chimney) cost 5/-. Buckets seem to have been lost down the College well quite frequently and their removal cost 4/- a time. A new chimney for the Principal's house cost £22 plus £1/10/- for its transportation from Edinburgh. Payments were also made to workmen for removing tree branches blown down in the Great Garden: on one occasion (2 September 1708) an entry reads 'for sawing ane great Elm tree that was blown over by the wind and for carrying the said tree from the foot of the Old Vennell to the College Close £1/15/0', and 'for ane dragsaw to saw therein the said tree, 6/0d'. On 12 August 1708, 4/- was paid 'for drawing naills out of the barren timber round the outside of the College yard'.

Thomas Young was required to make payments on occasions to the 'Toun Officers', an early form of police force. It was a College tradition that small sums of money were given to the College servants as New Year's gifts (usually recorded as 'drink money'!). The 'Toun Officers' were also included in this annual largesse — the University evidently believed in keeping on the right side of these officials, who had some responsibility for maintaining law and order. Two officers were paid 8/- each 'for arresting what was in Wm Steill's room' in the College, and 14/6d was paid to 'Toun Officers for apprehending 3 lads breaking the Colledge yeards' (presumably breaking into). There is the intriguing entry: 'To the Principalls order to a Toun Officer for getting off John Douglas Tennent to the College from going to Leith wi the Cable tow, getting him free at the Magistrates hands payed the officers 14/6d'. Two officers were paid 4/- each 'for taking washers to the Baylif for breaking down the wall of the private walk'. These 'washers' (washerwomen working for residents of houses in the neighbourhood of the College and its grounds) seem to have been something of a perennial nuisance. On 12 August 1708 the accounts record a payment of 18/- to 'a toun Officer for chargeing the Inhabitants that dwell near the College yards, and also the washers, not to drive any naills in the trees or put any fires near the wall or trees, under the pain of four pounds Scots'.[51] The washerwomen were using the College trees outside the walls as the means of attaching clothes lines; and the residents were lighting fires, probably to burn refuse.

With all the many dimensions of College life covered by the Thomas Young accounts, there are the occasional references to the gardens. Whilst it has been possible to be precise regarding the siting of the

Physic Garden as laid out from the spring of 1705 onwards, there are no records of its area at the time. Once the walls were built the garden's boundaries were established, with the Blackfriars Kirkyard wall to the north and the Blackfriars Wynd to the south. There was a wall (with a door) separating it from the Great Garden to the east, while on the west side another wall divided the Physic Garden from some College ground and from some houses which were not College buildings. There is no evidence in any of the College records throughout the eighteenth century that subsequent enlargements of the Physic Garden ever took place. John McArthur's 1778 map of the town includes the plan of the College and its grounds (Figure 2.1). This plan shows a rectangular Physic Garden which was the original site of the garden when first laid out. The area covered by the garden in the 1778 map is also the same as that when it was first established in 1705. An undated exact copy of McArthur's plan, copied by 'A.H.D.', also has scale measurements.[52] If these are reliable, then the Physic Garden measured 190 × 160 feet, equal to 30,400 square feet (= 3377.8 square yards) or 0.7 Imperial acres. As such it was smaller than the garden by Trinity Hospital in Edinburgh, which occupied some 1.3 acres. With the founding of the Physic Garden in the College there was now need for an overseer for its management and a gardener for its cultivation. These appointments and the subsequent developments are the subjects of the next chapter.

Notes

1. FM, 4 July 1704: 26632, p. 28.

2. A.G. Morton, 1981. *History of Botanical Science* (Academic Press, London), p. 49.

3. Ibid., pp. 120–1.

4. K. Thomas, 1983. *Man and the Natural World* (Allen Lane, London), pp. 52, 227, 271, 384.

5. C.J. Trew, 1985. *The Herbal of the Count Palatine* (Harrap, London), pp. 21–8, 53–68.

6. Munimenta, 3, p. 512.

7. F.O. Bower, 1903. Notes on botany in the University of Glasgow in the 18th century. *Transactions of the Natural History Society of Glasgow*, vol. 7, pp. 121–36.

8. A.L. Rowse, 1975. *Oxford in the history of the nation* (Weidenfeld & Nicolson, London), pp. 84–5.

9. S.M. Walters, 1981. *The Shaping of Cambridge Botany* (Cambridge University Press, London), pp. 15–29, 30–46.

10. J.D. Comrie, 1927. *History of Scottish Medicine to 1860*: Wellcome Research Studies in Medical History No. 4 (Baillere Tindall & Cox, London).

11. H.R. Fletcher and W.H. Brown, 1970. *The Royal Botanic Garden, Edinburgh 1670–1970* (HMSO, Edinburgh), pp. 3–10.

12. D. Hamilton, 1981. *The Healers: a history of medicine in Scotland* (Edinburgh, Canongate), p. 114.

13. H.R. Fletcher and W.H. Brown, 1970. *The Royal Botanic Garden*, pp. 11–25.

14. J.D. Mackie, 1954. *The University of Glasgow 1451–1951* (Jackson, Son & Co.), p. 28.

15. A. Duncan, 1896. *Memorials of the Faculty of Physicians and Surgeons of*

Glasgow (James Maclehose & Son, Glasgow), p. 18.

16. J.D. Comrie, 1927. *History of Scottish Medicine*, pp. 164–232.

17. D. Hamilton, 1981. *The Healers*, p. 114.

18. A.G. Morton, 1981. *History of Botanical Science*, pp. 237–8.

19. L.N. Magner, 1979. *A History of the Life Sciences* (Marcel Dekker Inc., New York & Basel), p. 302.

20. FM, 3 October 1704: 26632, p. 31.

21. FM, 6 October 1704: 26632, p. 31.

22. D. Murray, 1925. *Memories of the Old College at Glasgow* (Jackson, Wylie & Co.), pp. 247–9.

23. J. Walton, 1952. Natural History. In *Fortuna Domus* (University of Glasgow), pp. 296–8.

24. Anon. 1951. *The University of Glasgow through Five Centuries* (University of Glasgow), p. 31.

25. GUAA 43166.

26. GUAA 43167.

27. GUAA 45498.

28. GUAA 58023.

29. GUAA 45465.

30. P.B. McNab, 1903. *The History of the Incorporation of Gardeners of Glasgow* (J. Smith & Son, Glasgow), p. 183.

31. GUAA 47659.

32. GUAA 45459.

33. GUAA 58070.

34. GUAA 45457.

35. GUAA 45468.

36. GUAA 45456.

37. GUAA 45496.

38. GUAA 45456.

39. GUAA 45460.

40. GUAA 45447.

41. GUAA 45453.

42. GUAA 45479.

43. GUAA 45479.

44. GUAA 45525.

45. GUAA 45495.

46. GUAA 45525.

47. GUAA 45493.

48. GUAA 45497.

49. GUAA 45568.

50. GUAA 45538.

51. GUAA 45568.

52. GUAA 13471.

'ONE WHO SHALL HAVE CHARGE AND OVERSIGHT THEREOF ...'

Whilst decisions taken in 1704 at the 4 July and 3 October meetings of the Faculty led to the establishment of the Physic Garden, betweenwhile consideration was given to the appointment of an Overseer. This move is graphically described in the scroll recording the Faculty minutes for 7 September 1704.[1] In both its erratic penmanship and its sometimes individualistic spelling a clear impression is given of a scribe striving hard to keep up with Principal Stirling's dictation on an early-autumn afternoon:

> The faculty being resolved to prosecute ye own act of July 4th anent the improvement of some parts of ye great yaird for bottany and a physick garden: do now find it necessary to name one who shall have charge and oversight thereof and who may instruct the schollars who shall apply to him for the study of botany & being informed yt John Marshall surgeon in Glasgow is capable of discharging yt trust and he being specially commended yrto by the Dean of Faculties letter: therefore the Faculty does nominate the said John Marshall for the said imployment: and also to take care yt the whole big Yaird be kept in yt order in yth the Tackman by his Tack is obliged to keep the same\ & the faculty hereby grants him yearly for his salary two hundred & forty pounds Scots & ordered the same to be payed to him during his service to the Universitie besides a suitable fee for a gairdner to work at his direction and appoint the same 240 lib Scotts to commence from October next.

John Marshall's salary was identical with that paid to James Sutherland when he was in charge of the Physic Garden at Edinburgh — presumably an accepted 'going rate'. Marshall remains a shadowy figure. He was a son of Patrick Marshall (1631–97), a surgeon of Kilsyth in Stirlingshire, who had a second son, Henry. John Marshall served his apprenticeship in Glasgow, and is presumed then to have studied for a while in Paris — a presumption based on a book he gave to the Faculty of Physicians and Surgeons of Glasgow, in which he recorded his name, the city and the date 1677.[2] By some means or other, possibly through the Faculty of Physicians and Surgeons, the Principal and Masters must have been informed of Marshall's adequacy in botanical knowledge. He was married to Christian Stewart but no children of the marriage are recorded. Lillias, the daughter of his surgeon brother Henry, married Alexander Horsbrugh. Their daughter, also Lillias, married Robert Cowan, merchant of Glasgow, and their son Robert (1769–1808) was a medical student at the University (he enters the story at a later date). Robert's son, also Robert, was to be the first occupant of the Chair of Medical Jurisprudence, later Forensic Medicine, between 1839 and 1841. No portrait of John Marshall exists and until recently the only tangible link with him was in the book he presented to the Faculty of Physicians and Surgeons. Archival searches for the present book have, however, unearthed numerous precepts bearing his name and signature. The first of these records payment of the first instalment of his salary[3] (Figure 3.1).

C. Glasg. 9 March 1705

Mungo Cochrane
Pay to John Marshall Surgeon and Overseer of the College physick garden now designed Sixtie pounds Scots as part of the sallarie allowed him by act of facultie together w^i twentie four pounds for his pains & expenses in going to Ed^r to consult and advise about the sd garden and settle a correspondence wi some for carrying on the present design And this w^i his receipt shall be yor warrand
Jo: Stirling p^l

I John Marshall above designed grant me to have receabed from Mungo Cochrane payment of the contents of the above written precept. Writen & Subscribed At Glasgow the tenth day of Novr 1704 by me John Marshall

The expenses for going to Edinburgh were probably for consultations with James Sutherland. The date of Principal Stirling's authorisation is puzzling, unless Mungo Cochrane had received permission to pay Marshall in November 1704 (the date of the first payment of his salary had been specified at the 4 September Faculty meeting) and to submit the precept at a later date. Thereafter the salary payments were made at three-monthly intervals (Quarter Days), whilst for each year the College Accounts list the overall sum of £240 Scots. Marshall's salary indicates his relative status in the University, as shown in the College Accounts, Ordinary Revenue, for 1704–5:

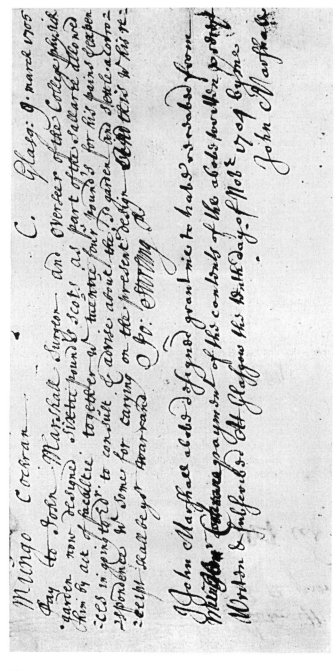

Figure 3.1. Precept showing the authorisation for payment of Marshall's first salary instalment, plus some expenses for a visit to Edinburgh

College Servants
Bibliothecarius	£253/6/8 Scots
Overseer of Physick Garden	240/0/0
Janitor	120/0/0
Bedellus	52/0/0
Bellringer	29/0/0

The Masters received sums more than double that of the Bibliothecarius and the Principal more than threefold the salary of Marshall, with additional benefits. Marshall's designation as Overseer (in due course he was made Master of Arts) remained his only official University title (as on all his salary precepts). The statement in University Calendars published since 1946 that for Botany 'A Lectureship was instituted in 1704' is incorrect.

Besides his Overseership, the minute of Marshall's appointment also outlined his responsibilities regarding the 'big Yaird' or Great Garden, in which he was to ensure that the tacksmen kept to their agreements about the general tidiness and appearance of their plots of ground. The minute also referred to the appointment of a gardener to work under Marshall. In the minutes of the Faculty meeting of 3 October 1704,[4] this aspect of the running of the Physic Garden came under discussion:

> ... And because a Gardiner will be presently necessary. It is recommended that the Principal with the advice of Dr Sinclare to look out for and agree with a Gardiner to work under and by the Direction of John Marshall, overseer of the said Garden, and to get att the Colleges Expense what may be needfull and by degrees doe everything which may forward the present design.

Robert Sinclair was Professor of Mathematics; John Marshall seems to have played no part in the ensuing selection process, nor are the consultative sources known. In 1706 the University drew up an agreement[5] on the sale of some land to the 'Corporatione of Gardeners' in Glasgow, for whom the Visitor and Collector of the said body acted, so there may have been advice from this quarter. Another relevant item of business at the 3 October Faculty meeting is briefly summarised at the end of the minutes: '... The which day John Marshall was called before the Faculty and gave his promise to be faithfull in the office whereunto he was chosen by the Faculty'.

The College Accounts for 1705–6[6] record that John Hume, gardener in the Physic Garden, was paid an annual salary of £60 Scots. A precept dated 25 March 1706 states[7] '... Pay to John Hume Gardiner threttie pounds Scots being half a year's fee from Martinmas 1705 ...'. The salary was thus paid in two instalments. The signature on the receipt of the precept, and on all that follow, is 'John Hoom' (Figure

3.2), and the spelling may reflect the pronunciation of the surname at the time. This is probably the same John Hume who was admitted to membership of the Incorporation of Gardeners on 5 January 1710.[8] Earlier precepts which seem not to have been clearly listed in the College Accounts are in the name of another gardener, John Kennedy. One dated 28 November 1705[9] cites '... Pay to John Kennedie Gardiner sixtie pounds Scots for his service to the College from mertimass 1704 till mertimass last ...'. He had already received a payment of £40 on 20 May 1705[10] for 'service to the College from mertinmass last'. On both receipts the signature was 'John Kennedy'. The last precept bearing his name is dated 28 June 1706:[11] 'Pay to John Kennedie Gardiner eighteen pounds Scots due for his house while he served the College and this wi his receipt & discharge to the College for his house rent shall be your warrand ...'. This suggests that John Kennedy may have been the occupant of the house which had to be dismantled and moved to make room for the Physic Garden. If so, the rent compensation was presumably because advance payments had to be made. Caution is, however, necessary in deciding on the house involved. References are to be found in accounts to payments of rent for gardeners' houses; and in the accounts of Thomas Young, the Bedellus, for 1708[12] reference is made to the gardeners' laigh (low) houses (p. 42) — probably small stone huts, windowed, for storage of tools. Kennedy may have been receiving refund from an advanced rent payment for such a 'laigh' house. There was no gardener's residence available in 1705, the year of dismantling and rebuilding. Evidence that he was the first gardener with responsibility for the Physic Garden is to be found in the Thomas Young accounts for 1705,[13] when, in the late summer, 16/- was paid for '200 nails for mailling the trees in the physick Garden for John Kennedie' (Table 3.1; Figure 3.2). At the same time '4 old hatts for the same use' were bought. 'Hatts' for the trees were purchased frequently over the years and were probably wood frames over which the branches were trained. The same summer accounts of Thomas Young for 1705 refer to £1/1/- paid for nails for 'nailling the trees in the Principalls garden', and '3 hatts for same' cost 6/-.

Enclosing ground for the Physic Garden brought additional problems. At the Faculty meeting of 12 March 1705,[14] the Principal and Mungo Cochrane were advised 'to commune with the Gardiners, anent the case they are seeking from the Faculty, and which the Faculty is resolved to give them, as to their Tack Duty of the College Yard, which they complain they will not be able to pay by reason of what is taken from them for the Physick Garden'. These gardeners were leaseholders of the Little Yard. This loss of ground for rent may underline some entries in the College Accounts which refer to a sum 'deduced ... for the Bowling Green now inclosed in the Physick Garden'. For the years 1707–9 this was stated as £12 Scots, and thereafter 'ten mercks.scots' (£6/13/4d) was deducted annually for an

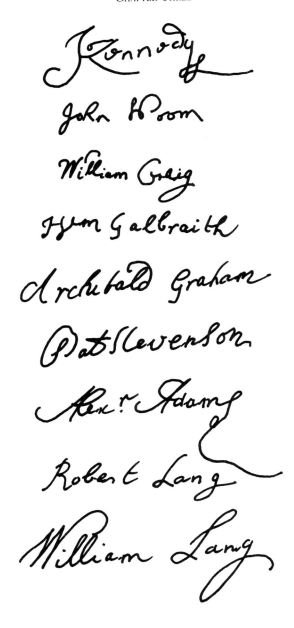

Figure 3.2. Signatures of the gardeners appointed with responsibility for the Physic Garden (Table 3.1). (Those of James Nichol and William Hume are not available)

Table 3.1. Gardeners appointed with responsibility for the Physic Garden

1704 – 5	John Kennedy
1705 – 19	John Hume
1719	John Nichol
1719 – 22	William Craig
1722 – 50	William Galbraith
1750 – 1	William Hume
1751 – 7	Archibald Graham
1757 – 60	Patrick Stevenson
1760 – 83	Alexander Adams
1783 – 1800	Robert Lang
1801 – 7	William Lang

indefinite number of years. This would seem to have been a necessary deduction to help balance the accounts.

Another claim for financial loss due to the institution of the Physic Garden was pressed by one John Allan in the early summer of 1711:[15]

To ye Principall of ye College of Glasgow on accompt of ye Losse I had in making up ye Phisick Garden

Im; ye taking down of ye house which was in my take by Counsar Robisson an years rent	24/00/00
It for ye back yard 5 years rent at 6 pound a year	30/00/00
It for 5 years of ye half of ye nurserie at 10 pound per year	50/00/00
It. for a glass window I put in ye house before ye house was taken away	03/00/00
It for ye Ground yt ye pale dick Stands on for 6 years at 1 pound per year	06/00/00
	113/00/00

'Ye pale dick' refers to a wood-paling fence ('dyk' or 'dick') which seems to have belonged to the College but to have included ground rented from the College by Allan. Principal Stirling gave authorisation for payment to be made: 'Mungo Cochrane Pay to John Allan Gardener sixtie pds scots of the above accot for I think an 113[lib] which he charges a great deal too much'. The extent of Allan's claim seems to have taken aback the Faculty somewhat, as reflected in Stirling's comment and in the relevant entry in the College Accounts for 1710–11, viz., 'To John Allan Gardner to precept deduce to him on account of the physick Garden being an extraordinar expense ... £60/0/0'.[16] It is to be noted that Allan's claim was backdated for five- or six-year periods — as if he was claiming for loss of rental on ground which he sublet to others. The claims also go back in time to when the gardener's house in the Little Yard was being dismantled and moved. Allan's claim for a year's rent suggests that he may have been the occupant of the house; 'my take by Counsar Robisson' could be rewritten 'my tack by Councillor Robisson', the latter being the Robert Robison (Robertsone) referred to earlier (p. 22) who paid the College an annual sum for renting the College Yards.

John Kennedy died in late 1705, as is shown in the Thomas Young accounts for 25 October 1705:[17] '... Given to the Gardiner who has wroght for the College and is to work next year in Jo. Kennedie's room by the principalls order — 14/6d'. To 'work in room of' was to be a replacement and this must refer to John Hume, who could have been one of the additional gardeners working under Marshall and Kennedy earlier in the year. In the 1705–6 College Accounts[18] there is a brief entry referring to payment of £24 Scots 'to John Keddedies relict', the only (indirect) reference to his death. The sum paid to Hume is similar to the 'drink money' payments recorded earlier in the accounts, so that some minor celebration may have accompanied Hume's taking up of the appointment. In fact, Hume was appointed from Martinmas 1705, and not 'next year' as given in the accounts.

The Thomas Young accounts are again the first sources of information on the initial laying out of the Physic Garden. On 2 January 1705,[19] £1/9/- Scots was given in drink money to the gardeners working in the garden. If Slezer's 1693 drawing of the College and its grounds (Frontispiece) is to be believed, the 'Little Yard' was bordered by trees and shrubs, so that the first major work of the gardeners would have been to dig out all the existing plants in preparation for the complete redevelopment of the site. Also on the same day, 14/- was paid 'for a lyne for the use of the Gardiners'. The question again arises whether this was a garden line or the Glaswegian interpretation quoted earlier. Since the Arms of the Incorporation of Gardeners of Glasgow, borne on the Deacon's Box of 1627[20] (for books, documents and cash), includes a garden line with metal spindle and cord, the spindle would raise the price. If the blazon represents the most important implements of the time, then with the line these were a spade, a rake, a dibble and a hoe. There is a further relevant entry in the Thomas Young accounts for 24 January 1705:[21] '... given to ye wrights for making of stabbs for ye use of ye sd Gardiners 00-08-00'. 'Stabbs' or 'stobs' would have been used for pegging out the ground, and could have been used with the garden line. Those working in the garden would have had to take into account the other activities going on — the dismantling of the house and the bowling-green wall, and the building of a new wall to enclose the garden. The evidence points to the main gardening effort of spring and early summer being put into digging over the ground, as shown in a cash payment made by Mungo Cochrane,[22] the College Factor (also recorded in the College Accounts):

Ane accompt of debursements be Mungo Cochrane to Gardners

for trinching ye physick Garden in summer 1705
To ten weeks of syxe gardiners at 12 lib pr week is   120 -0- 0
To John McCorkill for work at ye nurserie   2-12- 0

The cover note to the above states 'Workmens accompt for levelling the physick Garden' and Principal Stirling's authorisation of 3 July 1705 specifically mentions trenching and levelling work.[22] Trenching implies double trenching or double digging. Later in the year, as shown in the 1705–6 College Accounts,[23] £76 was paid to two gardeners for helping to 'frame and work the Physick Garden'. The framing would have been the stage of constructing the beds and the intervening and encircling paths. The £120 payment to six gardeners for ten weeks' work gives a weekly wage of £2. At a rate then existing of 8/- per day, this means a five-day week. By the same token John McCorkill would have worked for 6½ days, although this may not have been in one week. Assuming a similar wage for the two men 'framing' the garden, then this work would have been over 19 weeks. This stage could have been started when the trenching work was well advanced, and the 'framing.' could have gone on into the autumn.

The plantings would have had to wait until the ground was ready. The earliest record of plants in the 1704–5 College Accounts is for £8/17/0, to 'James Mitchell for Trees for the Physick Garden'. Mitchell's account shows that these were mainly fruit trees:[24]

Charge for 1 red primordian

plum	0.10.0	1 May cherry	0.10.0
1 early musile	0.10.0	1 red pear	0.10.0
2 orleanses	1.0.0	1 Golden rhine aple	0.10.0
1 morocco	0.10.0	1 medlar	0.16.0
1 chestnut plum	0.10.0	2 limes	0.06.0
1 red pedrigan	0.10.0	1 lilac	0.03.0
1 carnation cherry	0.10.0	2 horse chestnut	
		trees	0.08.0
1 Kentic cherry	0.10.0	1 pipe tree	0.04.0
2 heart cherry	1.0.0		8.17.0

The plum trees can be identified since in the main they were well-known varieties in the seventeenth and eighteenth centuries, e.g. Primordian, Muscle (musile), Orleans (orleanses), Morocco and Pendrigon (pedrigan). The one exception is the Chestnut plum, which may have been a local variety. Of the cherry trees, two varieties (Carnation and May) have been mentioned in the seventeenth-century lists of fruit trees earlier described. The Kentish cherry was well known south of the border and was grown in Scotland. 'Heart cherry' fails to mention whether it was the Black, Red or White variety. 'Red pear' is not very descriptive and 'Golden rhine' is probably a misspelling of Golden Reinette, which was a popular dessert apple of the early eighteenth century. The pipe tree could be either a *Philadelphus* (Mock Orange) or *Sambucus nigra*, the Elder. The former was so named because of its flower, and the latter because its cut stem could be freed easily from its pith, so forming a hollow tube. In old Scots, however, *Sambucus* was known as the 'bore' (or 'bour') tree. Since all the trees were to be planted in the Physic Garden, there is a natural tendency to assume that they were there to demonstrate some medicinal 'virtues'. All common fruit trees were listed in herbals and their health-giving properties emphasised. Both the Lime and Horse Chestnut were sources of 'simples'. Water infusions of Lime flowers were regarded as cures for apoplexy, vertigo and epilepsy. It was claimed at one time that epileptic people could be cured by sitting under the shade of a Lime tree. The inner bark produced a soft mucilage which was said to soothe and heal burns and scalds. Extracts of Horse Chestnut bark, in water or alcohol, were said to possess both astringent and febrifugal properties. If the pipe tree was the Mock Orange, it was probably for decorative purposes. If *Sambucus*, then its 'simples' value was considerable. The flowers, leaves and roots were used for a variety of purposes. It was said of the great Boerhaave that he used to touch his hat whenever he passed an Elder tree in tribute to its curative powers, a compliment he otherwise reserved for those times when he mentioned the name of God in conversation or lectures.

A letter addressed to John Marshall 'Surgeon and Master of the physic Garden at Glasgow' is of particular interest.[25] It came 'with a small Bundle of Trees directed for him and put up Decemb. 27 1705'. The sender was James Sutherland in Edinburgh, and the letter reads:

> Sir
> I have sent you with this Bearer a Bundle of Shrubs each of them marked with a figured stick viz
> Figur 1 German Tamarisk price 12 pence to be planted on a wall
> 2 French Tamarisk price 10 pence to be planted on a wall
> 3 Virginia Sumach — 10 pence to be planted on a wall
> 4 Sweet Olive of Bohemia — 14 pence to be planted on a wall
> 5 Three leaved Bladder Nut — 15 pence to be planted on a wall
> 6 Three leaved Ivy of Virginia — 06 pence to be planted on a wall
> 7 Five leaved Ivy of Virginia — 12 pence to be planted on the highest wall
> It will reach the top.
> 8 Climbing Dog's Bane — 12 pence. Requires a high pole to wind about.

9 Shrub Cinquefoil — 12 pence. Is to be planted as a standard
10 Myrtle leaved Sumach — 14 pence needs a warm wall
11 Shrub Dwarf Elder with Variegate leaves — 14 pence needs a warm wall
12 Cut leaved Elder — 06 pence. Is to be planted a standard
13 Whiteberried Elder — 08 pence. Is to be planted a standard
14 Red berried Elder — 08 pence. Is to be planted a standard

The sum is 7-13-0 Scots which ye may send myself by the Carier — that I may acquaint with him, seeing he must call frequently at me when spring advances and he is to get herbaceous plants. Plant the shrubs in fresh weather, so soon as ye can, in good ground exposed to the Sun. Ye must prune very little of the tops and roots of them, the White berried Elder has not much root, but will grow enough though planted without Roots

This with my humble Service is all at present from
Sir
Your most affectionate friend and servant
Ja. Sutherland
Direct from me at my chamber in Widow Hackets house the second Turnpike in the fishmercat Closse at the back of the Crosse

Principal Stirling's certification of the above is as follows:

Mr Alex^r Tran   Aprile 1706
Pay the above accompt of seven pounds thirteen shilling wt twenties shillings Scots more for the cariage and postage of letters to Mr. Marshall.

The tone of Sutherland's letter certainly suggests that a mutual respect had grown between him and Marshall. It seems that the shrubs sent over were a first instalment, and that collections of herbaceous plants were to follow in the spring of 1706. It is much to be regretted that the correspondence and lists sent over with these plants have not survived. The planting directions of mostly wall plants with the requirement for good ground exposed to the sun would probably have been meant for the east wall of the Garden or that by the more southerly orientated kirkyard wall. Notably Sutherland was to be paid directly, so he may have been permitted to sell the plants from the Edinburgh Physic Garden.

The plants in Sutherland's list can be regarded both as decorative and in some cases as having potential medicinal value. The French Tamarisk (*Tamarix*) is a source of a sugary secretion which hardens to form a type of manna and has a mild laxative property especially suitable for children. Extracts of roots of some Sumachs (*Rhus*) have astringent and diuretic properties. The Bladder Nut (*Staphylea pinnata*) is the 'Pipermuss' of the sixteenth-century German herbals. The Ivy of Virginia probably refers to the well-known Virginia Creeper, a decorative wall plant with striking autumnal leaf-colour changes. Dog's Bane was probably a variety of *Aconitum*, the rhizome of which was used for its curative properties. The Cinquefoil or *Potentilla* was a genus much favoured for the astringent properties of its root extracts, especially for internal bleeding (its generic name is derived from the Greek *potens* or powerful, as attributed to its virtues). The leaves, berries, flowers and roots of Elders, especially the leaves of the dwarf form, were highly valued as sources of 'simples'. Any variety of Olive was a source of oil.

Spring 1706 was going to be a busy time for Marshall and Hume. According to the Thomas Young accounts, drink money (£1/10/-) was paid to 'ye Gardiners of ye Physick Garden' on 16 February 1706,[26] so preparation of the ground was well in hand. The spring planting programme brought the need for extra labour, and in May 1706[27] Marshall was paid £8/16/- Scots for 'twentie two days of a man to assist the gardner', and on 6 July Patrick Buchanan (someone of this name had been admitted to membership of the Incorporation of Gardeners on 16 March 1693)[28] was paid £11/4/- direct for 'work wrought in the physick Garden being twentie eight days at eight shilling scots per day'.[29] Local nursery gardens were also sources of plant supply. An account settled in Marshall's name shows this:[30]

Accompt of plants furnished to the Physick Garden of the College of Glasgow, in spring 1706
impr. from Culross, Arskine, Jordanhill, Scotstoun, Cloberhill, Renfield, North Barr, according a yearlar Account by John Hume

	lb	s	d
	25	19	0
It. from Haulkhead according to Account	4	14	0
It. from Stirling	9	2	0
It. from Craigorth	2	17	0
it for Cariage from Stirling & Craigorth at twa several times	1	0	0
	43	12	0

Most of these localities are known today. Several (Scotstoun, Jordanhill, Renfield) are now part of the city of Glasgow. Again it is regrettable that no listing of the plants purchased is available: these all-important first spring plants must remain unknown. The College Accounts for the years 1704–6 include a number of entries recording payments to Marshall. These sums are not usually broken down into individual items except on occasions when his salary instalment was included. Making allowances for these salary payments, a sum of £366 Scots was expended on the Physic Garden, mainly in 1705–6. Principal Stirling maintained an active interest in developments, as evinced in a letter of his dated 20 December 1705 to John Erskine, eleventh Earl of Mar and Secretary of State for Scotland,[31] in which he drew attention to the University's actions '... to begin a Botanick Garden on account of the professorship of Medicine'.

Hedging plants were purchased on a number of occasions. One such order is from March 1705:[32]

> Accompt to John Marshall chyrurgeon to John Sym To 500 thornes bought and payed by Mr John Sym to John Watsoun which were my lyne — 05:00:00

Principal Stirling's authorisation states that the thorns were for the 'College nurserie'. Marshall's involvement implies the Physic Garden, although later records suggest that the nursery was common to both the Physic Garden and the Great Garden. It is possible that John McCorkill's work mentioned earlier was for planting the thorns and enclosing the nursery garden, or the individual plots into which it would have been subdivided. John Sym was the agent for the sale and it may be noted that in the account he uses the term 'payed ... to John Watsoun which were my lyne', this last being a Glaswegian usage of the word 'line' as earlier described. More thorns were bought by John Hume in 1706;[33] the account is undated but was found among papers from that year. Two-hundred-and-fifty thorn plants were purchased at 'twa shillings per hunder', which at £3 Scots were more expensive than Sym's 500 plants as above. Hume then asked for 14/- 'for going to severall parts through the countery to get them'; for 8/- 'for going to Erskine the last year being a whole night away and twa days'; 'going to renfield' cost 14/- and 'for going to Jordanhill' 10/-. The total charge was £5/6/0.

A further account from Haulkhead[34] in the name of a gardener John Good listed more plants for the Physic Garden. The account is undated but was found with 1706 papers:

2 fig trees	1.4.0	2 bean trifoils	0.10.0
2 vines	1.0.0	2 beech trees	0. 8.0
2 althea [frutens?]	0.12.0	2 Rhamnus	0.12.0

Of these, figs were commonly illustrated in herbals. The Althea plants (the second name is almost illegible) were probably Marsh Mallows. This was a medicinal plant in use for hundreds of years; its generic name is derived from the Greek *althomai*, to cure. Its principal virtue lay in its mucilaginous products, which had soothing and emollient properties which were claimed to have curative effects on kidney stones, gonorrhoea, toothache, vesical calculus, St Anthony's fire, constipation, coughs, asthma and numerous other complaints. 'Bean trifoils' were most likely plants of the Buckbean *Menyanthes trifoliata*, at one time extensively used by apothecaries and regarded as something of a panacea, leaf extracts being valued for nervous complaints, periodical headaches, heart palpitations, abdominal obstructions, uterine haemorrhages, dropsy, intermittent fevers and as an effective vermifuge for children. The last plant listed was either *Rhamnus catharticus*, the Common Buckthorn, or *R. frangula*, the Alder Buckthorn. Ripe berries of the former were a source of drastic purgative used in the past, but with unpleasant side effects including severe dryness of the throat and internal griping; a milder extract of the berries was used to treat dropsy and gout. The bark and berries of the Alder Buckthorn were sources of a similar purgative.

The Thomas Young accounts yield further information on the practical side of creating the Physic Garden. On 25 May 1706,[35] a woman was paid 8/- for 'giving room to lay in the gardiners worklooms', i.e. implements. A series of items was listed for 3 July 1706:[36]

Item payd for a new Syth to the Gardner for the Physik Garden	£01.06.8
Item for a sned & putting on the hands and Ring of mounting of sd syth	00.12.0
Item for grinding and setting up sd Syth and for a sharping stone to it	00.07.0
Item for a new Raik to the Gardner of the Physik Garden	00.14.0
Item payd for a Wattering Pann to the Physik Garden	02.18.0

The 'sned' was the shank of the scythe and the 'hands' the wooden pegs on the shank by which it was held. The 'ring of mounting' was the means by which the blade was attached to the base of the shank. The 'sharping stone' (whetstone) was a shaped stone of any hard-grained rock, obtainable from a local mason's yard. The purchase of the scythe suggests that by the summer of 1706 the main plots in the garden had been established and the intervening and encircling paths (the walks) had been fully 'grassed'; the walks in the College garden were usually sown with Dwarf White Clover seed (p. 114). On 24 August 1706,[36] 14/- was paid to 'the workmen for carrying the Rolling stone from ffrancis Stevinson's house to the phisick Garden'. Later (8 November), £3/14/- was given to 'ffrancis Stevinsons wife' for the rolling stone. This roller would have been used for the walks in the garden.

John Marshall and John Hume evidently established a sound working relationship which was to last until Hume's death in the autumn of 1718. Marshall died in September of the following year. In the 1707–8 College Accounts[37] Hume's salary is given as £72 Scots, so he had received an increase of £12 after his first year's employment. Marshall's salary remained fixed, at £240, as did Hume's also after its advance to £72. The 1 May 1707 was the date of the Act of Union of the two kingdoms and the creation of the United Kingdom of Great

61

Britain. An Act of Security at the same time included the provision that the Universities of St Andrews, Glasgow, Aberdeen and Edinburgh should continue for ever. Such a provision, however, then (as now!) was no guarantee of financial stability and in the early 1700s Glasgow University found that it was short of money at a time when it wished to augment existing salaries, to re-establish lapsed chairs and to create new ones. John Stirling (the 'masterful Principal' according to one historian of the University)[38] was the main driving force behind the University's attempt to broaden its academic base. In the spring of 1707, Stirling was planning a visit to London to present a memorial to Queen Anne requesting financial assistance for the appointments described. His forward planning included the Physic Garden:[39]

Mr. Alex[r] Tran   C. Gl. 7 Aprile 1707
Pay to John Marshall Overseer of the Physick Garden what
may be presently necessary for keeping up the same & carry on the
design in my absence.

                                                            Jo: Stirling

This 'open-cheque' approach to enable Marshall to make purchases was readily exploited. On the same day (7 April) he was paid £24 Scots, and £8 was claimed on 9 August followed by £6/0/9d on 12 August. £30/1/6d was received on 9 October, £24 on 24 November, £12/1/6d on 31 December, and £12 on 21 January 1708, making a total of £116/3/9d Scots. The details of the several purchases are not available.

The Faculty meeting of 26 June 1707 decreed that the Principal should seek extra financial help from Queen Anne 'for the augmentation of the Masters salary's and for the Further Advancement of Learning'. They then agreed to meet again on the forenoon of the following Saturday to draw up a memorial, the draft of which states:[40]

Memorial for the University of Glasgow
It is humbly represented that albeit the first foundation of the University of Glasgow there were professions in the several faculties founded: yet through want of funds diverse of e'm have been of late suppressed, such as not only that of Law, which was before the Reformation, but these of Medicine, Mathematicks, Oriental Languages and Humanity which were sett up since.

In consideration of the great necessity of the said professions the present Mr[s] have essayed to revive the professions of Mathematicks, Oriental Languages, Humanity & Botany by setting up a bottanick garden to promote the same. But there being no funds to maintain these sd. professions, tho' all most necessary, they will be obliged to let e'm fall again to the great prejudice of our country as well as the University unless the government be pleased to provide for support of e'm.

And since the other Universities in Scotland have already funds for maintaining the professions of Mathematicks, Oriental Languages & Humanity and that of Glasgow wants. And that the Parliament was pleased to recommend the several Universities to her Majesty for ane augmentation of the mr^s sallaries in consideration that their encouragements are much lessened of late by reason the number of students is not so great as formerly and that it has been the practice of all the princes since K. Ja: 2^d of Scotland who founded this University to bestow upon the same some mark's of their royal favour & munificence. It is humbly intreated her present majesty, who gives such ample proofs of her generous respect to the publick good will be pleased to tread in these laudable steps of her Royal predecessors And for the substinence of the above very necessary professions as well as the augmentation of the Mr^s sallaries Grant what may ansr yse end's.

In the draft, the last sentence had been written 'It is humbly intreated *and expected . . .*', but the two words in italics here are crossed out as sounding rather presumptuous.

The inclusion of Botany as one of the new 'professions' is of particular interest. Stirling was able to report back to the Faculty on 25 December 1707 that the testimonial had been given to Queen Anne and that a grant of money was forthcoming. It was not until 15 November 1708 that he could report that an annual gift of £210 sterling had been received from the Lord Treasurer. This gift, dated 22 September 1708, was to be divided:[41]

Professor of Oriental Languages	£40	To the Principal by way of augmentation	£22
Professor of Mathematicks	40	To the three Professors of Philosophy	11
Professor of Humanity	25	Professor of Greek	20
Professor of Botany	30		

What were the implications for John Marshall of a proposed Professorship of Botany with a salary of £360 Scots? It has been assumed by some historians of the University that he took to himself the title and was paid the salary. Neither of these assumptions is correct. His official title never changed from that of Overseer of the Physic Garden; he is only once described otherwise, as 'Teacher of Botany', and that in a marginal note to an entry dated 7 September 1704 in the 'Register of University containing the Proceedings and Acts from September 18 1701 when Mr. John Stirling was admitted Principal'.[42] There is no information on how Marshall taught his students. In the Chelsea Physic Garden of the Society of Apothecaries, the apprentices in the eighteenth century were taught the recognition of medicinally important plants by direct observation under the supervision of instructors, who were probably the equivalent of present-day Demonstrators. This was probably the mode of instruction used by Marshall. Reference to one of Marshall's students is to be found in the University records. On 20 September 1720,[43] the Faculty meeting minuted an application by one Andrew Graham for the degree of MD: '... The Faculty having taken the said motion into consideration, and several of their members having reported that the sd Mr Graham to be a person of learning and that he had studied Botany in the University ... do therefore appoint the Diploma creating Mr Andrew Graham Doctor in Medicine be drawn and sent to him ...'. The gardens as a whole were not open to the student body. Pass keys to gain entry were available only to members of Faculty (p. 17). The 1690 accounts[44] of Walter Corbet, a Hammerman, record for 20 February '... a pass key to Mr Tran to the gardine doors — £1/0/0' (this was John Tran, one of the Regents). Restricted entry remained unchanged, as already shown in the articles of Tack for Robert Robertsone as Tacksman of the Great Garden in 1691:[45]

> ... none belonging to the Universitie shall have the benefit of kyes or Libertie to walk in the said yeard Except the Masters and the primarii That's to say Noblemen and Barrons sons those sua priviledged are only to have access to the said yeard by the entries thereon the College and by noe other Gates and Entries. And each master for his own and students priviledged their access to the said yeard, is only to have the benefit of Two kyes on four their own and the other for the priviledged students use And that key which is to be communicat to the priviledged students is only to be a keye to Gyve them access to the said yeard by the entries thereon the College ...

Hence the only students allowed access were the sons of noblemen, who could do so only by obtaining a key from one of the Masters. This arrangement was not changed until 1721, as minuted in the Faculty meeting of 13 February:[46]

> The Faculty considering that none but the Masters have got keys to the Garden, but that it may be convenient that the sons of Noblemen who are scholars have free use of the said keys with certain restrictions, do therefore allow the said sons of noblemen a key to the Great Garden and Physick Garden, provyding they promise the Principal to allow no other persons the use of the said key, and at the end of every session to deliver it to him.

From 1705 onwards, only 'commoner' students wishing to study Botany were permitted entry to the Physic Garden, and then only in the company of John Marshall.

Further verification that Marshall did not benefit from Queen Anne's gift is to be found in a precept dated 4 December 1708,[47] authorising his salary instalment payment (£60) from the previous Martinmas. Queen Anne's gift was dated 22 September 1708 and by December of the same year revised salary payments were in hand, as shown by that paid to Alexander Ross for £300 Scots as Professor of Humanity[48] (a revived Chair). It seems that Marshall's salary of £240 Scots remained unchanged until his death. Whilst there seem to be no detailed records of the students taught by Marshall, Principal Stirling regarded the existence of the Physic Garden as essential to his plans for re-establishing the Chair of Medicine. As already shown, the major developments in the practice of medicine in seventeenth-century Glasgow remained outside the University and in the later years were centred in the Faculty of Physicians and Surgeons. The moves to re-establish the Chairs of Law and Medicine are described in the records of the Faculty meeting of 4 August 1713.[49] This referred to the Royal Visitation of 1644, which had advised that the professions of Law and Medicine should be revived, and that current views in the College favoured these appointments, with the additional backing of Lord Pollock, the Rector and 'severall persons of quality'. Faculty sought the release of money in King William's grant of earlier years to cover the costs of the two salaries. Principal Stirling was once more required to go south and present a memorial, and on 14 January 1714[50] was able to report that the Lord High Treasurer had informed him that a Royal Warrant was to pass the Great Seal in Scotland to release the annual grant of £230 sterling gifted by King William. The Professor of Law would receive £90 and the Professor of Medicine £40, the remaining £100 being put to yearly revenue deficiencies. A minute of the Faculty meeting on 1 June 1714[51] states that '... having good and satisfying information that Dr John Johnstoun in Glasgow is a person well skilled in Medicine and very capable to teach the same, does therefore elect and present the said Dr Johnstoun to be Professor of Medicine in this University'.

With Johnstoun's occupancy of the Chair of Practice of Medicine and the Physic Garden well established, Glasgow seemed set fair to develop its medical school, though well outpaced by Edinburgh. It was singularly unfortunate that this key appointment should have been to one who, in the words of one University historian,[52] was to become an 'inert' professor. Whilst Johnstoun seems to have given some lectures in the early years of his tenure, he subsequently developed an aversion to teaching. The Faculty, in order to maintain some semblance of medical teaching, was forced to appoint John Gordon, a surgeon in Glasgow, to give lectures in Anatomy. John Gordon is better remembered as one of a surgical partnership with William Stirling, to whom Tobias Smollett was apprenticed on 30 May 1736 when he commenced his medical education in Glasgow. After three years the budding author left for London, qualifying in the Barber-Surgeons Hall in December 1739. There is some suggestion that John Gordon may have been the source of 'Mr Potion', the apothecary in the early chapters of Smollett's *The Adventures of Roderick Random*. There is no information on whether Johnstoun or Gordon ever became involved in the Physic Garden. Later reports indicate that Gordon was a popular and successful teacher. Johnstoun's involvement became less and less, but he continued to occupy the Chair until 1751, with a series of substitutes lecturing in his place, presumably paid via the class fees.

Thus, for the last five years of his Overseership, John Marshall witnessed at least the beginnings of a medical school. Purchase of plants and seeds for the Physic Garden in this period largely go unrecorded. A precept for £13 Scots in Hume's name,[53] dated 17 October 1716, is for '200 Hollys at 13/- per hundred'. Since all Hume's purchases were for the Physic Garden, it is likely that these were hedging plants. The last precept involving Hume,[54] dated 22 August 1718, is for 'worklooms': a spade (£2/14/- Scots), a new scythe (£1/6/-) and 4/- for a 'sharping stane' and for 'upsetting and grinding' the scythe. A new garden line cost 6/- and three cartloads of horse dung 'for ane hot bed' plus loading and 'hurling' were £1/8/-. The new scythe is the first one recorded since a similar purchase twelve years before. The long life of the first scythe indicates its infrequent use on the walks in the Physic Garden. John Hume died in late 1718. He was also Collector (Treasurer) of the Incorporation of Gardeners of Glasgow at the time of his death. The minutes of the 4 November 1718[55] meeting of the Incorporation include:

> The said day the whole trade taking to yr consideration that John Hume, late Collector, deceased before stateing and clearing his accounts, and that there is a considerable sum of the trade's money in his hands inpowered the Deacon and Masters with the Collector to prosecute and pursue for recovering the same and do everything thereanent that the Trade could do.

Hume's death left his family in poor circumstances. A minute in the records of the Incorporation for 8 August 1720[56] states: 'The Collector is allowed to pay two Masters 10/- to buy coat, breeks, shoes, Stockins and shirt to Alexander Hume son of deceased John Hume'. This is a sad indication of the destitution faced by the family once the main wage-earner was dead, with the additional problem that the gardener's house at the College would no longer be available. On 11 November 1749, however, William Hume,[57] son of the deceased John Hume, was admitted to the Incorporation so that a family tradition was continuing.

Hume's successor was James Nicol (Nicholl or Nicoll). A James Nicoll was admitted to membership of the Incorporation of Gardeners on 2 August 1709,[58] being married to a Miss Reid, daughter of John Reid, Deacon of the Incorporation for 1701–2, 1704–5 and 1712–3. Nicol died at some time between November 1718 and February 1719, as shown by a precept dated 4 December 1719: '... pay to Bertha Reid, relict of Jems Nicol gardiner eighteen pounds Scots for her husbands service to the College bein a Qr salary from Martinmas 1718 to Candlemas 1719 ...'. The 4 December precept followed a petition by Bertha Reid, as shown in the Faculty minutes for the meeting on 1 December 1719:[59]

Upon a Petition by Berthia Reid Relict of James Nichol who had last winter served the College Sometime as Gardiner in the Physick Garden and that he had received nothing for his service humbly craving that the Faculty would allow her & her small children something as they shall think fit. The Faculty having considered the said petition do allow her eighteen pounds Scots being a quarters salary of the gardiners yearly salary from Martinmas 1718 to Candlemas 1719 and ordains a precept in her favour to be drawn for sd sum

Nicol's widow would seem to have had a long wait for payment. The pre-written receipt on the precept was signed 'BR'.

William Craig was appointed in Nicol's place: a William Craige was to be admitted to membership of the Incorporation on 16 October 1720.[60] Craig's salary commenced from Candlemas 1719, his second instalment being paid on Lammas Day (1 August). One of the first of Craig's submitted accounts is dated 1719:[61]

Imprs. half ane ounce of Savoy seed	00:04:00
Item a drop of Colliflower	00:06:00
Item a drop of Pumpkins	00:03:00
Item half a drop of Cucumbers	00:02:00
Item for millions and africa marygold	00:02:00
Item for a sythe	01:16:00
Item for six men at a merck a day	04:00:00
Item for Sharping Shears and ye Syth twice	00:04:00
Sum is	06:17:00
	John Marshall

Payment was made to Craig, who at the same time received his Lammas salary instalment, so that the above account would have been submitted in August 1719 and probably represents one of the last signed by Marshall, who died in the next month (Figure 3.3). All the plant purchases were for seeds; a drop was equal to 1/16 of an ounce. 'Millions' were melons and these, with the pumpkins and cucumbers, would have required a 'hot-bed' — as recommended in the 1626 edition of Gerard's Herbal for cucumbers and 'musk' melons, and described in great detail (especially for melons) in the 1750s by Gilbert White, the natural historian and keen gardener at Selborne in Hampshire. One is left with the suspicion that the Physic Garden was

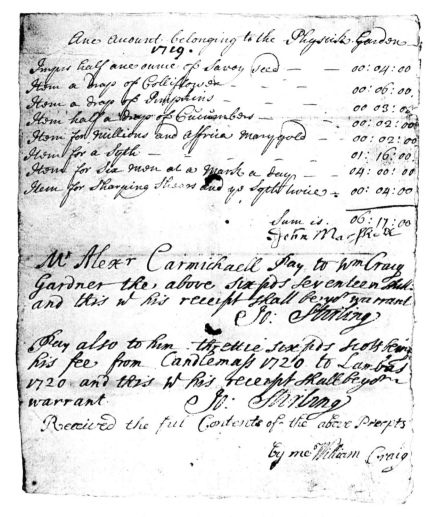

Figure 3.3. Account and precept of 1719 for the Physic Garden and for a salary payment in the name of William Craig. John Marshall's signature may be seen below the total sum; this is probably the last account countersigned by him

in part being used as a kitchen garden (for the professors?). It is true, however, that the health-giving properties of the common vegetables were described in herbals and some had virtues as sources of 'simples'. Cucumber leaves boiled in wine were said to be good for dog bites. Melon seeds yielded emulsions with cooling and diuretic properties, and marigolds were valued for promoting sweating in fevers. On 1 December 1720,[62] an account was presented by the Bedellus, Thomas

Young, which included £9/12/- Scots for a boll of 'Holland berries'. 'Holland'is a misspelling of 'Hollin' or Holly, and the quantity was 'a Boll of berries at a shilling per peck'. There were 16 pecks per boll (4 pecks per firlot and 4 firlots per boll). The cost per peck is given in sterling. The berries were purchased somewhere in the Highlands and transportation cost 12/-. Finally, 'a Hogshead and a little Barrell' had to be supplied for 'holding said Berries', and '2 girds for girding the Hogshead' (girds = hoops) cost 10/-. A man was then paid 4/- for 'treading sd Berries and Laying up Earth about the same'. All told, £12/5/6d Scots was expended. The hollies were clearly for hedging, probably in the Great Garden.

A major change in the status of Botany in the University preceded Marshall's death, and in due course came into effect. In 1718, King George I founded a joint Chair of Botany and Anatomy. After Marshall's death, a lengthy Royal Commission dated 23 February 1720[63] was read before Faculty, naming 'Doctor Thomas Brisbane to be professor and teacher of Botany and Anatomy the said University of Glasgow during all the days of his lifetime and to have and Enjoy all the powers and privileges of a professor of Medicine ...'. The salary was £30 sterling and the appointment *ad vitam aut culpam*, conditions which were to apply to all his successors up to the present century. Royal Commissions or Warrants (also called Patents) accompanied all appointments to Chairs with Royal Patronage, as they do to the present day. The preamble to Brisbane's Commission states that 'the office of professor of Botany in our University of Glasgow is vacant by the Death of Mr John Marshall late Botanist there', and this raises again the question of Marshall's status. All subsequent Commissions, however, give the name and title of the predecessor in the preamble and in the above case it would seem more a casual interpretation of the post occupied by Marshall.

Brisbane's first attendance at a Faculty meeting was on 9 March 1720. It seems that the aforementioned John Gordon had hoped that a Chair of Anatomy would be created for him, and he may have been encouraged to think so. Brisbane's 'pedigree' seemed entirely suitable. He had studied at Leiden under Boerhaave. He was the son of Matthew Brisbane MD, who had a practice in Glasgow and who was the first physician to be appointed Rector of the University (1679–81). Again it was most unfortunate for the University that the second occupant of a medical chair was to be as ineffectual as the first. Brisbane was sickened by the dissection of cadavers and so was totally incapable of teaching Anatomy, confining his lectures to Botany. This one-sided approach caused some alarm in the Faculty, as indicated in a minute of the meeting on 26 January 1721:[64]

In regard that there is now a professor of Anatomy in this University and that it may be necessary to make formal regulations with respect to ye teaching of Anatomy, therefore the faculty resolves to meet on Tuesday next at four afternoon to consider of the said Regulations.

In fact two meetings were necessary, on 31 January[65] and 7 February (Brisbane being absent from all the meetings so far), with the directive being made at last that 'all fsd Regulations be agreed to the Professor of Anatomy give a College of Comparative Anatomy sometime betwixt the first of December and the first of May, and that a guinea be the payment for such students getting such a College'. The term 'College' is used here in the old Scots form of a course of lectures. But these rulings brought no change, and on 23 November 1721 the students presented a petition to the Principal to which attention was drawn at next day's Faculty meeting,[66] which Brisbane attended. In answer to the petition, he acknowledged 'frequent trouble and uneasiness' about the matter but, having consulted his lawyers, 'their opinion was the patent being honorary could not be binding on him to do or not to do more yt he found convenient, and withall that their opinion was that the ffaculty could give no Laws of regulations in that affair, that he has all honour for the opinion of the ffaculty and should defer himself to ye judgement of the royal Commission to determine as they shall think fit'. In response, the Faculty postponed any decision but agreed to send all the details and correspondence to the Rector '... and express the sense the ffaculty has of the necessity there is that Anatomy be taught and of the Detriment will necessarily arise to the College by the students leaving if not taught'. There the matter seems to have rested in December 1721, with no apparent decisions being taken further. The suggestion has been made that Brisbane had some measure of support from the Principal and some members of the Faculty for the view that actual dissections were not the function of the professor but of an 'operator'. But the real state of affairs is revealed in the minutes quoted: Brisbane considered his post an 'honorary' one (reading the Commission leaves one wondering how: see Appendix) and that he had complete freedom to teach what he liked when he liked, and challenged the Faculty to appoint a Royal Commission to consider the matter. Nevertheless, there is ample evidence that he took an interest in the Physic Garden, at least in the early years of his appointment. This involvement is not evident in the College Accounts and Faculty records of the time, in which the names of William Craig and his successors mainly appear. The individual accounts submitted, however, usually bear either Brisbane's countersignature or mention him by name, as for example in a precept dated 4 October 1720:[67]

> Pay to Wm Craig Gardiner twelve pds scots for some necessaries to the Physic Garden to be bought at the direction of Dr Brisbane ...

An undated account associated with some 1720 papers in the name of William Craig is as follows:[68]

Ane Accompt laid out

Imprimas for a drop of Colliflour	00:06:00
Itt for twa drop of Cucumbers	00:05:00
Itt for a drop of Pumkins	00:02:00
Itt for a drop of Millions	00:02:00
Itt for a drop of Sunflower	00:02:00
Itt for a drop of Africa marygold	00:02:00
Itt for a drop of Lettus	00:02:00
Itt for a drop of Radishes	00:02:00
Itt for a drop of Tabacco	00:02:00
Itt for a drop of Turneeps	00:02:00
Itt for half ane ounce of Carses	00:02:00
Itt for half ane ounce Spinage	00:01:00
Itt for half ane ounce Broad Spanish Beans	00:01:00
Itt for half ane ounce of Pease	00:01:00
Itt for Oneons & Leeks	00:01:00
Itt for Beat Card & Carrats	00:01:00
Itt for ane ounce of Kidney Beans	00:03:00
Itt for ane ounce of Purpul	00:03:00
Itt for ane spade	02:08:00
Itt for ane Reak	01:08:00
Itt for ane syth	01:08:00
Itt for ane Sneed to the Syth	00:06:00
Itt for two Heaks	00:06:00
Itt for sharping of the Shezars	00:02:00
Itt for ane line	00:10:00
Itt for sharping of ye Syth four times	00:04:00
Itt for Six hunder of Naills	00:16:00
Itt for Hatts	00:08:00
	08:04:00
Received for trees	04:10:00
	–
	03:14:00
Itt for half ane hunder and ten ash trees	03:00:00
Itt for half ane hunder of fir trees	01:10:00
	04:10:00
Imp for Ten days work in the garden of a man at ten shill: a day which comes to five pounds Scots	05:00:00
	08:14:00

The above seeds were furnished by William Craig
T. Brisbane

Again most of the plant names are identifiable. 'Carses' were cress seeds. The 'Purpul' seeds are harder to identify: the name was applicable to a number of plants. It may have referred to the Purple Hedge-nettle or Dead Nettle, but could be broccoli. It is to be noted that young trees were sold (see 'Received for trees' and their sales credited to the account), which indicates that the nursery could be used as a source of income. Again the seed list is mainly for a kitchen garden, with three exceptions. If the Dead-nettle was the 'Purpul' plant listed, decoctions of its leaves were used for the treatment of dysentery, pleurisy and scrofula. Elizabeth Blackwell published her *Curious Herbal* in two volumes in 1737–9 (see p. 83), and for this she used source material from the Chelsea Physic Garden of the Society of Apothecaries. All the vegetables listed in Craig's account are to be found in the *Curious Herbal*, with descriptions of both their dietary and their curative virtues. Lettuce leaves were recommended for quenching thirst, provoking urine formation and flow, milk production in 'nurses', and for reducing temperatures. Radishes were valued as being anti-scorbutic and good for stone and gravel, and were diuretic. Cresses were to be used for treating scurvy, dropsy and palsy. Spinach leaves were regarded as possessing a cooling effect with high temperatures, and to be thirst-quenching and diuretic. Dried Tobacco leaves were recommended as a strong emetic. There is no record of Brisbane's lectures, but if he used Boerhaave's methods much time would have been spent in the garden as well as in the lecture room. It is possible that the health-giving properties of vegetables would have been included in Brisbane's lectures. It is known that later in the 1760s one of the gardeners ran a small shop in the gardener's house in the Blackfriars Wynd (p. 182), so that Craig may have done the same. Since the seeds were purchased with College money, however, a more official usage for the products of the garden should probably be envisaged. Of the tools and accessories listed, the 'Heaks' were wooden frames (cold frames?) and 'Shezars' were shears. The daily wage of 10/- Scots for a gardener is interesting; in 1724 and 1725, the wage fell to 8/- and 7/- per day respectively.

A further account for tools, seeds and plants was presented by Craig in 1721,[69] authorised by Brisbane. The seed orders repeated a previous one for 'drops' of 'Colliflour, Millans [melons], Cucumbers, Pumkeens, Tob^cc' all costing the same as in the preious year. Unidentified shrubs ('shirobes') and plants were bought for 10/- and 'Ane hunder of Turfe for laying the seed' cost 13/-. Further items were for '6 carts of Horse Dung to the Hotbeds' (£2/2/6d), with 9/- for 'drawing to the garden in a cart' and 3/- for 'ane man hurling it out'. Additional labour (four men) for the garden (20 days at 10/- per day) added another £10. The total sum was £20/15/6d. In the College Accounts for 1720–1, a payment of £92/15/6d is entered in the name of Craig for 'precepts and receipts'. These would have been his two salary instalments (£72) and the overall sum given above. These lists of plants and seed purchases are few and far between and exchange of seeds, cuttings etc. which probably went on is not recorded. No *Hortus Medicus Glasguensis* can be prepared from the incomplete data available, although from its beginning the Glasgow Physic Garden, albeit on a smaller scale, must have been modelled, to some extent, on that at Edinburgh if the advice of James Sutherland was being followed.

The various records from 1722 onwards have to be interpreted with care. In that year a second gardener, James Loudon, was employed by the University with responsibility for the Great Garden, and it becomes necessary to distinguish between the reasons behind particular purchases or employments. On 4 May 1722, two scythes were bought in the name of William Craig.[70] Then, in the 1721–2 College Accounts, £8/5/- was paid to Thomas Young for purchase of dung 'to the Physick Garden and Nursery'. The actual precept, dated 29 January 1722,[71] is as follows:

Accomp of dung furnished by Thomas Young To the use of the Nursery Jan^ry 29th Anno 1722

Impr for Dung to the sd Nursery and Hedge Dyke and for sowing the Holland seed there	06:00:00
Itt for hurling out Dung, at Six Pennies Scots per Cart there being 30 Carts thereof	00:15:00
Itt for ffilling and Cartage thereof down to the Nursery door, at a penny pr cart	01:10:00
Summa	08:05:00

The involvement of the Bedellus, Thomas Young, is a curious feature. It is not clear whether he was acting for himself or on behalf of the College as in the accounts he submitted in the 1704–9 period. Notably Craig's name is not mentioned, but is found on an account dated 6 February 1722:[72]

To 11000 bushes at 16/- pr 100 is		£07:06:08
To 2 hundred & ane half Hollies at		
5/- per 100 is		00:12:00
To 5 carts Horse Dung at 8s per cart		00:03:04
To Cariage from the Dunghill to ye Garden		00:00:10
To Naills & Hatts for Wall Trees		00:01:00
	Summa Sterling	£08:04:04

Evidently the number of unnamed bushes was incorrectly entered and the purchases would seem to be linked with hedging in the Physic Garden. Brisbane's name is referred to in a just legible scrawl: 'apryll second 1722 to the Coledg numbred forte stiks for the yeard by Doctor Bisbens order numered by Wm Waddell forte pens.'[73] It seems odd that a simple requirement like numbered sticks for designating rows of plants should necessitate outside labour. A further curious account was furnished by James Loudon (the man who later had responsibility for the Great Garden) on 10 September 1722:[74]

> Accompt of dayes wages due to John Millar whom I employed to work in the Physick Garden at the Principal of the Colledge his order.
>
> To fifteen days work at 8^d per day — is in all Six Pounds Scots

This was signed by Loudon, countersigned by Brisbane, authorised by the Principal and receipted by John Millar. But why was Loudon taking responsibility for the Physic Garden, the only time during his employ that he did so? The starting point for the affair was back in the summer, when some relevant decisions were taken by Faculty on 29 June 1722:[75]

> ... and Considering that it may be necessary in order to the prosecuting of the said proposal which the ffaculty approved of that there be for some time two Gardiners and William Galbraith gardiner being named as a person well qualified for taking care of the physick garden and other parts of Gardinery and James Loudon being also named as one skilled in training and dressing hedges & evergreens The ffaculty appoint Dr Brisbane to agree with the said William Galbraith to enter Gardner with the College att Martinmas next and they appoint Mr Jo: Loudon to agree with James Lowdon to enter likewise at the same time, and the Faculty considering that after Martinmas next they will not have occasion for Wm Craig do yt Order him to be warnd away from their service

John Loudon, at that time a Regent and later (1725) to become Professor of Logic, was given supervisory authority over the Great Garden by the University and was to play a major role from 1724 onwards. William Craig, by the Faculty ruling of 29 June, was clearly under notice to leave the following Martinmas and was required to work out his notice. No reasons are given for this move, but evidently Brisbane was given the task of informing Craig that his job was to be terminated. Craig seems not to have taken too kindly to this state of affairs. The Faculty meeting of 5 July 1722[76] makes this quite clear:

> The pcl acquainted the Faculty that being informed by Dr Brisbane and Mr John Loudon that Wm Craig who for some time has had the charge of the physick Garden as Gardiner has rooted out and destroyed some valuable plants in the sd. Garden upon Monday last, & had att the same time behaved himself very rudely and indecently towards both the sd Masters he the sd pcl had by advice of the Masters present in ffaculty on Tuesday last take in the key of the Garden from the sd William Craig and discharge him from all

further attendance upon & to do with the sd Garden, and had put
the key of the said garden in the hands of James Lowdon who was
ordered to be feed as one of the Gardners for the Interim till Wm
Galbraith who is to be agreed with to take charge of the P. Garden.
The ffaculty approves of what has been done in this matter and
ordains Thomas Young to receive from the sd Wm Craig the tools
and utensils belonging to the garden.

The ffaculty orders new locks to be made for the physick Garden &
Nursery In regard that there are too many keys of the present locks
that it is impossible to secure the sd physick Garden and nursery.

So, having been told by Brisbane of his notice to leave the
University's employ, Craig responded by attacking the plants and
showing a pronounced lack of respect to his superiors afterwards. As a
result he was immediately sacked by the Principal, with the inevitable
result that he was turned out of house and home. James Loudon was
then taken on as a replacement in advance of his appointment due in
the following Martinmas, and hence his hiring of the man to work in
the Physic Garden in September 1722. James Loudon was paid £36
Scots at the following Martinmas for his services to the University in
the interim:[77] something of a bonus, since he actually worked for only
four months but received half a year's pay. Thereafter he was paid at
the regular six-monthly intervals for his work in the Great Garden.
Echoes of the affair lingered on into 1723, as shown by a precept dated
13 February 1723:[78]

> Mr A Carmichaell Pay to Thomas Young thretty three shillings four
> pennies for the extracts of Mrs Craig's assignays their discharge to
> the University for the whole & rent due by it to the sd Mrs Craig
> and this without receipt shall be your warrant

An 'extract' was a judgment, the 'assignays' (assignees) were those in
receipt of certain rights and 'discharge' means that they had resigned
all further claims on the University. It would seem that, whilst Wm
Craig had to vacate the gardener's house in Blackfriars Wynd, he was
owed some money for rent paid in advance. A further relevant precept
winding up the affair is dated 23 July 1723:[79]

> Mr A Carmichaell Pay to Wm Craig Gardiner the above two pds
> seventeen shill and Eight pennies Sterlin and this wi his receipt &
> discharge to the College of all he can crave shall be y^{or} warrant
>
> Jo: Stirling
>
> Of the above sum there is seven shill. Sterlin to be pd to Wm.
> Galbraith Gardiner to the Physick Garden on the act of Ro^d Dick
> Gardiner to Castlemilk to whom Wm Craig ows
>
> Jo: Stirling

The actual claim made by Craig has been detached from the top of the page, so why he received this £34/12/- Scots is not known, but he evidently owed another gardener £4/4/- Scots for work done and for which the University had already paid him. Eventually this money was received by Jon Dick (not Robert), as recorded in a receipted precept of 20 September 1723.[80] Meanwhile William Galbraith had taken up his appointment as gardener for the Physic Garden at Martinmas 1722 and was to continue as such until 1750: the longest period of service of any of the succession of gardeners so employed. His annual salary on appointment was £72 Scots, the same as for Hume, Nicol and Craig, and was to remain so for the 28 years of his service to the University. This unchanging sum is not a reflection of a non-inflationary period of financial stability. It was based on a concept of labour costs exercised by the Faculty. Their view was that the outlay of £72 covered the annual labour involved in running the now established Physic Garden, which was not regarded as full-time employment all the year round. When Galbraith was free from work in the Physic Garden he could earn money by other part-time employment. The house, an important additional feature at that time, was still available throughout the year on a rental basis.

Galbraith's name appears for the first time in the College Accounts for 1722–3 with a payment of £46 Scots for '5 precepts and receipts for Trenching the Physic Garden'. Only two of these survive, the first being as follows:[81]

A accompt of days wrought by John Galbreath withe Physicke Garden and Nurserie since Janur 1723 until the 19 day of Aprill
Janur	17 days
ffebrur	24
March	17
Aprill	17
	———
	71 day

at eight pence per day is 28=08=00

Note that the daily sum is in sterling and the total in Scots money. This account was countersigned by Brisbane and payment made to Galbraith. Whether John Galbreath was a relative of his is not known. A side note on this precept states '... to cart hire from Pesly with lavender 00=08=00'. 'Pesly' was Paisley and lavenders make good dwarf hedging plants. The second relevant precept[82] records payments for further work by James Galbreath in April and May to the sum of £10/4/- Scots. Plant purchases on 15 April 1723[83] included 'Ane sweet bay tree with the pot it grows in =01=04=00: An hundreth and fourtie set of Globe Gulifours 00=18=00: two Evergreen oaks 00=05=00'. The Sweet Bay (the Bay or True Laurel, *Laurus nobilis*) would have been an obvious choice for a Physic Garden, since the leaves, fruit and oil were all regarded as being of medicinal value, as well as for the attractiveness of the plant itself. Infusions of the leaves and berries were used to treat hysteria, amenorrhoea and flatulent colic; the berries were sometimes used to promote abortion. The oil was obtained by distillation of the leaves and was used for sprains or earache. The evergreen oak (*Quercus ilex*, the Holm or Holly Oak) was again decorative and the 'Gulifours' (gillyflowers, stocks/pinks) are well-known bedding plants. Later in the year £3 Scots was expended by Galbraith[84] 'for getting some herbs at Ed[r] for the use of the Physick Garden at Dr Brisbane's desire', but the individual plants were not defined. At some time in the year,[85] Brisbane authorised Galbraith's purchase of 'six flour pots of which three att ten shilling scot per pott and three at eight shilling' from a local potter. An undated precept[86] countersigned by Brisbane and receipted by Galbraith states: '... Ane thousand rooted sets of box for mending the hedges of the physic Garden receibed from Robert boots Gardner ... the price three pounds Scots'. Dwarf box hedges were used for subdividing the individual plots in the Physic Garden and these replacements were probably required in the early 1720s.

An account sent in in February 1724[87] by 'Wm Stuart junior Gardner in Glasgow' was issued under the names of both William Galbraith and James Loudon for 'the number of ten Aple trees and ten Pear trees for planting in the College Yard ... att 12 pence per yierd the aples and 14 pence per yierd the pears summa lib 13=00=00'. The two gardeners being involved rather suggests that the fruit trees were to be divided between the Physic Garden and the Great Garden. The price 'per yierd' is not easy to interpret; it probably has nothing to do with length. 'Yierd' is possibly a misspelling of 'yeird' or 'yird', which has various associations with earth or soil (e.g. 'yeard' for yard, also 'yaird' or garden). The description given in the account may be for a tree with a ball of soil enclosing its roots. More fruit trees were bought for the Physic Garden in 1724, each time with payments made to Galbraith but with the orders countersigned by Brisbane. Two medlar trees costing £1/10/- Scots[88] and three peach trees (£3 Scots) 'for the north wall of the physick Garden'[89] were duly delivered. The 'north wall' was the 'kirkyard dyke' mentioned earlier (p. 31), and would have been more south-facing than any other.

A laboriously penned letter and invoice, dated 15 October 1724,[90] is addressed on the outside to 'William Galbraith garner at Blackfriars Wiend'. This was the address of the gardener's house after it was moved and rebuilt in 1705–6. The letter continues:

William recive fromm the bearer your sheers and pruning kneif they are both good and strong I shall bide your reprouf of both the loest pries of the shiers is 5 shillings & 6 pence and knief ten pence which is the loest price I ever tooke for anay thought not so good. I ad no more

John Brown Gorbils
Oct. 15 1724

In the letter, '& 6 pence' is scratched out; Principal Stirling's authorisation for payment is for £3/10/- Scots. 'Gorbils' (Gorbals) was then a small village just south of the River Clyde near the main bridge (its old name was Bridgend).

The records of plant and seed purchases and of plantings are sparse after 1724. An account presented by Galbraith on 20 December 1725[91] includes:

3 cartload of hors dung for a hot bed	01-04-00
for loading it home	00-07-06
for cyclamen	00-12-00
for 3 plants of laurustinus	00-12-00
for 3 black poplars and bolt of rose slips and other plants from renfield	00-08-00
for 3 red bines ['bine' = 'boyne', a container]	00-06-00
for 4 old hats for the trees	00-12-00
for 2 sharping stons for the syth	00-06-00
	04.07-00

This account also bears Brisbane's countersignature, (Figure 3.4). The plants were mainly decorative. The *Laurustinus* is *Viburnum tinus*. A 'bolt' of rose slips refers to a bundle of rose plants. The black poplar (*Populus nigra*) has buds which yield a resinous aromatic substance when distilled and this was used for external and internal treatments of various sorts in the past.

A brief digression is necessary here to review the general state of the University over the years from 1704. During his 27 years' tenure of office, the 'masterful Principal' John Stirling coaxed money for the University from the Government and increased the number of Chairs and students. He was, however, rather high-handed in his dealings both with the students and with some of his colleagues on Faculty such that these were also years of student indiscipline and disturbance and of dissension among members of Faculty. A move such as that taken in 1721, when it was decreed that only students who were sons of noblemen should have admission to the gardens, would hardly allow for domestic peace. As already mentioned on p. 70, the suggestion has been put forward that Brisbane was able to evade his responsibilities regarding anatomy-teaching because of some ambiguity in his Commission of Appointment.[92] It has also been suggested that because of this ambiguity all subsequent Royal Commissions for Brisbane's successors in office specifically laid down that they were to be 'professors and teachers of Botany and Anatomy'. This suggestion of ambiguity in Brisbane's patent was evidently made without knowledge of the contents of the document. In fact, the statements in the patent regarding Brisbane's conditions of employment are identical with those of his successors (see Appendix). There was no ambiguity; Brisbane

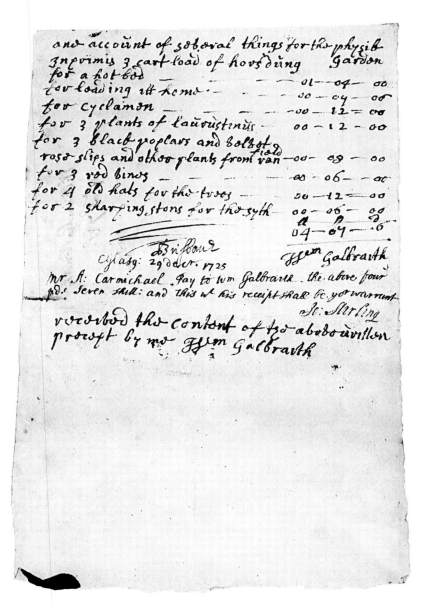

Figure 3.4. A William Galbraith account for various items for the Physic Garden. Thomas Brisbane's signature can be distinguished faintly below the list of items

could not face carrying out the dissections essential to the lectures and remained quite determined not to do so.

This general background turmoil resulted in the appointment of a Committee of Visitation on 31 August 1726[93] to investigate the affairs of the University and recommend any changes necessary. Their report, issued as a series of statutes on 19 September 1727, was to influence the running of the University up to 1858. Of particular interest, however, is their specific mention of the teaching duties of the Professor of Botany and Anatomy (Figure 3.5). Brisbane was required to teach Anatomy if ten students presented themselves before 1 November, and if no students came forward he was to give one public lecture each week up to the commencement of his Botany lectures. These latter were to be given from 15 May to 1 July if five students made application. The seasonal balance of his lecture courses was sensible enough: summer was the obvious time to obtain flowering plants in abundance, and the lower temperatures of the winter months would be better for cadaver dissections. Despite the Committee's report and recommendations, Brisbane still refused to teach Anatomy, and it is uncertain for how long he taught Botany over the years. A possible clue lies in the accounts for the Physic Garden presented by the gardeners. These were usually countersigned by the person in charge, as by John Marshall in his time. Brisbane continued this practice, so it seems reasonable to assume that such continued authorisation indicated a continuing interest in the Physic Garden and in Botany. If so, these signatures can be traced up to 1731. Thus his countersignature is to be found on two accounts sent in by John Mather, a seed merchant in Glasgow:[94]

Acct. Wm. Galbreath to John Mather for a parcell of fine flower seeds furnished by me for the Coledg of Glasgow s use

		Lib. sh. d.
1730	To 30 Different Kinds of fine flower seeds at 6 pence	
Apr 3	each particular seed	— " 15 " —

The Different Kinds of Seeds ment'd the writtin acct being 30 sorts viz:

Curled Indive	Yellow Do.
Cardoons	Whit Do.
Summer Savoy	Catch Fly
Basil	Musk Pease
Lande Cress	Palma Christi
Amaranthus Bicolor	Snails & Caterpilers
ffrench Mary Gold	Horns & Hedgehogs
African Ditto	Oak of Jerusalem
Marvel de Peru	Scarlet Beans
Noli me Tangere	Red Candy Tuft
Belvidere	Whit Dito

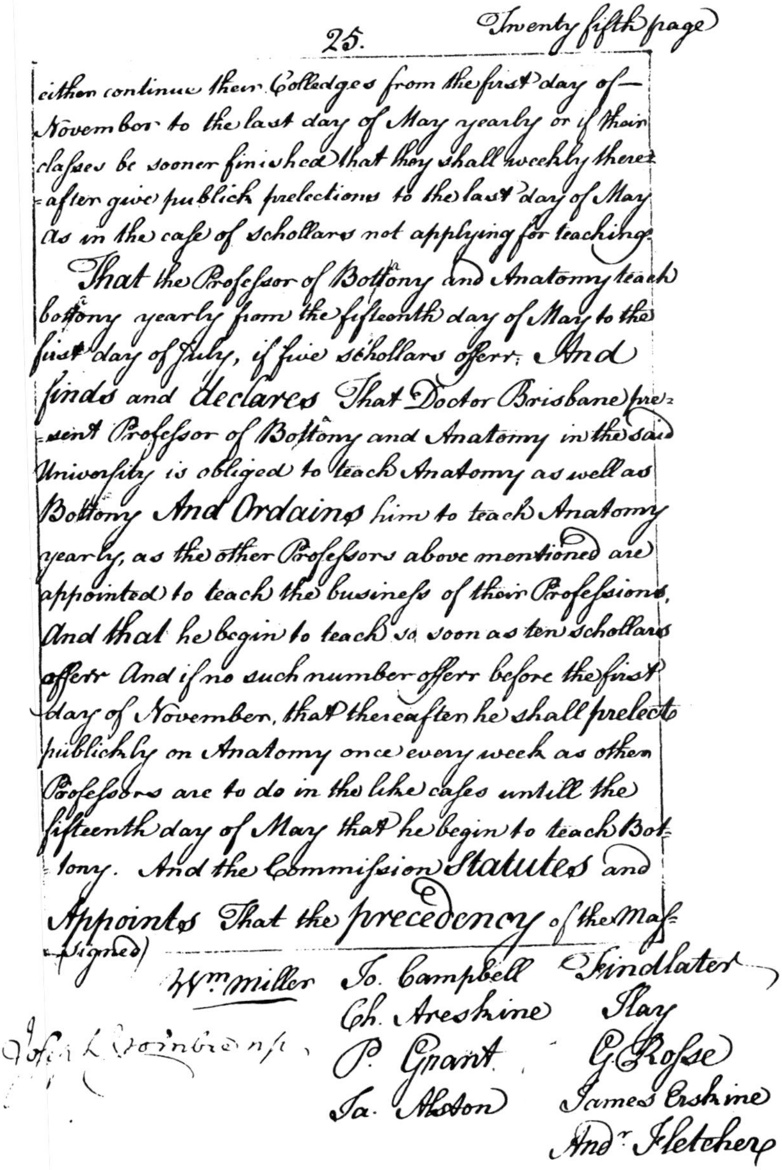

25.   Twenty fifth page

either continue their Colledges from the first day of
November to the last day of May yearly or if their
classes be sooner finished that they shall weekly thereafter give publick prelections to the last day of May
as in the case of schollars not applying for teaching

That the Professor of Bottony and Anatomy teach
bottony yearly from the fifteenth day of May to the
first day of July, if five schollars offerr. And
finds and declares That Doctor Brisbane present Professor of Bottony and Anatomy in the said
University is obliged to teach Anatomy as well as
Bottony And Ordains him to teach Anatomy
yearly, as the other Professors above mentioned are
appointed to teach the business of their Professions,
And that he begin to teach so soon as ten schollars
offerr And if no such number offerr before the first
day of November, that thereafter he shall prelect
publickly on Anatomy once every week as other
Professors are to do in the like cases untill the
fifteenth day of May that he begin to teach Bottony. And the Commission Statutes and
Appoints That the precedency of the Mas-
(Signed)

Wm. Miller   Jo. Campbell   Findlater
               Ch. Areskine   Ilay
Joseph Loinbianfi.   P. Grant   G. Rosse
               Ja. Alston   James Erskine
                              Andr. Fletcher

Figure 3.5. Page 25 of the Report of the Committee of Visitation of 1726,
specifying the duties of the Professor of Botany and Anatomy

Sweet Sultan	Venus Looking Glass
Rose Lupines	Sencibale Plant
Small Blew Do	Humble Plant
great Blew Lupines	Whit Walflower
	ffrench Honeysuckle

In all 30 sorts att 6 pence the piece

Mather twice stated that 30 seed samples were sent, although 31 names are listed. Many of the names are immediately recognisable, with the usual complement of vegetables. The remainder is a mixture of plants which were purchased either for their decorative value or possibly because of some claimed medicinal virtue of the time. The majority of those named are still garden favourites: e.g., *Amaranthus*; Marvel de Peru (*Mirabilis jalpa*); Noli me Tangere (*Impatiens noli-tangere*), the Touch-me-not Balsam; Belvidere (Belvedere, *Kochia scoparia*, the Summer Cypress); and Sweet Sultan. This last refers to the genus *Centaurea*, all of which are sweet-scented and were either the purple or white *C. maschata* or the yellow-flowered *C. sauvaleneus*. The lupin selection was clearly one to ensure maximum display of colour. The catch fly was probably a species of *Silene*, the sticky secretions of which are known to trap insects. Less obvious names such as 'Snails & Caterpilers' were probably genera such as *Medicago* and *Scorpiorus*, both with fruiting bodies resembling the animals mentioned. 'Horns & Hedgehogs' were plants with spiny seed cases (e.g. *Ranunculus arvensis*, *Medicago echinus*, *Echinaria capitata*). Palma Christi probably referred to the Castor Oil plant (*Ricinus communis*), an obvious inclusion in a Physic Garden, and Oak of Jerusalem (*Chenopodium botrys*) was used as a source of expectorant. Venus Looking Glass (*Specularia speculum*) is still a popular garden plant. The Musk Pease is more difficult to identify — so many plants are credited with a musk-like scent. Mather's listing of 31 names whilst charging for 30 seed samples probably lies in the names 'Sencibale' and 'Humble'. The term 'Sencibale' was an alternative for 'Sensitive', commonly used for *Mimosa pudica*, the well-known plant the leaves of which collapse as a result of physical contact. It was also called the 'Humble plant' because of this leaf response.

A second Mather account was sent in during 1731:[95]

1731 Acct. The Coledge of Glasgow to John Mather

		Lib.	sh.	d.
March 23	To 12 Different sorts of flower seeds per Acct. to Doctor Brisbane @ 6 sh	3	12	—
	12 Double Anemonies @ 3 sh	1	16	—
	12 Double Ranunculua @ 3 sh	1	16	—
Aprill				
5	To 16 Different sorts of flower seeds got			
12/15	by Wm Galbreath Gardener	4	16	—
	To 12 Double Clove July flower carnations			

& yellow July flower plants raised from the seed at 12 sh pr	7 "	4 "	—
3 fine pinks @ 6 sh	— "	18 "	—
3 Sweet Williams @ 6 sh	— "	18 "	—
1 ffrench Honeysuckle 6 sh	— "	6 "	—
4 plants finest Sweet Thime	— "	12 "	—
Scotts Money	£21 —	18 —	

For much of the 1730s relatively few data are available on purchases for the Physic Garden. A payment of £3 Scots was made to Galbraith on 18 December 1732[96] for 'two cartload of dung the last year = 00 = 18 = 00' and 'ane cartload of cows dung for planting of fine flowers = 00=08=00' (the 'fine flowers' are not named). A new scythe cost £1/4/- and 'four old hatts for wall trees' was 12/-. At some time in 1733,[97] 3/6d sterling was paid for 'Ane English spade' and 2/- 'for ane sythe'. These, together with '2 strong plants of white hellebor' (1/-) brought the bill to '6 hillings and 6 pense'; the relevant entry in the College Accounts gives the overall cost as £3/18/- Scots. The White Hellebor (*Veratrum album*), though a somewhat violent emetic and cathartic, was used in old medicine.

Brief mention has already been made of Elizabeth Blackwell's *Curious Herbal*. This was advertised for sale in 1737 under its full title: *A Curious Herbal containing five hundred cuts of the most useful plants which are now used in the practice of physic*. Aberdeen-born Elizabeth Blackwell had made an unfortunate marriage and her physician husband had gambled away her dowry and then landed himself in debtors' prison. Her skill at drawing was turned to good account when she enlisted the help of Sir Hans Sloane and the Society of Apothecaries in publishing a herbal. She lodged near the Chelsea Physic Garden and made drawings of some 500 plants from this source, making all the engravings herself. Financially the herbal was a success, sufficiently so to obtain her husband's release from prison. Mrs Blackwell advertised her herbal widely, and one sale was made to the Glasgow University Library; this is recorded in a receipt which is mainly printed, but with handwritten insets (italicised in the following):[98]

London *15 April 1737* 173

REceived *One* guinea & *14s from Mr William Forbes Quastor for the Library of Glasgow* being the first Payment for the Paper of a CURIOUS HERBAL, or a set of CUTS of the most useful Physical Plants, engrav'd on Five Hundred Folio Copper Plates, from Drawings after the Life, the second payment of Guinea to be made when Three Hundred Plates are delivered, and the last when the whole number is compleated

Elizabeth Blackwell

All these written additions are in the lady's hand. Additional writing to the side and underneath (in a different hand) states:

> *Received 1£ 15s as the payment of the second moiety from Mr Forbes as also for charge on shiling seven pence half pence Glasg. febr. 23 1738*
> *Jo: Johnstone*

John Johnstoun, the 'inert' Professor of the Practice of Medicine, had taken over responsibility for the purchase of the herbal after the first part had been paid for by the Quaestor to the Library (the Quaestor was responsible for the financial affairs of the library and at the time was William Forbes, Professor of Law, who had in fact succeeded Brisbane). The back of the receipt bears more handwriting:

> *Then Received by me from Mr Alex' Dunlop Quastor one pound seventeen shillings and Elevenpence sterling for the last subscription and charges for Mrs Blackwells herbal*
> *Jo: Johnstoune*

Alexander Dunlop, Forbes's successor as Quaestor, was Professor of Hebrew and Semitic Languages. The overall cost of the herbal, including despatching costs, was £5/8/6d. Johnstoun's involvement is probably a further indication of Brisbane's lack of interest in Botany at that time, but it is also true that one of the sections of the herbal was dedicated to Johnstoun along with other physicians, who received similar dedicatory recognition. What seems to be the last tangible link between Brisbane and the Physic Garden is to be found in an entry dated 18 July 1738[99] in some accounts actually to do with the Great Garden, viz. '... Common sythe allowed to Wm. Galbraith by Dr Brisbane 0.2.0.' (recorded in sterling).

As already mentioned (p. 34), the question of the permanency of the siting of the Physic Garden has been raised by previous historians of the University, and in one case it is positively stated that a new garden was laid out somewhere in the University grounds by order of the Faculty at some time in the mid-1750s.[100] The background to these speculations appears to be some matters which are incompletely reported in the minutes of Faculty meetings. One such example is for 15 April 1741:[101]

> The Faculty has under consideration the turning of the present Physick Garden into a Bowling Green and allotting a suitable part of the Great Garden for a Physick Garden: This affair is appointed to be fully adjusted against the time fit for Transplanting Shrubs and Plants, in case it be found convenient to make the change.

No further reference to this proposed change is to be found in any of the following records of the Faculty meetings. It has also been suggested[102] that this minute might be regarded as an indication of the continuing uncertainty surrounding the running of the garden and its future. The proposal to change the garden back into a bowling green would have been a return to the *status quo* following the incorporation of the bowling green into the garden in 1705. Bowls was a popular pastime of the Professors and it is possible that moves to reinstate the bowling green may have been a result of Brisbane's lack of interest in the teaching of Botany. Laying out a new Physic Garden as suggested by one historian would not have gone unnoticed in the College Accounts, the minutes of Faculty meetings and the various precepts covering garden expenditure. None of these sources gives any indication that a change of siting took place.

Brisbane died on 27 March 1742, having been virtually a professor in title only for most of his time. His professional interests were maintained in building up an extensive and profitable practice in the town. His successor, Robert Hamilton, was admitted to office on 3 June 1742,[103] following the reading of his Commission. A son of the Reverend William Hamilton of Boswell, he had graduated MD at Glasgow in 1742 and was admitted to the Faculty of Physicians and Surgeons in 1743, being President for the two years 1745–7. There is little information on the running of the garden during the early years of Hamilton's tenure of office. The College Accounts include £4/16/- Scots as 'depursements to the Garden' in Galbraith's name in the 1738–9 period[104] and two payments of £12 Scots, also to Galbraith, for 'Extraordinary work in the Physick Garden' (probably overtime) for the years 1744–5 and 1746–7.[105] The last annual payment of Galbraith's salary was recorded in the 1750–1 College Accounts. He was followed by William Hume in 1750–1. This is probably the same William Hume who was the 'lawfull son of the deceased John Hume', the same John Hume who was gardener to the Physic Garden from 1704 to 1718. William Hume was admitted to the Incorporation of Gardeners on 11 November 1749.[106] Whilst involved for only a short time under Hamilton, he was to be employed later in the Great Garden (p. 116). Hume in turn was succeeded by Archibald Graham at some time in 1751–2.

Of greater significance, however, was the teaching connection formed with the University by William Cullen in 1746 (Figure 3.6). Born at Hamilton in April 1710, Cullen entered the University of Glasgow in 1727 to study Metaphysics, Ethics, Natural Philosophy and Mathematics. He did not graduate and was next apprenticed to the surgeon John Paisley, whose lectures (in place of the 'inert' John Johnstoun) from 1730 to 1740 were the only source of anatomy-teaching in the University. Paisley was followed by John Love in the 1740–1 session, and he in turn by Robert Hamilton from 1741 to 1742 before the latter assumed the Chair of Botany and Anatomy. Cullen

Figure 3.6. William Cullen, from a portrait in the possession of the University of Glasgow

went to London in 1729 and became surgeon on a merchant ship for two years in the West Indies. It was here that he developed his interests in Botany, especially of those plants with medicinal virtues. On his return to London he was apprenticed to an apothecary for a while. He returned to Scotland in 1731–2, setting up practice in the village of Auchinleck. A small legacy enabled him to attend the Edinburgh medical school from 1734 to 1736, after which he returned to Hamilton as medical attendant to the Duke and Duchess of Hamilton. He was able to keep up his botanical interests by supervising a small Physic Garden owned by the Duke. Soon after his arrival he took as pupil the young William Hunter, from the nearby village of Longcalderwood, who in turn was to gain fame as an anatomist in London. Cullen graduated MD at Glasgow in 1740, moved his practice to Glasgow in 1744, and in 1746, by arrangement with Johnstoun, gave a six-month lecture course on the practice of medicine. He was appointed to the Chair after Johnstoun in 1751. Cullen's teaching interests were not restricted to Medicine. In 1747 he instituted lectures on Chemistry; one year later on Botany (given in Latin).

Hamilton meantime re-established the teaching of Anatomy under the control of the appointed professor, travelling to London in 1746 to obtain anatomical preparations. His success brought problems. The public regarded such teaching with suspicion, primed as they were by the escapades of the 'Resurrection Men'. Mob attacks on the College, brought about by rumours, took place in 1744 and 1745; further attacks of a more serious nature, with arrests, followed in 1748 and 1749. These local insurrections ceased after consultations had taken place between the Faculty and local magistrates. Hamilton continued to teach Anatomy until 1756, when he succeeded Cullen in the Chair of Practice of Medicine. Few references are to be found to Botany and the Physic Garden during this period. Cullen's lectures from 1748 would have ensured a fair bearing for the botanical side, and an established garden with a competent gardener would have maintained its plant stocks by propagation and its own seed collections. The paucity of precepts and accounts for the 1730s and 1740s might well be due to loss of documents. All precepts, however, were recorded in the College Accounts and in these there is a seeming dearth of information on Physic Garden expenditure over this period.

Archibald Graham continued to work in the Physic Garden until some time in the 1757–8 session, when he was replaced by Patrick Stevenson. Graham was thus under the supervision of either Hamilton or Cullen — probably the latter. The two professors were evidently dissatisfied with the state of both gardens, as indicated in the minutes of the Faculty meeting of 31 May 1754:[107]

A proposal was given in by Dr. Hamilton and Dr. Cullen concerning the great garden, to make it more useful to the study of Botany, and about getting a good gardiner. And these two Professor

Robert Simson and Dr Dick are appointed a Committee to consider the proposal and report to the next meeting

This minute may be the basis of the suggestion already referred to that a new Physic Garden was laid out in 1754. The actual proposals by Hamilton and Cullen were contained in a memorial (Figure 3.7):[108]

To the Honourable the Rector & other members of the University of Glasgow

The Memorial of
Dr Robert Hamilton Professor of Botany and Anatomy
Dr William Cullen Professor of Medicine

Whereas the quarters of the College Garden by the decay of fruit trees with which they were formerly planted are now almost waste & neither of ornament nor use

And Whereas Dr Robert Simson has formerly informed the Society that our noble Patron His Grace The Duke of Argyle has been pleased to observe that it would be highly ornamental to the Garden & very usefull towards promoting botanical knowledge in this University to plant the quarters of the Garden with such curious exotic Trees and Shrubs as our Soil and Climate will bear: & that further His Grace has been generously pleased to offer and encourage the executions of this work by furnishing the Nursery necessary to it.

We think it in special manner our duty to suggest this subject to the consideration of the University meeting & to move that the meeting may as soon as they conveniently can take the proper measures for planting their Garden in a manner becoming a Society devoted to Taste & Science & move that they may not neglect to show immediately a proper regard to an offer which the Love of Arts & a special affection to this University has produced.

We beg leave to observe further that as the present Botanic Garden from the nature of the Soil & its situation very much exposed to the smoke and soot of the Town is very unfit for the purposes of it & as that quarter of the great Garden adjoining to the Masters Houses can not be planted with Trees without very much incommoding the said Houses. We humbly propose that this quarter be employed as a Botanic Garden for which we judge it is sufficiently fit & we conceive it may be properly employed in this way without producing any dissimilarity that might affect the general plan of the Garden.

On this occasion we cannot avoid observing that the study of Botany in this University has been very much retarded by the want of a proper Gardiner & that the present appointments are insufficient for engaging one. We hope therefore the Society will

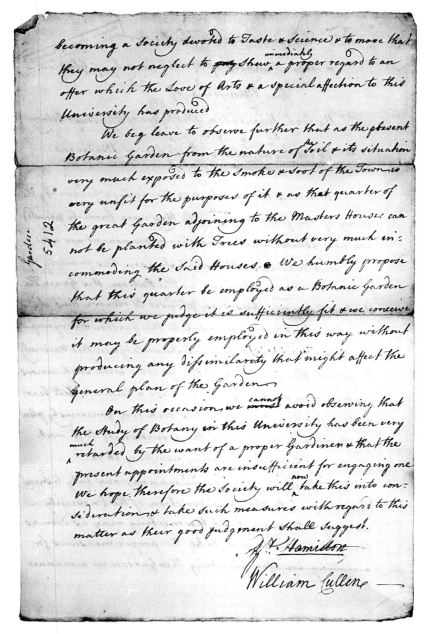

becoming a Society devoted to Taste & Science & to move that
they may not neglect to pay shew a proper regard to an
offer which the Love of Arts & a special affection to this
University has produced

We beg leave to observe further that as the present
Botanic Garden from the nature of Soil & its situation
very much exposed to the Smoke & Soot of the Town is
very unfit for the purposes of it & as that quarter of
the great Garden adjoining to the Masters Houses can
not be planted with Trees without very much in:
commoding the said Houses. We humbly propose
that this quarter be employed as a Botanic Garden
for which we judge it is sufficiently fit & we conceive
it may be properly employed in this way without
producing any dissimilarity that might affect the
general plan of the Garden

On this occasion, we cannot avoid observing that
the Study of Botany in this University has been very
much retarded by the want of a proper Gardiner & that the
present appointments are insufficient for engaging one
We hope, therefore the Society will now take this into con:
sideration & take such measures with regard to this
matter as their good judgment shall suggest.

J. F. Hamilton

William Cullen

Figure 3.7. Part of the Memorial of Robert Hamilton and William Cullen in
which the unsatisfactory state of the Physic Garden and the lack of a good
gardener are mentioned

now take this into consideration & take such measures with regard to this matter as their good judgement shall suggest.

R. Hamilton

W. Cullen

There is no evidence that the committee formed by the Faculty made any recommendations, nor did any changes take place following the above memorial. Archibald Graham continued in employment until 1757, despite being the subject of the complaint regarding the need for a 'proper Gardiner', and by this date Cullen had resigned and Hamilton was dead. The memorialists expected the Faculty to take some notice of the veiled criticism by the Duke of Argyll (Archibald Campbell, third Duke, 1682–1761), who clearly disapproved of the state of the Great Garden. Campbell, the 'uncrowned King of Scotland', held considerable political power and, as a patron and supporter of the University, had been instrumental in securing Cullen's appointment to his professorship. The Faculty seemed not to have been impressed by the complaints, which, though concerned mainly with the Great Garden, also pointed to the state of the soil and unsuitable siting of the Physic Garden. The chemistry of soil was one of Cullen's principal scientific interests. After his marriage in 1741 he became a consultant on rural and agricultural matters. In 1749 he entered into correspondence with Henry Home, Lord Kames (1696–1782), who, on acquiring an estate, became an enthusiastic agricultural experimentalist. In one letter, Cullen questioned whether plant roots had 'elective' properties regarding 'soil juices', or if there was a non-selective uptake of nutrients and a specific conversion of materials within the plant body; he was inclined '... to the latter opinion'.[109] In early 1750 Home proposed experiments on plants which he considered could live on air alone (i.e. cabbages), which by being less dependent on the soil and rapidly putrefying would cheaply 'augment the quantity of my dung'. Cullen pointed out that a complete answer could be obtained only from using many plants through a growing season with a suitable garden, 'circumstances I cannot command at present'.[110] Cullen was not convinced that such a method of manuring would be any more profitable than dung obtained after 'passing through the body of an animal' — with the additional returns from the sale of meat.

Agricultural use of lime was more extensive in eighteenth-century Scotland than in the rest of Britain and in Europe. Cullen, in reply to some letters from Home, questioned whether lime was itself a plant nourishment or whether 'it operates only in preparing nourishment', or if both were true.[111] This interest in lime application recalls the memorial with Robert Hamilton and the statement on the soil of the Physic Garden. Lime was frequently purchased by the University. William Pinkerton was paid £16/13/4d Scots for '5 chalders of lym at 50 merks Scots' on 16 January 1708,[112] and received a further £20 Scots for '3 chalders Blackhall lym' on 7 November 1716.[113] (A chalder was a variable local quantity of 20–64 Imperial bushels.) Lime for building purposes was usually accompanied by payments for 'riddling and sowering' it ('sowering' = slaking), as in the 1708 Thomas Young accounts.[114] The gardens as a whole were of a cold clay soil. Cullen's dissatisfaction with the gardens may lie behind his comments to Home on the lack of opportunity to carry out experiments on plants and air. The joint memorial referred to the harmful effects on the Physic Garden of smoke and soot from the town. Soot deposition on soil and leaves would be harmful enough, but the memorial may have included recognition of the effects of acid rain. The proposed re-siting of the garden near the professors' houses in the northwest region of the Great Garden would have placed it not far from the original site (Figure 2.1), nor are there any indications that the soil would have been any better. The 1778 plan of the University (Figure 2.1) confirms that there was no change in the position of the Physic Garden.

Cullen's annual teaching programme followed the plan of the 1727 Committee of Visitation, with Medicine and Chemistry taught in the winter and Botany and Materia Medica in the summer. The Botany lectures were solely taxonomic in scope, based on Linnaeus's 'sexual system' of plant classification.[115] Linnaeus wrote his many books in a technical Latin based on medieval and Renaissance sources. The suggestion that Cullen gave his botanical lectures in Latin 'because of the formidable array of botanical terms used in the subject'[116] rather misses the point; the specialised terminology was the basis of the Linnaean system of classification. Cullen had regarded the Linnaean system as 'the most uncouth jargon and minute pedantry' on first acquaintance in the later 1730s, but in time came to recognise its merits.[117] Lectures of a taxonomic nature would have required a supply of demonstration material from the Physic Garden, as well as 'simples' for the Materia Medica lectures. Cullen's main claim to medical fame lies in his book *Nosology* (1760), a system of classification of diseases and their symptoms based on Linnaean principles.

Cullen was elected Professor of Chemistry and Medicine at Edinburgh University in November 1755, the letter of resignation of 22 March 1756 pointing out that Robert Hamilton's appointment as his successor at Glasgow could only follow his formal relinquishment of the post.[118] Cullen had been instrumental in revitalising the teaching of Medicine at Glasgow and with Robert Hamilton had made up some of the ground lost during the 'inert' professorships of Brisbane and Johnstoun. His removal to Edinburgh may have been due in part to internal dissensions in the Glasgow Faculty. Robert Hamilton similarly became involved in some non-agreements. On 25 March 1752[119] he wrote to Robert Simson, Clerk of Faculty, seeking consideration for a vacant professorial house and also asking for an increase in salary, having heard that some other professors were making like applications. A second undated letter complains at some length about the clashing of Faculty meetings with the times of his lectures.[120] In this letter there is also reference to a disagreement with John Anderson (Professor of Oriental Languages 1755–7, and of Natural Philosophy 1757–96). Anderson — of 'active, fearless and combative disposition'[121] — seems to have quarrelled at one time or another with most of his colleagues. On his death he left a legacy for the foundation of an alternative university, Anderson's College, of which the present-day University of Strathclyde is a lineal descendant. Hamilton's lengthy letter is probably one of his last: he died in May 1756 of a fever.

Interest in the Physic Garden was expressed from time to time by other members of Faculty. Robert Dick, Professor of Natural Philosophy from 1751 to 1757, described a visit to Oxford in a letter to Robert Simson dated 14 September 1754:[122]

> ... I have visited Oxford lately, and found it very thinly inhabited, most people being in the Country ... The Physick Garden contains about three acres, and is kept in a very good order, there being about 900 exotics in pots, with large stoves and greenhouses. Among the exotics are Coffee, Tea, Cotton trees, Sugar Cane etc.... There is a plant of Aloes a very noble and strong one, which flowered two years ago. Pine Apples in abundance, the mode of disposing of which is settled, one to the Head of the College, two to another, so many for the Professor of Botany, so many to the Gardiner etc ...

There is some hint of criticism about the Glasgow garden in the above letter, written within a few months of Hamilton and Cullen's joint memorial. The implications are that the gardener Archibald Graham was not proving a very successful operative.

With Hamilton's translation to the Chair of Practice of Medicine, Joseph Black was admitted to the Chair of Botany and Anatomy on 25 March 1756. Black entered the University in 1744 to study the Arts course, but did not graduate.[123] He attended Cullen's lectures on Chemistry and gave him some assistance in laboratory work, but left in 1752, again without graduating. After attending medical classes at Edinburgh, he presented his MD thesis (*De Humore Acido a Cibis Orti, et Magnesia Alba* — 'On the acid Humours arising from food and magnesia alba') in 1754. The thesis, with its accurate gravimetric study of the release of carbon dioxide ('fixed air') from magnesium carbonate, was in itself a milestone in quantitative chemical analysis. Black was a conscientious teacher who would have carried out fully his teaching duties in Botany and Anatomy. In March 1757, after Black had been translated to the Chair of Practice of Medicine in succession to Robert Hamilton, the Commission of Thomas Hamilton, brother of Robert, was authorised as Professor of Botany and Anatomy. Black's fundamental studies on latent heat were carried out in his later years at Glasgow. In 1766 he followed Cullen to Edinburgh on being elected to the Chair of Chemistry, and remained there until his death in December 1799 (this sad event taking place whilst he sat of a sofa with a bowl of milk held between his thighs, and even then none was spilled). Cullen and Black were to become prominent members of the informal group of philosophers who collectively gave to Edinburgh in 1730 to 1790 an intellectual lustre unsurpassed by any other capital city in Europe — the 'Scottish Enlightenment'. Black left no imprint on the running of the Glasgow Physic Garden during his year of office, which coincided with the last year of employment of Archibald Graham as gardener.

Thomas Hamilton was the same age as Joseph Black and was admitted to the Faculty of Physicians and Surgeons in 1751. His apprenticeship was served under a John Crawford prior to his entry into practice in partnership with John Moore, and in 1752 he replaced William Hunter as Cullen's surgical assistant in the town of Hamilton. He was admitted to the Glasgow Chair on 12 April 1757,[124] after reading a dissertation on 'The Teeth' before the assembled Faculty as his 'Qualification for Office' (no such requirement was asked of Joseph Black or of his predecessors). Hamilton, a close friend of both Hunter brothers, William and John, was a man of great social accomplishments, popular in the town and University, and a notable clubman. He married Isobel Anderson and they had two sons: William, born 31 July 1758; and James, born 28 December 1759, who died when two years old. William Hamilton literally followed in his father's footsteps and became the third member of the Hamilton family to hold the Chair of Botany and Anatomy.

Thomas Hamilton's appointment, in the same year that Patrick Stevenson became gardener, seems not to have been marked by any recorded changes in the running of the Physic Garden. Stevenson's salary remained at £72 Scots, as with all his predecessors, and the Professor's remained the same as for Thomas Brisbane at £360 Scots. Thomas Hamilton was to occupy the Chair for the next 24 years and in all this time there are few references, either in the College Accounts or in the precepts or other accounts, to expenditure on the Physic Garden with the exceptions of Stevenson's salary statements, and these terminated in 1760–1. There is mention in the 1759–60 College Accounts of £19/15/- Scots being paid to Deacon Muir 'for work about the Physic Garden'.[125] Muir was a mason who frequently did repair work for the University, but the exact nature of his work in the garden cannot be traced. One entry can be found in the College Accounts linking Hamilton's name with garden expenditure, viz., 'To Mr Thomas Hamilton for an account of wright work paid by him to Mr Nisbit for use of the Physick Garden, precept 29 October 1760 £246/11/8d'.[126] The actual precept is as follows:[127]

Mr Thomas Hamilton Dr To Geroge Nisbet Wright Glasg^w
April 1757
In the Physick Garden

for a hot bed box 4 planks	£0 2 0	
30 cast double floorin & 20 cast dor nails	0 0 10½	

½ of a Gotenbourg plank three Days work	0	1	9
three days work	0	3	6
four Sash broads to Do timber Glas &c	2	8	0
pd for painting the box	0	4	6
May one 3 footed stool	0	1	2
26 Dozn pins @ 4^d pr Dozn	0	8	10
Mended 2 losans in hot bed	0	1	6
To sheath a floor 30 Gotenbourg planks & sawing	4	15	0
Making ready Do. 11 days & pd cartage	0	13	4
One chist small Drawers wood, locks &c	1	2	0
One box & frame to cistern wood nails & work	0	4	2
Deem^r pd cartwage of planks from My Shop to Coledge	0	0	6
400 Double 300 Single floorin & 200 plansher	0	6	3
12 days laying floor, puting up a press			
shelfing a closet & a New Door	0	14	0
One sided sanded plank to the Door	0	0	11½
One Small Sash Windo	0	3	6
pd a plaisterer for 12½ feet cornice & for			
17 yds plaister work	0	8	6
pd for mending a lock	0	0	4
One sash casement windo	0	3	10
one lock	0	1	2
March 15th 1758			
Mended 8 Sash lozans in hot bed	0	6	0
One very lerge chist of Drawers Desk			
& Glas case	7	7	0

£20 10 11²/₂

(Note that the above sum is in sterling and that given in the accounts is in Scots money.)

The carpenter's work seems to have been divided between the Physic Garden and Hamilton's household requirements. For the latter the chest, desk, glass case, plastering work and sash windows would be relevant. The remaining expenditure was concerned with a 'hot bed box'. Several references to horse manure and hot-beds have been given in earlier pages. The planks, nails, glass ('sash broads' = shutters; 'losans' = panes) etc. would suggest the construction of a large hot-bed frame rather than a hothouse or greenhouse. A '3 footed stool' could have been used by the gardener and the 'box & frame to cistern wood' could also have been used in the garden or in the house.

The Professorship of Botany and Anatomy under Thomas Hamilton seems to have been of broad scope, including in time lectures on Surgery, Midwifery and Materia Medica. Whilst in Cullen's time both Botany and Materia Medica had been taught with enthusiasm, Hamilton was either too busy or too unfamiliar with these subjects to do them justice. He conscientiously gave the lectures and attendant dissections in Anatomy, and in 1768 instituted lectures on Midwifery. William Irvine, one-time assistant to Joseph Black, gave lectures on Materia Medica, and may have given those on Botany but this is uncertain. He in turn became Lecturer in Chemistry. Hamilton was taken ill with the palsy in August 1777 and was allowed two months' leave of absence in October of that year to help in his recovery. Whilst recovering sufficiently to return to his teaching duties, he did not regain his former health. The Faculty meeting of 31 October 1780[128] considered a letter from Hamilton in which he emphasised the precarious nature of his health and asked that his son William be employed to give the Anatomy lectures in the coming winter session, '... which desire the Meeting, knowing the state of the sd Professors health and abilities and good character of the said Mr William Hamilton did and hereby do unanimously agree to'.

With William Hamilton's first official engagement by the University an important point is reached in the history of both the Physic Garden and the teaching of Botany in the University. Of significance also is an event back in 1760–1, when Patrick Stevenson left the employment of the University and was succeeded by Alexander Adams. Of all the gardeners, Adams was destined to be the one who raised the status and scope of the work and its responsibilities. Both of these men, the future Professor and the gardener, deserve chapters in their own right. Moreover, the emphasis placed so far on the Physic Garden has forced into the background the importance of the Great Garden in the life of the University. To restore the rightful balance, there is now a need to explore the extent to which archival documents help to clarify the organisation and day-to-day running over the years of this important amenity of the Old College. The next chapter will seek to do this.

Notes

1. FM, 7 September 1704: 26631, pp. 19–20; also 26632, p. 29.
2. A. Duncan, 1896. *Memorials of the Faculty of Physicians and Surgeons of Glasgow* (James Maclehose & Sons, Glasgow).
3. GUAA 39483.
4. FM, 3 October 1704: 26632, p. 31.
5. GUAA 8528.
6. CA, 26623.
7. GUAA 45445.
8. P.B. McNab, 1903. *The History of the Incorporation of Gardeners of Glasgow* (J. Smith & Son, Glasgow), p. 184.

9. GUAA 45448.
10. GUAA 45449.
11. GUAA 45460.
12. GUAA 45568.
13. GUAA 45447.
14. FM, 12 March 1705: 26632, p. 35.
15. GUAA ??.
16. CA, 1705–6: 26623, p. 77.
17. GUAA 45456.
18. CA, 1705–6: 26623, p. 77.
19. GUAA 45459.
20. P.B. McNab, 1903. *The History of the Incorporation of Gardeners*, p. 15.
21. GUAA 45459.
22. GUAA 45464.

23. CA, 1705–6: 26623, p. 81.
24. GUAA 45455.
25. GUAA 45956.
26. GUAA 45479.
27. GUAA 45527.
28. P.B. McNab, 1903. *The History of the Incorporation of Gardeners*, p. 183.
29. GUAA 45526.
30. GUAA 45951.
31. D. Murray, 1927. *Memories of the Old College of Glasgow*, p. 248.
32. GUAA 45467.
33. GUAA 45500.
34. GUAA 45468.
35. GUAA 45498.
36. GUAA 45495.
37. CA, 1705–6: 26623, p. 81.
38. J. Mackie, 1954. *The University of Glasgow 1451–1951*, chapter XI, p. 153 *et seq.*
39. GUAA 45955.
40. GUAA 27211.
41. Note at back of College Revenue Book.
42. Register of Proceedings and Acts, p. 29 (Ref. no. 26632).
43. FM, 29 September 1720: 26634, p. 2.
44. GUAA 47659.
45. GUAA 50823.
46. FM, 13 February 1721: 26634, p. 18.
47. GUAA 39487.
48. FM, 18 December 1708: 26632, p. 51.
49. FM, 4 August 1713: 26632, p. 110.
50. FM, 14 January 1714: 26632, p. 111–12.
51. FM, 1 June 1714: 26632, p. 121.
52. J. Coutts, 1909. *History of the University of Glasgow 1451–1909*, (J. Maclehose & Son, Glasgow), p. 487.
53. GUAA 42053.
54. GUAA 45852.
55. P.B. McNab, 1903. *The History of the Incorporation of Gardeners*, p. 31.
56. Ibid., p. 31.
57. Ibid., p. 193.
58. Ibid., p. 184.
59. FM, 1 December 1719: 26631, p. 312.
60. P.B. McNab, 1903. *The History of the Incorporation of Gardeners*, p. 187.
61. GUAA 42338.
62. GUAA 42339.
63. Royal Commission, 23 February 1720.
64. FM, 26 January 1721: 26634, p. 16.
65. FM, 31 January, 7 February 1721: 26634, pp. 17, 18.
66. FM, 24 November 1721: 26634, p. 31.
67. GUAA 42365.
68. GUAA 42340.
69. GUAA 42429.
70. GUAA 42544.
71. GUAA 42527.
72. GUAA 42621.
73. GUAA 42521.
74. GUAA 42529.
75. FM, 29 June 1722: 26634, p. 65.
76. FM, 5 July 1722: 26634, p. 69.
77. GUAA 42544.
78. GUAA 42652.
79. GUAA 42664.
80. GUAA 42665.
81. GUAA 42620.
82. GUAA 42618.
83. GUAA 42617.
84. GUAA 42672.
85. GUAA 42675.
86. GUAA 42755.
87. GUAA 42674.
88. GUAA 42756.
89. GUAA 42758.
90. GUAA 42761.
91. GUAA 39862.
92. J. Coutts, 1909. *History of the University of Glasgow*, pp. 485–6.
93. Report of 1726 Committee of Visitation, p. 25 (Ref. no.26638).
94. GUAA 40307.
95. GUAA 40233.
96. GUAA 40394.
97. GUAA 40574.
98. GUAA 8846.
99. GUAA 40931.
100. D. Murray, 1927. *Memories of*

the Old College of Glasgow, p. 248.

101. FM, 15 April 1741: 26648, p. 99.

102. F.O. Bower, 1903. Notes on botany in the University of Glasgow in the 18th century. *Transactions of the Natural History Society of Glasgow*, vol. 7, pp. 121–36.

103. FM, 3 June 1742: 26639, p. 155.

104. CA, 1738–9: 26624.

105. CA, 1746–7: 26624.

106. P.B. McNab, 1903. *The History of the Incorporation of Gardeners*, p. 193.

107. FM, 31 May 1754: 26640, p. 115.

108. GUAA 5412.

109. A.L. Donovan, 1975. *Philosophical Chemistry in the Scottish Enlightenment*, (Edinburgh University Press), p. 86.

110. Ibid., p. 87.

111. Ibid., p. 88.

112. GUAA 45578.

113. GUAA 42062.

114. GUAA 45568: entry for 18 June 1708.

115. W. Blunt, 1984. *The Complete Naturalist: a Life of Linnaeus* (Collins, London), Appendix (by W. Stearn), pp. 242–9.

116. J. Coutts, 1909. *History of the University of Glasgow*, p. 489.

117. J. Thomson, 1827. *The Works of William Cullen, M.D. Vol. 1* (W. Blackwood, Edinburgh, & T. & G. Underwood, London), p. 445 *et seq.*

118. GUAA 45264.

119. GUAA 26226.

120. GUAA 31117.

121. J. Coutts, 1909. *History of the University of Glasgow*, pp. 227–9.

122. GUAA 26308.

123. R.G.W. Anderson, 1986. Joseph Black, in *A Hotbed of Genius* (Edinburgh University Press), pp. 93–115.

124. FM, 12 April 1757: 26640, p. 220.

125. CA, 1759–60: 26672.

126. CA, 1759–60: 26672.

127. GUAA 6375.

128. FM, 31 October 1780: 26692, p. 38.

'AT THE PRINCIPALL OF THE COLLEDGE AT HIS ORDER...'

John Stirling commenced his 26-year tenure of the Principalship in 1701, and during his time a large number of the precepts and accounts relative to the Great Garden were headed as shown above or with a minor variation. The Principal and Faculty exercised a direct control over the running of the Great Garden. As already shown, in 1701 there were three gardens or yards: the Great Garden and the Little Garden, the latter being taken over in 1704 for the Physic Garden, and a small garden north of the College buildings. The value to the College of the Great Garden was twofold: as a place of recreation (the Principal had a small garden of his own), and as a source of income by letting parts of the ground to the tacksmen. John Marshall's (1704) conditions of appointment made him overseer of the Physic Garden and also required that he should watch over the general upkeep of the Great Garden by the tacksmen. But, whilst he had some direct responsibility for the management of the Physic Garden, he had no say in the running of the Great Garden. In 1701, the walled Great Garden extended from the rear of the College buildings to the Molendinar Burn, covering an area of about 9 acres (Figure 4.1). Further land beyond the burn was to become enclosed during the course of the century.

A pertinent precept, issued at some time in the 1702–3 session, ordered payment of £16 Scots to 'William Hattrick Gardiner for Dressing the Grass as per precept'.[1] Grass played a role in the life of the University. A green area of several acres' extent at the rear of the College offered a striking and much-appreciated contrast between the populous and noisy High Street and nearby town and the peaceful tree-lined and studded lawns to the rear. Slezer's drawing (Frontispiece) gives an impression of the appearance of the garden in 1669–70. The sale of grass cuttings as fodder to the townspeople was a source of income for the tacksmen. Mechanical grass-cutters were to be

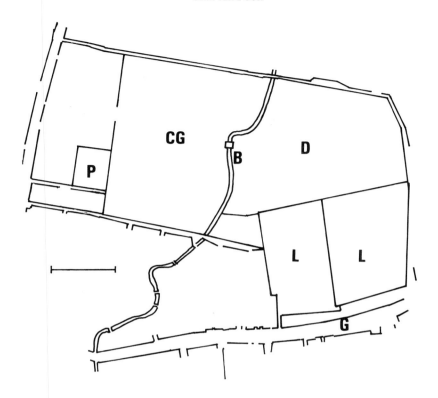

Figure 4.1. Plan showing in outline the gardens and other land in the possession of the University

P = Physic Garden **CG** = College (Great) (Dovehill) **L** = Land south of Dowhill **G** = Garden **B** = Molendinar Burn **D** = Dowhill Gallowgate Street

Scale line: 300 feet

an invention of the early years of the next century, so the regular mowing of the walks and the plots was by hand, and for this the College supplied the scythes and 'sharping stones'. One of the striking features of the purchase of implements over the years is seen in the regular annual payments for scythes (syths, sythes, sayths, sayeiths, siths) and for 'sharping stones' (Table 4.1). Next in frequency came spades and hedge shears.

In the early 1700s much of the Faculty's attention was focused on the establishment and organisation of the Physic Garden, and relatively few references to the Great Garden are available. The Thomas Young accounts for 1705[2] include 3/- paid for 'great garron nailes for the Great yeat of the College Yeard' ('yeat', 'yett', or 'yate' =

Table 4.1. Implements and associated purchases for the Great Garden, from precepts and accounts dated as shown (all in Scots money)

? 1721	ane spade	£02 - 02 - 02
	ane syth	01 - 10 - 00
4 Feb. 1722	naills & Hatts for wall trees	00 - 01 - 00
4 May 1722	2 sythes	03 - 00 - 00
30 June 1724	2 sith sneds	00 - 08 - 00
24 Sept. 1724	ane pair Hedging shears	03 - 00 - 00
15 Oct. 1724	1 pair shears	03 - 00 - 00
	1 pruning knife	01 - 10 - 00
24 April 1725	two sayeiths	03 - 00 - 00
13 May 1725	3 sayth stanes	00 - 06 - 00
25 Aug. 1725	sharping of Gardiners shears twice	00 - 04 - 00
29 Oct. 1725	3 red bines	00 - 06 - 00
	4 old Hatts for the trees	00 - 12 - 00
	2 sharping stanes	00 - 06 - 00
7 Dec. 1725	ane pruning knife	00 - 12 - 00
	2 sythes stanes	00 - 06 - 00
24 June 1727	for a pruning knife	00 - 12 - 00
29 June 1727	a bottle of oyl to the Axle trees of the Wheelbarrows	00 - 08 - 00
28 April 1728	a riddle	00 - 12 - 00
17 May 1731	4 long sythes	05 - 08 - 00
	1 short Do.	01 - 02 - 00
25 April 1732	4 long sythes	05 - 08 - 00
	4 spades	03 - 12 - 00
	2 shafts for them	00 - 06 - 00
7 June 1732	Price of a spade	02 - 00 - 00
	4 sythes	04 - 16 - 00
18 Dec. 1732	1 new sythe	01 - 04 - 00
	4 old Hatts for the trees	00 - 12 - 00
14 March 1733	Two spades and two shafts for them	04 - 00 - 00
12 May 1733	4 long saythes	05 - 08 - 00
24 July 1733	2 sythes	02 - 14 - 00
	besoms	00 - 01 - 00
9 Aug. 1733	12 Syth stones	01 - 04 - 00
13 May 1734	4 long sythes	05 - 08 - 00
20 July 1734	For ane shears grinding	00 - 06 - 00
9 Jan. 1735	2 pairs of shizers[a]	04 - 16 - 00
1 June 1736	2 Sythes	02 - 14 - 00
23 Aug. 1736	2 pairs shizers[a]	04 - 16 - 00
18 Nov. 1736	For grinding Hedge shears	00 - 06 - 00
25 March 1737	By 2 spades	04 - 00 - 00
	By 2 Sythes	02 - 14 - 00
	By 12 Sythe stones	01 - 14 - 00
27 April 1738	A riddle	00 - 12 - 00

27 July 1738	To 3 Long Sythes	04 - 01 - 00
9 Oct. 1739	A dozen of Syth stones	01 - 03 - 00
	To grinding sythes and Hedge shears	00 - 02 - 00
30 May 1752	4 Sythes	04 - 16 - 00
6 June 1752	6 sharping stones	01 - 00 - 00
28 July 1753	4 Sythes	04 - 16 - 00
	6 sharping stones	00 - 15 - 00
1 June 1754	4 sharping stones	00 - 10 - 00
20 July 1754	4 Sythes	04 - 16 - 00
16 April 1755	A beatter for beatting the banks	01 - 04 - 00
14 June 1755	4 Sythes	04 - 16 - 00
4 July 1755	Mending a frame for a rolling stone	01 - 04 - 00
9 Aug. 1755	To iron work for 3 wheel barrows	04 - 07 - 00
4 Sept. 1755	2 hooks for clearing of hedges	00 - 12 - 00
17 Jan. 1756	To a shod[b] for a shovel	00 - 10 - 00
24 Jan. 1756	To a spinel[c] to a Gardiners Reel	00 - 06 - 00
10 July 1756	To 4 sythes	04 - 16 - 00
18 May 1767	To a frame and furniture for a hourse for the Great Rolling stone for Rolling the garden	17 - 05 - 00
7 May 1771	1 Spade	02 - 08 - 00
	1 Large Rake & shaft	01 - 13 - 00
	1 Syth and 4 sythe stones	01 - 12 - 00
15 June 1775	One spade	
	1 Dutch how	
	1 Small garden rake	
	1 lock for garden door	09 - 00 - 00
12 June 1779	1 sythe & 4 sythe stones	01 - 12 - 00
	1 Dutch howe	00 - 14 - 00
	One Garden line	00 - 12 - 00
20 July 1780	Mending the Wattering Cann	00 - 08 - 00
11 June 1781	1 scythe & other tools	04 - 10 - 00

Notes: a. shizers = scissors
      b. metal rim for a wooden shovel
      c. a spindle

gate), and on 3 August 1708[3] 4/- was paid to 'two officers for takeing washers before the Baylif for breaking down the wall of the private walk'; trouble continued with the local washerwomen, possibly through their attempts to use boundary trees (outside the wall) to attach drying lines. A lengthy and repetitive document prepared in 1706, the parchment cracked and illegible in places, is the only surviving documentary link between the old College and the Incorporation of Gardeners of Glasgow.[4] The bond is an agreement between the College and the Incorporation regarding the feu payable to the College on some land purchased by the Incorporation from Sir William Fleming, one-time Rector. The land in question was not part of the College gardens. Whilst there seem to be no other eighteenth-century documentary links between the College and the Incorporation, many of the gardeners employed by the University over the years were recorded in the list of members of the Incorporation.

References to the Great Garden are more frequent from 1720 on. The 1 December 1720[5] account presented by Thomas Young included £9/12/- Scots for 'Holland' (holly) berries which were probably intended for the nursery, and then later for hedges in the Great Garden. On 25 March 1721,[6] Thomas Young was paid £4 Scots for 'twenty carts of stones for a sink in the great Garden' — an allusion to the problems of drainage, to which there are numerous references over the years. As already mentioned, James Loudon's appointment was intended for work in the Great Garden and to commence from Martinmas 1722. His interim appointment to take temporary charge of the Physic Garden followed the sacking of William Craig (p. 75). Loudon's appointment allows an approximate time to be placed on an undated note in a College Revenue Book:[7]

The College Large Yard did yield by Tack formerly 300£ Scots per annum, but now by reason of enlarging and walks, & doing things to beautify same, the rent is reduced to 210£ Scots, and makes a prt of General Revenue. This rent will be further reduced if some other things are done to the yard that are thought proper and if yearly expences already increased by a second Gardiner who has 72£ Scots per annum.

The second gardener was James Loudon, and it is evident that some replanning of the Great Garden was in hand. The Faculty meeting of 29 June 1722[8] considered a proposal for the 'better ordering and beautifying of the Great Garden by Inclosing the four quarters yrof with proper hedges'. This initial proposal was followed by a further move on 6 December 1722:[9] '... In pursuance of the Resolve 29 June last anent Beautifying the great Garden the Faculty orders that so much ground be taken from the present Tacksmen of the sd Garden as will for both enlarge the walks around the yeard to 24 foot in breadth & for conveniently planting hedge along the walks'. One outcome is seen in a precept dated 10 June 1723[10] 'To John Good Gardiner for advise and drawing a scheme for the Great Garden — £25 : 04 : 00'. As a result of the introduction of Good's scheme, Jame Loudon and Walter Galbraith jointly presented to Faculty at the end of 1723[11] 'Ane account of ground taken of the College Yard for Enlarging the walks and borders in the year 1723

	fall	Ell	feet
John Allan	19	25	03
John McArter	20	35	02
Alex. Miller	21	03	00
James Stuart	18	01	00
	79	28	05

William Galbraith
James Lowdon'

In square measure used at that time there were 36 ells to one fall. Further estimates of ground lost were to be made by Galbraith during the process of redesigning: 'Amount of land taken for enlarging the walks and borders of the College yards this present year 1723 coming to half ane aikr four falls and fourteen ells measured by me William Galbraith';[12] and 'An account of the measure of ground taken off the Coledge yards for Wales and borders the borders about the walls being contained likewise amounts to an akre and twentieth falls twentie nine ells and two feet'.[13] An acre ('aikr' or 'akre') was equal to 160 falls in square measure.

Accounts for the purchase of plants for the Great Garden are sparse in the first years of Loudon's employment as gardener. In February 1722, 'Beatches for the Hedge of the Garden' amounting to 'Eleven hunder and an half of trees' were supplied by Hugh Tod of Stewarton for £41/8/- Scots.[14] On 1 March 1723, George Jameson of Hamilton supplied 'six scor Lym trees' for £20 Scots.[15] The College Accounts for 1722–3 include the entry 'To James Lowden Gardner for 12 precepts and receipts for working and levelling the garden walks £167/10/-'.[16] This covers the wages of hired workmen — the latter description is to be found on almost all relevant precepts, whereas Loudon was always careful to describe himself as 'gardiner'. From the more fully documented wage payments of a similar nature, it is evident that the hired men were paid on a Saturday from authorised precepts made out to Loudon and with cash from the College Factor. No one worked for more than six days in a week, the Sabbath rule being strictly enforced. From 1724 until 1727, increasing numbers of workmen were hired for various jobs in the Great Garden, all under the management of Loudon. Their periods of employment varied, with some working over several months and others engaged for a few weeks or less. The individual workmen are all named in the accounts presented; some 61 documents are available for the three-year period. The accounts from April to August 1724[17] quote wage rates of 8/- Scots per day. In the following November and December[18] the rates were reduced to 7/-, and remained so at all seasons over the rest of the period for which accounts are available. No reasons are given for this wage reduction. The above accounts are also somewhat confusing in that, whilst the individual daily payments are given in sterling, the totals for each are in

Scots money — in the same way that the totals are recorded in the College Accounts.

In 1724, five workmen were involved from April to August. John Wilkie received £32 Scots for 80 days' work in this period. John Dunlop worked during the period April to August and again in November and December, a total of 133 days, and received £50/13/- Scots. John Hutchison was similarly employed for 128 days, receiving £48/17/6d. John Miller and Robert Brock both worked from April to July, for 71½ days (£28/12/-) and 67½ days (£27/10/-) respectively. Alexander Weir and Alexander Mitchell joined the workforce in July and August and again in December, with the former earning £7/15/- for 20 days' work and the latter £11/10/6d for 30½ days. Casual labour was taken on in November. Patrick Ferguson (39 days for £13/13/-) and Robert Taylor (17 days for £5/19/-) were also employed in December, whilst Daniell McDonald (five days for £1/15/-) and James McGichen and Robert Buchanan (both ten days for £3/10/-) were employed in November only. No descriptions of the actual work done are available for 1724, but the more explicit accounts of later years show that the summer work entailed rolling and mowing the walks, mowing the other grassed areas, digging and weeding the borders and the nursery, and dressing and 'snedding' (cutting) the hedges. The total expenditure is similar to that for 1723, when the extra labour was involved in working and levelling the garden walks. The work programme for November and December is more difficult to interpret, but may have been involved with the continuing problems of drainage of a clay soil, and possibly remodelling of borders, although little cultivation would have been possible.

Some of the men employed in November and December 1724 were re-engaged in the following January 1725,[19] but for all the workmen employment ceased in the following May. John Dunlop (98 days for £34/6/-), John Hutcheson (89½ days for £31/6/6d), Patrick Ferguson (70 days for £24/10/-) and Robert Taylor (84½ days for £29/4/6d) were all engaged over the four months. Alexander Mitchell worked from January until March (57½ days for £20/2/6d), whilst Alexander Weir worked for 3½ days only in January. Just why no further labour was taken on in the summer is not easily explained. Another of the Thomas Young accounts[20] gives part of an explanation:

1725 Accompt of Debursements To the use of the Colledge of Glasgow by Thomas Young Bedellus to the Colledge, att Severall Occasions per order of the Principall of sd Colledge

Apryl 6th Impr. To Workmen when working in the College yeard
          pr sd order   00:04:00
May 15th To the College Gardeners when the sd Workmen were
          dismissed from furder work in sd yeard
          pro tempore pr sd order   00:12:00

24th To Men who Rolld the Walks in sd yeard		00:12:00
28 To Ditto per sd order		00:12:00
June 1st To Ditto per sd order		00:12:00
7th To Ditto per sd order		00:12:00
19th To sharping=stones for use of ye Colledge Gardener		00:06:00
26th To rollers of sd Walks pr sd order		00:12:00
July 14th To the College Gardener when Mowing sd Walks of sd yeard pr sd order		01:18:00
August 13th To Rollers of sd Walks pr sd order		00:12:00
25th To Sharping of gardeners shears twice, for snedding the hedges of ye Colledge yeard & Nursery		00:04:00
Sept 3rd To Rollers of sd Walks pr sd order		00:12:00
To the College Gardener when Mowing sd Walks of sd Yeard pr sd order		02:04:00
29th To Rolling Walks pr sd order		00:12:00
	Summa	10:04:00

The 15 May 1725 is close to the date when the hired labour was paid off. There is no comparison between the £10/4/- outlay as recorded above and the £155/15/- paid out during the equivalent period in 1724. The work programme in summer 1725 was centred on maintenance of the walks. It is, however, possible that the concentrated work on the walks of the two previous summers may not have needed to be repeated in 1725. The total annual bills for hired labour for the Great Garden in 1723 and 1724 were £167/10/- and £255/1/- Scots respectively.

December 1725[21] was a busy time in the Great Garden, with seven workmen employed for varying periods. Alexander Mitchell and Patrick Walker worked for twelve days (£4/4/- each) and John Hutcheson for eleven days (£3/17/-), while the remainder worked for shorter periods: Adam McCallum for six days; Adam McClealand for 5½; John Graham younger for 5; and John Graham elder for 1½. The overall labour bill for December was £18/11/- Scots. The work involved was defined, i.e. '... wheillin of earth from about the new buildings into the large Garden'. The new buildings were houses for the professors and were under construction on the north side of the College. This house-building programme had started in 1722 and between then and 1728 eleven houses were built — much envied by the well-to-do citizens of the town, few of whom were housed so elegantly in residences so private. These houses were to become the New Court, and their construction removed part of the garden area on the north side of the College. Soil was too valuable to waste and the seven hired men were set to wheelbarrowing it into the Great Garden. It was presumably topsoil from digging out the foundations of the new houses. The temporary labour hired in the previous winter of 1724 may have been similarly employed, but this is not stated. This transportation of soil continued into January and February 1726,[22] involving seven men: Adam McCellan (January only), Alexander Mitchell, John Hutchinson, Patrick Walker, John McFarlane, George McTaggart and Patrick Ferguson. The overall cost of these two month's work came to £34/6.6d Scots, equivalent to 98 man-working days. This transported soil was used to build the 'Mound' or 'Bank' on the west side (Figure 4.2).

Whilst 'wheillin earth' was the principal occupation of the workmen in the winter months of late 1725 and early 1726, other work was in progress. On 7 December 1725, £1/6/- Scots was paid for '3 threave of straw to cover ye young elms etc. in Nurserie at 8 pence per threave & 2 pence for carrying it from Gorbels'.[23] A similar quantity of straw in 1706 cost £1/4/- Scots. As mentioned earlier, a threave of straw was 2 stooks, each stook containing 12 sheaves. Evidently there were problems of frost damage. On the same day, £1/4/- was claimed '... Att rolling the Walks twice wt. ye big rolling stone to 2 men imployed at it 6 pence each time before the setting down of the Colledge'.[24] It is not clear just when this rolling of the walks was carried out, and 6d per piece (piece here meaning a period of time — one day) was less than paid to the men wheeling the barrows. It should again be noted that the daily sum is in sterling. On 3 January 1726,[25] 'the principall allowed in compleament to the workmen last December' the sum of £1/4/-, probably for drinks at Hogmanay. On 5 February 1726,[26] £1/19/- was paid to some men 'for hagin a whitil'. To 'hag' means to chop down, and 'whitil' appears to be a hastily written abbreviation for 'whitelegs' or short branches. Some minor requirements were dealt with on 16 April 1726:[27]

> For barrowin anoter stand for to carrie water to the cows and horses
> and for ceitin for man for sade work   00:06:00
> and for half a stowk of straw for to make ropes to laye above the
> hollies to keep them from wind waven   00:02:00

The 'stand' was a barrel; the location of the cows and horses is not stated but was probably on the Dovehill. The straw ropes were used to protect the young holly plants from being blown about ('wind waven').

Whilst the hired labour was involved in a variety of occupations, there was some plant-buying. Reference has been made (p. 77) to purchase of fruit trees under the joint names of William Galbraith and James Loudon, which would suggest that the trees were for the Great Garden and the Physic Garden. On 10 February 1725,[28] £32 Scots was paid 'for two hundred of Lyms for the said Large Garden' to Allan Bowie 'Gardner'. In the next month (5 March) more Lime trees were obtained:[29]

An accompt of Limes bought by Mr James Lowdon distinct from

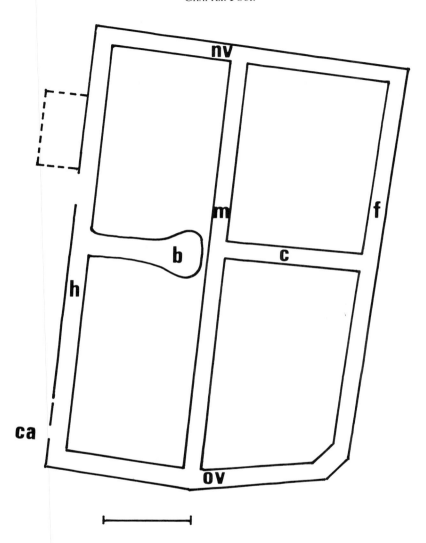

Figure 4.2. The walks in the College Garden

h = Head Walk **nv** = New Vennel Walk **ov** = Mound (also Mount) **ca** = causeway
Old Vennel Walk **m** = Middle Walk **c** = The broken line shows a rectangular area
Cross Walk **f** = Foot Walk **b** = Bank or at the rear of the Common hall.

Scale line: 150 feet

them that came before for the use of the Large Garden of the College of Glasgow

	Scots
Impr from George Bowe gardner of Cesnock	16:00:00
Item from George Bleckes gardner at Loudon halfe a hunderd of suckers of limes at 3 pound per hundred	01:10:00
Item for horse hires for bringing them hither	01:16:00
Item for a baite for men and horses when they came	00:06:00
The sum	19:12:00

George Bowe, or Bowie, had acted as an agent for Allan Bowie in the 5 March transaction. The above account consisted of a mixture of young trees and layered plants, the latter being the commonest form of *Tilia* propagation, and these are described as 'suckers' in the list above. The 'baite' (= bait) was refreshment for man and horses. In due course James Loudon submitted his claim for expenses:[30]

Impr. Att Kilmarnock to amman to assist him in procuring a hundred Limis a cheap as possible	00:12:00
It. At the place of Lowdon to the Gardners to procure him if possible a hundred succers of Lims at a Chep Price	00:12:00
It. at the place of Cesnock to the Gardners for undertaking to procure him two hundreds and a halffe to Lime trees and to take care to send them hither	01:16:00
It. for a hors hire from the place of Lowdon to lochnorie wither the Limis were and to haining where more were	01:04:00
It. At the above two places procuring a charge penyworth spent and given	01:06:00

More Lime trees were acquired at the end of the year. Loudon's account for 10 December 1725 states:[31]

An account of Lymes bought for the use of ye Large Garden of the Colledge of Glasgow by order of the Principal of the Colledge for three quarters of an hundred of Lyme plants bought from William Barr Gardener at Jordanhill at 15 pounds Scots per hundred

lib sh ds
11=05=00

By the end of 1725, some 425 Lime trees had been purchased for the Great Garden. There is no information on where they were planted, but they were probably used to line some of the walks — and possibly for the boundary region outside the wall, bearing in mind the problem of the washerwomen who found the boundary trees so convenient for their drying lines. In addition, 1,150 Beech trees were purchased in February 1722.

Certain of the localities visited by Loudon in pursuit of Lime trees can be identified. His longest journey would have been to Kilmarnock, some 21 miles to the southwest of Glasgow. Cessnock is a district $2^{1}/_{2}$ miles in a direct line southwest from the site of the Old College and just south of the River Clyde, and Jordanhill lies some 5 miles to the northwest in a direct line; both would have been small villages in the early 1700s. All that seems to remain of Haining is a Haining Road in the district of Renfrew, 7 or 8 miles west of the College in a direct line and again south of the river. Lochnorie cannot be placed.

The Faculty meeting of 25 May 1727[32] took two decisions on the Great Garden, one of minor and the other of major significance:

> The Faculty allows six pounds Scots to be given to a man to assist James Loudon in weeding the borders and nursery in the Great Garden.
>
> The Faculty orders the head walk paralel to and next to the College to be made and putt in order as soon as possible and also that the square piece of ground lying at the back of ye Common Hall be levell'd and putt in some order as conveniently can be after the walk is finished and appoint Mr. Carmichael, Mr Loudon, Mr Morthland and Mr Robert Simson to oversee the work and that Mr Loudon pay the workmen and order Mr Carmichael to lodge in Mr Loudon's hand sixty pounds Scots.

The position of the new 'head' walk can be visualised running north to south at the rear of the College buildings and the square of ground behind the Common Hall (Figure 4.2). Those enlisted to supervise the work were Robert Simson, Clerk of Faculty and Professor of Mathematics; Charles Morthland, Professor of Oriental Languages; and John Loudon, that same year made Professor of Logic and previously Regent. Alexander Carmichael was the College Factor at the time. John Loudon's being in overall charge has led on occasions to difficulties in interpretation of accounts and precepts owing to confusion with the gardener James Loudon. The completion of this project entailed the hiring of 46 workmen, employed mainly from May until October.[33] Before John Loudon took overall charge, however, James Loudon supervised the work of five men through March and April.[34] These were John Hutchinson, John Dunlop, Alexander Mitchell, John Donaldson and Charles Mcarthur, of whom Hutchinson, Dunlop and Mitchell had been employed off and on since 1724. The names of all the men employed in 1727, together with their monthly hours of work and wages, are summarised in Table 4.2.

The five men hired by James Loudon in March and April were engaged to deal with one of the continuing drainage problems which beset parts of the Great Garden, described in the heading of the relevant account:[35]

Table 4.2. Number of days worked by 'Workmen' employed in the Great Garden 1727 (days/month)

	March	April	May	June	July	August	Sep/Oct	Wages
John Hutcheson	11½	15½	4½	18½	16½	8	18½	£32/11/-
John Dunlop	11½	14½	3½	13½	1	–	–	15/08/-
Alexander Mitchell	11½	16	5	18½	18	11½	–	28/03/6
John Donaldson	10	12½	4½	16	16½	25½	10½	33/08/-
Charles M^carthur	10½	19½	5	19½	16	21½	23	40/05/-
Thomas Lewis	–	4	–	–	–	–	–	01/08/-
Alexander Stewart	–	2	5	19½	8	12	–	16/05/6
John Mitchell	–	4	5	19½	8	12	–	16/19/6
Nicol Campbell	–	–	1	2	–	–	–	01/01/-
Ninian Rodger	–	–	–	13	19½	8	13	18/14/6
James Duncan	–	–	–	10	–	–	–	3/10/-
Thomas Dounie	–	–	–	6	16	8	–	10/10/-
William McAidie	–	–	–	5	–	–	–	01/15/-
Thomas Beetle	–	–	–	2	–	–	–	00/14/-
John Glen	–	–	–	1½	9	2	–	04/14/6
Solomon Irvin	–	–	–	1½	4½	–	–	02/02/-
Joseph Gedde	–	–	–	5	14½	–	–	06/16/6
John Graham	–	–	–	5	14½	–	–	06/16/6
William Crown	–	–	–	–	26½	–	–	09/05/6
William Pennyfeather	–	–	–	–	11½	2	–	04/14/6
Solomon Aran	–	–	–	–	17½	1	–	06/09/6
William Coupland	–	–	–	–	16½	–	–	05/15/6
Robert Walker	–	–	–	–	5½	11½	19½	12/05/6
Joseph Osburn	–	–	–	–	9	2	–	03/17/-
Edward Lister	–	–	–	–	5	–	–	01/15/-
Joseph Witham	–	–	–	–	5	7	–	04/04/-
William Cren	–	–	–	–	5½	8	–	04/14/6
William Hyde	–	–	–	–	–	18	17	12/05/-
Archibald Campbell	–	–	–	–	–	7	–	02/09/-
Alexander Knox	–	–	–	–	–	14½	10	8/11/6
Samuel Haill	–	–	–	–	–	2	–	00/14/0
James Ridgeway	–	–	–	–	–	3	–	01/01/-
Thomas Takeman	–	–	–	–	–	1	–	00/07/-
Samuel Spiller	–	–	–	–	–	11½	3	05/01/6
William Colstoun	–	–	–	–	–	17½	13½	10/17/-
John Turner	–	–	–	–	–	2½	–	00/17/6
John Campbell	–	–	–	–	–	9	–	03/03/-
William Dykes	–	–	–	–	–	5½	–	01/18/6
Robert Woodfield	–	–	–	–	–	5½	–	01/18/6
William Smith	–	–	–	–	–	9½	–	03/06/6
Matthew Alstell	–	–	–	–	–	10	–	03/10/-
William White	–	–	–	–	–	4	–	01/08/-

	March	April	May	June	July	August	Sep/Oct	Wages
William Loanie	–	–	–	–	–	4	–	01/08/-
Roger Chaslett	–	–	–	–	–	8	–	02/16/-
Samuel Windwright	–	–	–	–	–	$6\frac{1}{2}$	$5\frac{1}{2}$	04/04/-
John Lennox	–	–	–	–	–	–	4	01/08/-
							Total (Scots)	£361/-/-

Acct of Workmens Wages employ'd by James Loudon Gardner to the College of Glasgow by order of the Principal & Masters of the said College, in digging and carrying off the clay from the Wet ground, at the North-east end of the Middle Walk in the College Garden making syvers [=drains] for draining away Water, wheeling off Rubbish & Earth from the New Building, & other things Necessary fr the said Walk

This work occupied the five throughout March and April, and towards the end they were additionally engaged in 'removing Rubbish from the Little house desing'd for holding the Gardners tools, beating the Loose Ground on the banks & carrying Waters to the Elms and Hollys set on it'. The Middle Walk lay north to south, and the newly established Head Walk would come to lie parallel to it (Figure 4.2). The 'banks' describes the raised ground — the 'Mound' lying to the west of the Middle Walk. At this time the walk on the north side of the garden, parallel to the wall, was called the New Vennel Walk. On the south side, lying parallel to this and the Cross Walk, was the Old Vennel Walk. The Foot Walk lay on the east side, near the Molendinar Burn.

The drainage work on the Middle Walk involved some outlay by James Loudon, and his detailing of expenses allows some interpretation of how the problem was dealt with:[36]

Acct of money laid out by the above James Lowdon Gardner for Stones for making Syvers & Laying on the wet ground of the above walks And for Straw to lay Betwixt the stones & the Earth for preserving the Walk from being wet

Impr. To Robt Brown for 27 carts of whinne stones brought from
the whinne Stone quarry to the College Garden at
2sh 6 pense Scots pr. cart   3 7 6

It. at Bargaining wi the Carter & to engage him to lay on the
Greater loads   0 4 0

It. To two other Carters for bringing Carts of round Stones from
an Old Dyks at Greensyde to the Garden at 2 shs pr Cart   012 0

It. To the Caswayersmen for the stones the gathered about the
New Building   0 6 0

It. For twenty thrave of oat straw at 9 shs per thrave of which
  16 Thrave from Andrew Chambers in Gorbels and 4 thrave
  from him afterwards and 6 sh for carrying it from the gorbels
  to the College Garden   9 6 0
It. Spent at Bargaining   0 3 0
It. for the Lend of a Stand to carry Water   0 2 0
It. for a Gimblet for boring the paling put up at the end of the
  said Walk   0 2 0

    14 2 6

The whinne (=whin) stone was hard stone used for road-making. The
'whinne stone quarry' was situated north east of the College, about ⅔
mile from the College by the route then available; note the charge of
30d Scots for cartage, which on a round trip works out at about 23d per
mile. 'Caswayersmen' were causiers who laid the paving-stone floor (p.
42), but as a sideline collected small stones for James Loudon.

Whilst May 1727 was to see the start of work on the new Head
Walk, Alexander Stewart was hired by James Loudon in the same
month for five days[37] (£1/15/-) for 'assiting to Roll the Walks, in
Carrying water to ye Elms and hollies on ye Bank in Cleaning ye
Borders and Weeding ye nursary'. John Loudon's charge of events was
put to effect immediately. The Faculty resolution on the new Head
Walk having been taken on 25 May, the accounts and precepts show
that work commenced two days later, with five workmen involved in
the last week of May. The overall work programme is clearly defined in
the first account submitted:[38]

Accompt of Workmen's Wages Imployed by James Lowdon
Gardiner to the College of Glasgow in making a new Walk in the
large Garden parallel to the backfront thereof, in cleaning the
ground of Rubbish, digging out the stiff Clay which occasion'd the
Grounds being wet, wheeling it to the burnside to make up the low
ground without the Garden wall, Wheeling Stones for laying on the
wet Ground & making sivers to carry off the water, wheeling
Rubbish from the new Buildings for laying above the stones when
covered with things proper and for helping to fill up the low places
of the Ground Working and Rolling and dressing the other Walks,
borders and bank, and weeding the Nursarie in the said Garden at
different times when the weather stopt the wheelbarrows from being
imployed in the said work

The burnside in the above refers to the Molendinar Burn (Figure
4.1). Payment of the workmen's wages via James Loudon came from
the £60 Scots given to John Loudon by the Faculty act of 25 May. With
increasing numbers of workmen employed through June and July, the
wages bill of £95/17/- Scots by 8 July was £35/17/- over the amount

allowed by Faculty in the first instance, a discrepancy duly noted by John Loudon at the bottom of the first page of the accounts. It seems likely that thereafter the increasing costs were borne by John Loudon and reclaimed at a later date. All wages were paid to the men by James Loudon from money given to him by John Loudon throughout the summer. One entry in the accounts reads 'Paid for paper by the said James Loudon for writing out the Accompts of the Workmen's wages £6/6/-',[39] and later 6/- was claimed for 'a pocket Book for keeping the Acct of the workmen's wages'.[40] James Loudon was the responsible timekeeper. Extra payments were made at intervals. On Saturday 17 June, 18/- was paid out in addition to the workmen's wages 'By Extraordinary work in Assisting to drive the levelling pins and other Work at By hours not otherwise counted in Ale & Money'. The traditional 'drink money' allowances were thus appearing in the accounts, as with Saturday 1 July when 12/- was paid 'To Drink to the Workmen this week at Extraordinary work'.[41] The latter half of July 1727 seems to have been blessed with exceptionally fine weather. Allowing for the fact that ale was 2/- Scots per Scots pint, the sum paid represents 18 Imperial pints of ale between 13 workmen, though some were not employed for the whole week. The account for the week ending 22 July includes the comment 'The weather this and preceding weeks favouring the Imploying of more hands than ordinary', and on 29 July 'To engage them to work closer, the weather being exceeding warm, allow'd for Ale this week 0-12-0'. Similar sums were expended in the following weeks. The general work description remained unchanged through to September. Only in the last week of October was there any change, when earth was wheeled to make up a border between the stone wall of the Physic Garden and the new walk because the ground was at a lower level.

Whilst the fine weather allowed the work to proceed apace during July and August, one unforeseen difficulty arose. As described previously in dealing with the water-drainage problems of the Middle Walk, straw played an important role in establishing a drainage path when placed between the stones and the earth. In August 1727, however, there was a serious shortage of straw in the Glasgow neighbourhood and James Loudon had to find an alternative. This he found in the common Bindweed (*Convolvulus*), large quantities of which were growing on part of Glasgow Green, as shown in the relevant account:[42]

Impr: for procruring Liberty from the tacksmen of the town green
      to cut the Bindweeds in the upper part of the green,
      spent   0 = 10 = 0
It. To the men imployed to cut them for continuing at work
      some hours beyond their stated time each of two days
      5sh & a third day 4sh   0 = 14 = 0
It. to Robert Brown & other two Carters for leading 14 carts

of said Bindweeds from the upper end of the sd Green to
the Colledge at six p. p cart   4 = 04 = 0
It. at Engaging the Carters spent   0 = 03 = —
It. for a Cart of Stones to Lay on ye Syvers and wet ground
over what has been provided before   0 = 02 = 06
                                                                      —————————
                                          James Loudon   5 = 13 = 6

'Procruring the liberty of the tacksmen' sounds rather like buying
drinks to allow free access to the Bindweed. It would certainly have
suited the tacksmen to be rid of the surface growths of a troublesome
weed, although the persistent rhizomes would still have been left
underground. 'Engaging the Carters' suggests a similar expenditure to
that outlayed on the tacksmen.

The 1726–7 College Accounts record that £615/16/- Scots was
repaid to John Loudon on precepts and receipts concerning work in
the Great Garden.[43] These included the work on the Middle and Head
Walks, and a sum of £134/10/- Scots paid to William Millar, gardener
of the Abbey, Edinburgh, for nursery seeds and plants, variegated yews
and 'Hollies' in the spring months of the years 1723–6. In addition
more 'Hollie Berries' were obtained from John Graham of Buchanan.
Between March 1727 and the end of the year, the overall labour and
materials costs recorded in the College Accounts as being paid to John
Loudon for work in the Great Garden came to £481/6/- Scots.
According to the records of Faculty meetings,[44] John Loudon's
accounts for the outlay of £414/13/- for the work from March to
October 1727 were eventually accepted on 10 December 1728. All
available precepts show that he was repaid at £30-50 Scots at a time,
and not running up such a large debt. One precept under John
Loudon's name[45] records the sowings on the renewed part of the
Middle Walk and the new Head Walk. For this 20 lb of White Dwarf
Clover seed were purchased in March 1727, costing £15/16/- Scots. If
sown at the rate of 1 oz per square yard (a minimal allowance), this
would mean that some 320 square yards of ground were involved.

The extensive work programme of 1727, with its large hired labour
force (Table 4.2), was not to be repeated on such a scale in future years.
The workmen involved come down to us as names on account forms,
some men being regularly employed year after year and others more
casually. The most they could earn was £2/2/- Scots per week (no
Sabbath working was permitted), 7/- being for a full day's work. It is
difficult to equate such a sum to a standard of living. At that time, ale
cost 2/- per Scots (Stirling) pint (3 Imperial pints) and a 'fardel' of oat
bread about 8d Scots. According to an old Dunbarton measure, there
were 3 fardels per kaik and '4 kaiks per pek', or 12 fardels per peck.
One kaik seems to have been the same weight as a lippie (1¾ lb), which
makes a fardel just over 9 oz. By a similar estimate, 1 lb of oatmeal cost
about 10d Scots. It is not altogether surprising, yet not without

interest, that 86 per cent of the surnames of the 61 workmen hired can be found, with minor variations, in a present-day Glasgow telephone directory. Each man had to be paid on the Saturday of his working week. It was the responsibility of James Loudon to have the individual hours of work fully documented (in his pocket book) and then some time on the Saturday to make out the weekly account (on paper especially bought for the purpose) for presentation to the Principal or his substitute, who duly authorised the cash to be obtained from the College Factor — all on the same day. For the most part the accounts are legibly presented and follow a set format. On occasions they were written in a hurry, e.g. '... by order of ye principall of th Coledg of Glasgow to wit in large Gardne'; and surnames were misspelt, Mitchell becoming Mithel, Hutchison becoming hutchsn, Taylor becoming tyler, etc. Nevertheless, each Saturday without fail the workmen were paid. Financial matters (so far as James Loudon was concerned) became easier in 1726 and 1727 when John Loudon took over as Supervisor on behalf of the Faculty. John Loudon gave the cash to James Loudon after receiving his account of timekeeping, submitting claims for reimbursement later. It is as well to remember that, whilst the workmen were paid at the rate of 7/- per day, the £72 Scots per annum received by James Loudon and Walter Galbraith was equal to less than 4/- per day, though the annual sum received was a guaranteed one. As mentioned earlier, however, neither of them was regarded as full-time employees throughout the year, but the work programme of 1726 and 1727 would have given James Loudon little spare time in the summer months. A notable event in the history of the University occurred on 28 or 29 September 1727 with the death of John Stirling, the 'masterful' Principal whose last attendance at a Faculty meeting was on 10 July 1727. His successor was Neil Campbell, minister at Renfrew, appointed by the King in December 1727 and admitted to office on 8 February 1728. Henceforth, the authorisation signature on the precepts were those of Campbell.

April 1728 saw the return of hired labour for work in the Great Garden. The work programme entailed[46] 'digging out the old Gooseberry Bushes & decayed barren fruit Trees in the large Garden of the said College, digging the whole of the Ground in the four Plots of the said Garden & the old cross Walk, in order to their being sown with Rye Grass & Clover Seeds, Raking the whole of that Ground before Sowing, in Rolling as much of it as the Weather would allow them to overtake in time; in Wheeling Earth to make up a border on the east side of the new Walk, in the places where the Ground in the plots next to it fell considerably lower than the Walk: In digging out ths stiff Clay from the places where the Ground in the plots was considerably higher than Do. Walk & wheeling it to fill up the Bottom of the low Ground be South the large Gate of the said Garden: Beating & mowing the Bank on the West side of the Middle Walk: Digging and raking the borders; weeding the nursery & borders at such times as the

Weather stopt them raiking from Thursday 4th April to 28 June 1728'. The individual sites mentioned in the above can be found in Figure 4.2.

In April 1728, 72 lb of Red Broad Clover seed were purchased[46] 'for sowing together with Rye Grass Seed on the Whole of that Ground of Do. Large Garden within the Hedges'. The rye-grass seed was obtained from a supplier in Hamilton and amounted to 'three Bolls, three fourlets & one peck', all told 61 pecks or 244 lippies. Assuming 1 lippie to be $1\frac{3}{4}$ lb, the overall quantity was 427 lb of rye-grass seed. The Red Broad Clover seed cost £18/14/- Scots, and the rye-grass seed £22/17/6d. Hence the members of Faculty enjoyed the soft underfooting of Dwarf White Clover on the main walks, whilst the larger plots of mixed clover and rye grass were for harvesting. In March 1728,[46] a further 10 lb of White Clover seed was required from William Millar of Edinburgh 'To supply what has been too thin sowen on Ditto New Walk'. One questionable feature of the work programme for 1728 is the reference to men digging the whole of the ground in the four plots (Figure 4.2), raking, sowing with rye grass and red clover, etc. The surface area of the Great Garden at that time has been given as about 9 acres. As described earlier, some land was lost in the formation of the new walk, extending the borders, etc. If, therefore, the extent of the grassed area in the four plots is taken to be 6 acres or 29,040 square yards (probably an underestimate), then to obtain a dressing of 1 oz of seed per square yard, 29,040 oz is very much more than the 427 lb (or 6832 oz) of rye-grass seed purchased. Nor would the 72 lb of Red Clover seed (1152 oz) added make a significant difference; with a combined seed weight of 7984 oz, a dressing of 1 oz per 3.6 square yards would have been obtained. Reference to the 'whole ground' in the work description may, however, have referred only to those parts of the four plots to be fully grassed.

One important difference arises in the status of some of the workforce hired in 1728 when compared with previous years. For the first time the accounts include different rates of pay, viz., 'The Bredd Gardiners at 8 sh, the rest at 7 sh Scots per day'. 'Bredd' is an abbreviation of breder, or bredern (brither), a person admitted to a trade or corporation. The 1/- extra per day earned by the 'Bredd' gardeners probably recognised those who had served a full apprenticeship. The distinction is apparent in the several accounts submitted, where the person so designated always has the description 'gardiner' after his name, and this was the standard practice of James Loudon himself when entering his own name in the headings to accounts. The 'rest at 7 sh Scots per day' were the same as the 'workmen' of the previous accounts. Of the eight Bredd gardeners employed by the College in the spring and summer of 1728, four identical names can be found in the membership of the Incorporation of Gardeners. These are William Hume (son of John Hume), John Lennox, Henry McKie and Alexander Miller (Junior). The status of being a 'Bredd gardener' did not require membership of the

Incorporation. The two Alexander Millers named in Table 4.3 were father and son and both were 'bredd' gardeners, but 'Alex Miller Senior who tho' a bredd Gardener, yet being put to the easiest of work because of his age was allow'd but 7 sh pr day'. In passing, it may be noted that an Alexander Miller was one of the College's tacksmen in 1723, along with a John McArthur, one of the workmen in 1728. With the elder Miller we see some consideration being given for the old age of a temporary employee.

In the accounts, an additional note is to be found for the week ending 20 April 1728: ' ... Allowed them at finishing the first plot having then wrought several hours after their stated time at finishing the first plot, to get the grass seed timeously covered by raiking, 00:12:00'; and for one week later, 'At finishing the second plot allow'd them for extraordinary work 00:06:00'. The rewards were as usual in pints of ale, 18 (Imperial) pints in the first week and 9 in the second.

Table 4.3. Number of days worked by 'Bredd' gardeners and workmen employed in the Great Garden in the spring and summer of 1728

Week ending	April				May				June					Total wages
	6	13	20	27	4	11	18	25	1	8	15	22	29	
Bredd gardeners														
Robert Adam	–	–	–	–	1½	–	–	–	–	–	–	–	–	£00.12.00
Wm Cunningham	–	–	–	–	–	4	5	5	5	3½	1	6	4½	13.12.00
Wm Hume	–	–	–	–	2½	–	–	–	–	–	3ª	–		02.01.00
John Lennox	–	3	4	4½	3½	–	–	–	–	–	–	–	–	06.00.00
George Lowdon	–	4	4½	½	–	3½	–	–	–	–	–	–	–	05.00.00
Henry McKie	–	5	4	2	–	–	–	–	–	–	–	–	–	04.08.00
William McKie	–	5	4	2	–	–	–	–	–	–	–	–	–	04.08.00
Alexr Miller (Younger)	–	–	–	–	5	5	3½	6	3½	1	6	4		13.12.00
Workmen														
John Allan	–	–	4	4½	3½	4	2	–	–	–	–	–	–	06.06.00
James Dickson	1	1½	–	–	–	–	–	–	–	–	–	–	–	00.17.06
John Donaldson	3	5	4	4½	3½	4	5	6	4	–	½	5	–	15.11.06
John Hart	–	–	–	1	–	–	–	–	–	–	–	–	–	00.07.00
John Hutchison	3	5	4	4½	4	3½	5	6	6	2	–	5	–	16.16.00
John McArthur	1	1½	–	–	–	–	–	–	–	–	–	–	–	00.17.06
Alexr Miller (Elder)	–	–	1½	4½	5	–	–	6	6	3	½	4	–	10.03.06
Patrick Mitchell	–	–	1½	2½	4	2	4	6	6	3	½	4	–	11.14.06
Ninian Rodger	2	1½	–	–	–	–	–	–	–	–	–	–	–	01.04.06

Total (Scots) £113/11/00

Note: a. For some undisclosed reason paid at 7/- rate in this week

Table 4.3 summarises the workloads of the hired men in each week. Up to three days only were worked in the first week. Four of the bredd gardeners were involved in the first full week of work ending 13 April, and probably these four shaped most of the 18 pints of ale with the five workmen who were hired in the week ending 20 April. In the week ending 27 April more work seemed to have been done for less ale. Usually, however, the ale 'bonus' was allowed on only one day in the week, so that the treats afforded in the week ending 13 April were something extra. The reasons are not too hard to find. In these first two full weeks of work in April the preparation of the ground by digging and raking, sowing the grass and clover seed, and then raking and rolling would need to be finished in the cooler, wetter month to allow seed germination and growth of the seedlings to be sufficiently advanced before the onset of the drier summer months. Proper sowing of a new 'grassed' area called for some expertise, hence the employment of the bredd gardeners, who were probably involved mainly in this aspect of the work programme while the less skilled work occupied the workmen. In each following week there was the allowance for ale on one day (9 pints). Noticeably only two 'plots' within the hedges were regrassed, which may mean that the actual area dealt with was closer to the 7984 square yards indicated by the quantities of seed ordered. At some time in the week ending 4 May, 12/- was expended on 'a riddle for riddling Earth for covering the dwarf white dutch Clover-seed sown on the places of the new Walk where the seed was formerly sown had not come through close enough up'. The patchy growth on the new Head Walk was already in need of repair.

The following year again saw renewed work in the Great Garden, and once more James Loudon purchased Lime trees:[47]

Accompt of Lime Trees bought by James Loudon Gardiner in the College of Glasgow from George Bowie Gardiner in Cessnock for the use of the Large Garden of the said College

	£	s	d
1729 Impr. Paid for a hundred Lyme Trees reckoning the Aprile six score to the hundred	£20	—	—
Item for the Charges of the said James Lowdon at Going to Cessnock and Returning including what he spent at the Gardners at Cessnock at prigging down the price which was Long held at 22£ the lowest after asking 24£	3	6	0
For the Cariage of the said Trees from Cessnock to the College Garden	2	8	0
	25	14	0

James Loudon's excursion to Cessnock to buy Lime trees had involved some haggling ('prigging'), and evidently expenditure on drinks to clinch any such deal was an accepted University expense. Loudon had succeeded in beating down Bowie's price by £4 Scots and had himself outlayed the £25/14/-, which was eventually repaid on 9 June.

Hiring of extra labour commenced in March 1729,[48] with again a clear statement of the overall work programme planned until June, viz.: '... Accompt of Workmen's Wages employed by James Loudon Gardner to the College of Glasgow in Wheeling Earth partly from the new Buildings, partly from the back front of Ditto College to the south End of the New Walk parallel to the back front of the College and next to it, being that part of the Said Walk which was not finished the preceding Year, reaching from the Great yard of the Said Garden to the Old Vennel, and in dressing the border of the East side of Ditto New Walk: Planting a Holly hedge on Ditto Border, Carrying Water and Watering the Hollys, Planting Lyme Trees at proper Distances on the East side of that & of the Middle Walk, Rolling the Walks, Beating and Dressing the Bank on the West Side of the Middle Walk, Mowing the whole of the Walks, Weeding & dressing the Borders and Nursery' (see figure 4.2 for the various sites). A smaller workforce was then employed (Table 4.4). Of the two bredd gardeners taken on, William Cunningham worked over the three months and was joined in May by Alexander Miller. Their expertise was probably required for the planting of the new holly hedge and the Lime trees on the east side of the new Head Walk and the Middle Walk. It should also be remembered that James Loudon's appointment was based on his expertise in hedge-planting and management. Meanwhile two of the workmen were engaged on the other, less skilled, jobs until early May. Of these, John Hutchinson's name has appeared on all the submitted accounts from 1724. The investment in hedging plants over the years (beeches, hollies, variegated yews) indicates the patterns of enclosures of the plots, and the sizeable expenditure on Lime trees (nearly 500)

Table 4.4. Number of days worked by 'Bredd' gardeners and workmen in the Great Garden in the spring of 1729

	March			April			May					Total wages
	3–13	22	29	12	19	26	3	10	17	24	31	
Bredd gardeners												
Wm Cunningham	15½	2½	6	5	4	5	6	3	3	5	1	£22.08.00
Alexʳ Miller (Younger)	–	–	–	–	–	1	6	3	2	5	2	07.12.00
Workmen												
John Donaldson	2	3	5	5	4	5	6	–	–	–	–	10.10.00
John Hutchison	1	2½	5	5	4	4	5	6	–	–	–	11.07.06
Jas. Kirkwood	1	–	–	–	–	–	–	–	–	–	–	00.07.00
Patrick Mitchell	–	–	4½	–	–	–	–	–	–	–	–	01.11.06

A View of the Middle Walk in the College-garden.
Academy Glasgow. 1762.

Figure 4.3. The Middle Walk in 1762. The Cathedral spire is visible, as is the Bank or 'Mound' on the left (west) side

underlines the Faculty's evident concern for the future attractiveness of the garden. One result of this can be seen in the 1762 appearance of the tree-lined Middle Walk (most likely Limes), with the Cathedral spire in the middle distance and the Bank or 'Mound' on the left-hand side (Figure 4.3).

Care of the garden amenities was not restricted to the plots within the walls. On 17 June 1729,[49] Faculty instructed that a committee consisting of John Simpson (Professor of Divinity), John Loudon and Robert Dick (Natural Philosophy) meet with the Dean of Guild and 'perambulate the outside of the College garden, to see the condition of the trees, the harm done to the garden wall by laying dunghills against it, building furnances upon it, and the harm done by burning bark, and placing fires at the roots of the trees, that the Magistrates may give orders to discharge these and such like abuses for the future under a penalty'. This echoes a similar concern for the perimeter trees outside the walls expressed in Thomas Young's accounts of 1708 (p. 45), especially the fires lit against the trees by inhabitants of houses around the perimeter. Just under twelve months later (11 May 1730)[50] another Faculty ruling was made, that 'The Faculty appoint Mr Loudon, Mr Dunlop and Robert Simson to take some of the servants along with them tomorrow and intimate to the people who live in the Vennel on the North side of the College Yard that they must remove their dunghills, furnances etc. from the walls of the said garden, and the ground belonging to the College adjacent thereto against Saturday next with Certification that if they do not the College will dispose of them as they think fit'. Evidently the pleasures of the groves of academe were marred somewhat by unpleasant reminders of the extra-mural world, with all the environmental problems associated in those insanitary days with the disposal of ordure and garbage. Eight days later the committee reported[51] that the inhabitants of the Vennel had promised to clear away their refuse, but in fact failed to do so, with the result that ' ... The Faculty appoints the said committee to order the College servants to take away the said dung etc. beginning at the upper end of the vennel, and in case of any reluctance that the said Committee apply to a justice of peace in order to obtain the assistance of a constable for that end'. On 27 May,[52] the committee was able to report that the walls had been cleared of all refuse by the College servants. The Vennel's inhabitants would hardly have objected to their neighbourhood being cleaned up free of charge. We can visualise this sedate group of professors setting out with a protective escort of College servants to 'perambulate' outside the College walls and inspect these unpleasant heaps of domestic waste. The call 'gardyloo' was more a feature of the streets of Edinburgh, and, whilst the Glasgow of that time may have lacked the high tenements, problems of local hygiene seemingly pressed in on the College. The rumbling 'night soil' carts were well known.

The fate of James Loudon as College Gardener becomes somewhat obscure in the 1730s. On 17 March 1730,[53] Faculty decreed that:

> The Principal, Dr. Johnstoune, Mr Loudon, Mr Dunlop and Robert Simson be appointed a committee or any two of them or anyone in absence of the rest the rest being advertised out of town to take care of the walks, hedges etc of the large garden, to see them cut in due time and to pay the workmen and keep account of work and expenses. As also to take care of every other thing necessary about the garden

From the date of the minute, we may assume that James Loudon left the employment of the University at Candlemas 1730. The work programmes of spring to autumn of the late 1720s seem not to have been repeated, suggesting that the major developmental work in the Great Garden had been completed. Precepts for Loudon's salary are not available after 1730, whilst William Galbraith's continue at regular intervals. A precept for the purchase of two scythes in the name of Loudon was made out in July 1733 and one for four scythes on 13 May 1734, and these probably referred to John Loudon.[54] One matter held over from the 1728 summer work programme concerned the provision of 'morning drinks'. One Marion Shearer, a charge keeper (innkeeper), sent in a claim for £5/10/- Scots,[55] made up from £4/10/- for morning drinks to the men mowing the walks, and £1 for bread and ale to the 'people imployed at making hay in the sd Garden'. At the charge of 2/- Scots per pint, this came to 45 Stirling pints (= 135 Imperial pints) for the men mowing the walks. This late claim also bears the indication that some hay-making went on in the summer, and the refreshments supplied are separate from those provided by James Loudon for the same period, since the Shearer orders stemmed from Thomas Young, the Bedellus. Marion Shearer's bill, however, was dated 26 June 1733 with an appended complaint under the changes for ale and bread in 1728 'Both of which was ordered by the deceased Thomas Young and payment of which was promised after his death by his son William Young but no payment of it ever got by the sd. Marion Shearer'. Thomas Young died at some time in 1728–9 and was succeeded as Bedellus by his son William. William Young again ordered morning drinks and bread from Marion Shearer for the men mowing the walks in the summers of 1729 and 1730 and again failed to pay up. Another paragraph of complaint and charges was added to the above bill for a total of 6 gallons and 3 pints of ale, 17 cakes and 2 fardels of oat bread, all told £5/17/4d Scots. The men mowing the walks and making hay were probably a separate workforce from that of James Loudon, and may be included in the £231/9/- Scots paid to John Loudon in workmen's wages as entered in the College Accounts for 1727–8.[56] The Scots gallon was equal to 3 Imperial gallons, so that 153 Imperial pints of ale were dispensed during the two summers.

There is a lack of similar accounts and precepts between 1730 and 1733. This is due to John Loudon adopting a different method of accounting, a form of 'double entry' where sales were balanced against expenditure; this will be described later. Marion Shearer's bill for the summer of 1733[57] provides a further insight into the provision of morning drinks. She had not prepared an account with individual dates, but, 'having chalked ym down as they were given, ye Number of days was 37, and each day given ym a pint of ale at 2d and a farle of bread at ½ penny, yt being ye price of ye bread ye Summer, ye Meal having been cheaper ym last year, ye whole of ye 37 parts of ale is 0 = 06 = 02, and ye 37 farles of bread is 0 = 01 = 06½'. Marion Shearer's accounts were in sterling, and 1 farle = 1 fardel. Through the summer of 1733 two bredd gardeners were employed, James Loudon, now no longer the College gardener but hired as required, and William Cunningham. Over 37 days in that summer they shared 1 Stirling pint of ale and 1 fardel of oat bread on each day. Both were paid at 8/- Scots per day for 'ordinary' work and 10/- per day when engaged on 'mowing the walks', the latter perhaps somewhat harder and more continuous work through the summer days.

The 1733[58] accounts are complicated by the inclusion of payments made in the name of Alexander Dunlop, Professor of Greek (one of the Faculty 'management' committee), who with John Loudon was responsible for the overall supervision of the work in the garden. Whilst John Loudon carefully documented both the names of the gardeners and the number of days worked, Dunlop claimed the overall sum without indicating either feature. In February 1733 James Loudon, William Cunningham and a workman, John Donaldson, were each employed for three days at pruning the hollies and hornbeams and digging over the ground in the nursery. In the following March, Loudon and Cunningham were engaged in 'digging ye borders & other ordinary work' for nine and 7½ days respectively, and 'Do. work' in April involved Loudon for 18½ and Cunningham for 18 days. Each was employed for 15 days in May, and in two working weeks between Monday 14 May and Saturday 26 May their main occupation was mowing the walks. This was to continue at intervals throughout the summer. Between Monday 18 June and Saturday 14 July, Alexander Dunlop paid out £15/6/- Scots for the hire of the three gardeners. Both Loudon and Cunningham were employed for twelve days in the remaining weeks of July, only two of these being attributed to mowing the walks, followed by the same employment over three of the four days worked in the first week of August. Dunlop again took charge between Monday 6 August and Saturday 13 October, recording that £32/8/- Scots was paid out to the two gardeners Loudon and Cunningham, so that in the 68 days available they worked a combined total of 81 days. Loudon and Cunningham continued to be employed at various times through the remaining weeks of October and in November, with Loudon alone engaged through December. The actual work involved lay in the category of 'ordinary work'. At some time during the summer, the two went to Langside Woods (about 2 miles in direct line from the College) in search of twigs to make besoms for sweeping the cut grass and clover on the walks. This simple exercise of twig-collecting was charged at 12/- Scots. Between 18 and 24 November, James Loudon went on an unsuccessful search for 'Beech plants to supply for Beech hedges' and was allowed 8/- Scots in expenses. Also purchased in the course of the year were two spades, two scythes and twelve scythe stones, the last two items a measure of the mowing activities in the summer months. The overall hired labour costs in 1733 came to £112/5/- Scots.

James Loudon was once again the first gardener hired in 1734,[59] and the overall work programme was much the same as in 1733 — clipping and pruning the hedge plants, mowing, rolling and sweeping the walks, and digging over and dressing the borders — with the wage rates scaled and for the same amounts as in 1733. Apart from two days of unspecified work in January, the main programme started in the week beginning Monday March 11 with Loudon 'clipping and dressing ye Lime and Beech hedges' over four days. In the week beginning 1 April Loudon (three days), Cunningham (one day) and Patrick Mitchell (a workman at 7/- per day, for 2½ days) were all engaged in 'beating ye bank after great rains and rolling walks etc.', suggesting that some ground slippage may have occurred on the bank and that the walks needed heavy rolling to remove excess water. For the remaining three full weeks of April all three men were employed for 15 days, mainly at digging and weeding the borders, Loudon and Cunningham mowing the walks over the five days of the final week. In this same week, 4/- Scots was paid out for 'grinding two scythes' and the same sum for 'barking ye new garden Line to save it from rotting' ('barking' was to give a protective covering to the line, perhaps by waxing). In May Loudon, Cunningham and Mitchell were employed for 13, 14 and 13 days respectively; Mitchell continued to dig and weed the borders until the end of the month. Loudon and Cunningham were paid at the higher 'mowing' rates for four days in the first week of the month, so that digging and weeding would have been their lot for the ensuing weeks. In June Loudon worked for 16 days and Cunningham for 18, with the higher mowing rate paid to both for five days in the second week, two days in the third and one day in the last week of the month. Neither Loudon nor Cunningham were employed by the University after 10 August 1734. In the intervening weeks from the beginning of July they worked for 20 and 22 days respectively, of which twelve days each were given over to mowing the walks. The remainder of the time was spent on 'ordinary work', including digging and weeding the borders. The 1734 labour costs accounted for by John Loudon came to £77/1/- Scots, giving a total of £189/6/- for the years 1733 and 1734. From the Principal's authorisation of the precepts and from the receipts, it is clear that Loudon was not repaid these sums until 25 March 1737, with part of the sum held over until 25 May 1738 because a section of the accounts had been mislaid.

From 20 July 1734, two other bredd gardeners, John McFarlane and John Ewing, were hired at first for a few days and then from 21 August until 17 October for three or four days per week. During August they were involved mainly in cutting the grass of the walks and rolling them and in weeding the borders. Throughout most of September they were trimming the hedges, and then digging the borders for eleven days during October. Their separate bill came to £26/4/- Scots,[60] making the total labour costs for the two years £215/10/- Scots. For some reason McFarlane and Ewing were paid separately, with the relevant precept made out in McFarlane's name. Marion Shearer[61] was again called on to supply the ale for morning drinks and oat bread, and again she relied on her chalked-up records to derive the total charge, based on the quantities supplied per day. In 1734 she supplied 35 Stirling pints of ale (still at 2/- Scots per pint) and 35 fardles of bread on the same number of days, the latter being more expensive in 1734 at ^{2}/3d sterling per fardle. Ale and bread came to £4/13/4d Scots in 1734, and from the Shearer accounts it is evident that Loudon and Cunningham were the principal beneficiaries in the summer. The supply of refreshments ceased after 10 August. The Shearer bills for 1733 and 1734 were paid directly by John Loudon, and these charges were then included in his accounts. Marion Shearer was unable to read or write and her accounts, to which she appended her mark 'M' in the presence of two witnesses, had to be written for her based on her own chalked markings.

After the extensive redevelopment work of the late 1720s, the accounts and precepts for the 1730s give us a picture of the routine maintenance of the Great Garden and show that periodic employment was given to three or four men each year, mainly through spring and summer. The regular attention to cutting the grass and clover on the walks, to rolling them, to digging, hoeing and weeding the borders, clipping and dressing the hedges, cutting the grass on the larger plots with hay-making, all carefully supervised by representative members of the Faculty, further emphasises the value placed on the garden and the appreciation of the need for proper management of the amenity. There is no information on James Loudon's change of status at some time in the 1730–3 period. This demotion brought a significant change in his earnings from the University. In 1734 he was paid £32/10/- Scots for periodic employment, compared with the guaranteed £72 per annum he had earned as a College gardener. One must presume that he would have made up his depressed earnings by other garden employment in the town, as would have been the normal annual employment of his 1733–4 companion, William Cunningham. William Galbraith meanwhile continued in post as gardener to the Physic Garden; clearly, of the two appointments, that for the teaching garden was considered of greater importance by the Faculty.

Accounts and precepts for the routine maintenance of the Great Garden as described for 1733 and 1734 follow similar patterns over the years, with work programmes virtually unchanged from April to October. The available precepts allow the work and costs to be followed up to 1758. In 1735,[62] the payment for mowing the walks was raised to 11/- Scots per day to bredd gardeners. All other ordinary work was still at 8/- per day. Alexander Dunlop was again responsible for paying the gardeners (unnamed) that year, and claimed £74/10/6d Scots for the year's wages. The 1736[63] documentation shows that the hired gardeners (again unnamed) were employed from 1 April to 12 October, some 145 working days of which 104 (72 per cent) were accounted for. John McFarlane was responsible for the final wages precept, equal to £119/2/6d Scots. On occasions payment was made to an 'Asestant' for one of the gardeners. Between 9 July and 3 August two men were each paid 6/- per night as nightwatchmen for 'watching the fruit',[64] presumably having to maintain night-long patrols around the many ripe fruit trees in both the Great Garden and the Physic Garden. The overall cost of these nightwatchmen was £13/4/- Scots.

Two sets of precepts and relevant accounts are available for 1738,[65] both attributable to Dougald Weir, the Bedellus at the time. The first of these has a variety of entries, reminiscent of those of Thomas Young for 1705–8 (p. 38). Work in the gardens and purchases associated are documented along with numerous other aspects of the maintenance of the College fabric. These entries reflect Weir's additional duties as a 'Master of Works', a title actually given to a later Bedellus. A separate set of accounts is a straightforward documentation of the employment of the gardeners in the Great Garden from 8 May to 9 October. In the 'Master of Works' accounts four gardeners are recorded, John McFarlane, Gilbert Weir, James Kirkwood and James Atchison (also Etchison), who were engaged on eleven days between 15 June and 21 July 'working at and laying ye sink'. Such summer work was presumably linked with the winter drainage problems. The 1738 accounts for the Great Garden list 95 days between 8 May and 9 October on which four men were employed. At the start, four men (John McFarlane, William Gerva, James Atchison, Thomas Runnel) were engaged on 8 and 9 May at mowing the walks (11/- Scots per day) and each received a further bonus of 6/- for 'extraordinary work' — probably overtime (not drink money), which rather suggests that the walks had become somewhat overgrown. After 17 May, McFarlane, Atchison and Gilbert Weir were the three employed for all the routine work until 24 July, when Atchison was replaced by Matthew Hamilton; Andrew Hill replaced Weir on 14 September. The two sets of accounts complement one another. The days when the gardeners were 'working at the sink' in June and July were days when no work was done by them in the Great Garden. On 17 June, half a day's work on the drain by the three men balanced half a day's work by the same three at rolling the walks. Only for 21 July is there a double entry, when McFarlane, Atchison and Weir each received 8/- for work on the drain and 11/- for mowing and weeding on the same day. Since otherwise the two accounts are exactly complementary, it is likely that one of the entries was wrongly dated — probably the account referring to the drainage work, because the spacing and writing is less meticulous than in the garden accounts. One feature of the latter is the annual excursion, viz. 'one Day at the wood making Besoms' (the wood being Langside Woods). On this occasion there is an additional note: '... allowed by Mr Loudon 1 sh for the Birk'. The 'Birk' refers to the birches used as a source of twigs for which John Loudon allowed 1/- sterling in payment, the two men so engaged being paid the standard 8/- Scots for the day's work. On 9 October John McFarlane was allowed 3/- sterling for '12 sythe stones' and 2/- for 'grinding sythes and hedge shears', probably reflecting some expenditure earlier in the year when the mowing was in full swing. The cost of labour and additions for the Great Garden in 1738, based on Dougal Weir's accounts, came to £127/10/- Scots. In the College Accounts for the same period, however, the sum is accredited to John McFarlane, as in previous years. McFarlane may be envisaged as the 'senior partner' in the group and presumably was responsible for paying his companions.

The variety of entries in Dougal Weir's 'Master of Works' accounts for 1738[65] indicates the multifarious activities of the tradesmen attending to the maintenance of the College buildings, outside and inside. Some are puzzling on first reading, an entry on 19 July being as follows: 'To Alex^r Livingston at taking the sclates and timber off the Brandy house and carrying them to a convenient place in the College ...' ('Brandy' here is probably a misspelling of 'brandrie', a wood frame for a roof or for partition walls; presumably the 'house' was a workshop for their construction). In October it was necessary to clean out the College well, seemingly an unpleasant job, since the six men so engaged were twice a day rewarded with 'Buns and ale ... and one Mulch. of spirits'. At the end of the cleaning session a peck of salt was put down the well, perhaps as a cleansing agent. One entry of relevance to the gardens was made on 18 June: 'To the Regality and Trades officer at going through the trades in the town and Suburbs to prevent of false keys to the College Garden ... 0..5..0'. The 5/- sterling fee was evidently necessary to counteract a growing nuisance. On 13 February 1721 (p. 64), Faculty had decreed that scholars who were sons of noblemen should have keys along with the Masters. Some blacksmiths were successfully making copies and those townspeople who could afford these 'false keys' could enjoy the garden amenities. This problem remained, however, and at the Faculty meeting of 26 March 1742[66] the following minute was entered in the records:

> The College Garden being much spoiled by many persons purchasing keys thereof from Blacksmiths in the Town and Country. The faculty appoint new keys to be made for each of the Masters and for nobody else. And that Intimation be made in the Glasgow newspaper that whosesoever shall make any keys for the College garden without appointment of the Faculty or shall be found opening doors with such keys shall be prosecuted according to Law as makers or users of false keys and appoint the keys to be made of a convenient size for the pocket and of good strong work

The privilege extended to the sons of noblemen on 13 February 1721 was presumably lost as a result of this new decree. Perhaps therein lay the source of the copies so successfully made and sold by the local blacksmiths. There is an undated draft memorandum which may have a bearing on the matter: 'To know if the ffaculty would allow the old Garding locks to be put on the doors for some time to disappoint some folks their counterfeit kees using that so many'.[67]

At some time in 1743, consideration was again given to regrassing the plots in the Great Garden:[68]

> Estimate of the Expenses that the College Large Garden will cost in trinching, dunging, soing and Raiking for Grass etc.

To trinching	£12: 0:0
To dung	4: 0:0

To 4½ boll of good grass seed at 10s per boll	2: 5:0
To 40lb of Clover at 6^d per lb	1: 0:0
To Raiking at 2/6 per acre	0:10:0

The overall estimate (£19/15/- sterling or £237 Scots) included the hire of labour for double trenching the 4 acres of plots under renewal. Compared with the previous seeding of April 1728 (p. 116), the cost of the rye-grass seed remained at 7/6d Scots per peck, whilst the clover seed had increased from 5/2d to 6/- Scots per lb. The combined quantities of seed (8704 oz) would have allowed 1 oz of mixed seed per 3.3 square yards of ground, close to the 1728 allowance of 1 oz per 3.6 square yards. However, there is no confirmatory evidence either in precepts or in the College Accounts that this re-seeding actually took place.

Trespassing by townspeople remained a constant problem, as further shown in the Faculty minutes for 1 June 1748:[69]

Some of the inhabitants in the two Vennels on each side of the College Garden and at the Spout mouth having pulled down part of the Bridge at the South East Corner of the said Garden in order to make a publicke passage through the College ground betwixt these vennels, the meeting appoint Mr Barclay their writer to take out Law Burrows ['Law Burrows' = Law Borrows: to redeem costs] against the inhabitants of the two places.

The site of the offence was the bridge over the Molendinar Burn where it flowed under the Old Vennel (Figure 4.4). The Spout Mouth inhabitants would have lived in houses on the burnside where it emerged from under the Old Vennel.

At some time in the early 1740s John Bryce became Bedellus, after Dougal Weir, and was also given the additional title of Master of Works — the first time that records of this entitlement are to be found. In this position he assumed responsibility for paying the gardeners' wages, which in 1745[70] came to £92/16/6d Scots, but neither accounts nor precepts are available for that year. The accounts and precepts which are available (1752–6)[71] show that in each year similar numbers of gardeners were employed, usually from April to October, and that the annual cycles of maintenance work were identical with those described for 1733–4. The annual sums of wages and additional costs were similar:

1752	£97/7/6d Scots
1753	£88/4/6d Scots
1754	£92/16/— Scots

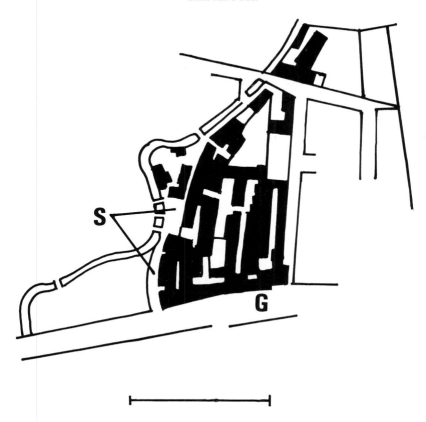

Figure 4.4. The Spout Mouth area south of the Old Vennel
S = Spout Mouth **G** = Gallowgate Street
Scale line: 300 feet

| 1755 | £100/2/— Scots |
| 1756 | £100/19/— Scots |

Over these five years the wage rates remained unchanged, 8/- Scots for 'ordinary' work and 11/- for mowing the walks. Each year there was the excursion to Langside Woods to get birch twigs for besoms. In 1752, the labour force consisted of William Hume (previously employed in the Great Garden in 1728, and briefly in the Physic Garden in 1750), Gilbert Weir, James Stevens and John Stevenson — all paid at the rates of bredd gardeners. Additional help is recorded for 30 May, when Hume, Weir and 'a soldier' were engaged on rolling the walks. In 1753 Hume was joined by James Deuart, Daniel Sinclair and John Tennent, who were employed at various times from April onwards, and joined by Daniel Campbell from 4 August. Hume was taken on for one day in January of that year to sweep the fallen leaves from the garden walks, and noticeably this was on the second day of the month! William Hume continued to be employed each year up to and including 1756, always from April to October, whilst all other gardeners were engaged for shorter periods. In 1754 he was joined at various times by James Deuart, Daniel Campbell and Daniel Sinclair, whilst the 1755 workforce, in addition to Hume, included Archibald Graham, Daniel Campbell, John Din, William Kinniburgh and 'Pitter' King. On 16 April in the same year, Bryce paid 2/- sterling for a 'new beatter for beatting the banks'. We must imagine the nature of this specially constructed 'bank beater'. Another distinctive feature of these 1755 accounts is to be found in the statements of the actual times devoted to mowing named walks in the gardens. In all previous accounts the individual days given over to mowing are listed, often in succession, but with no indications on how the work was apportioned. On 3 May 1755, however, Hume and Graham are listed as having spent five days continuously mowing the walks, and on 10 May three days at the same work are entered. The entry for 28 June shows that three days were spent mowing the Head and New Vennel Walks, and on 12 July they are listed as having spent five days mowing the Middle, Foot and Old Vennel Walks. Thereafter these time allocations are recorded exactly as described: three days up to 26 July for the Head and New Vennel Walks and five days up to 9 August for the remainder, probably including the smaller Cross Walk although this is not defined. These two sets of times are again entered in succession on 16 August and 6 September.

In 1756, Hume, Graham, and Campbell were employed for most of the spring and summer and were joined for a short period in October by James Scott. Again in this year's accounts, the timings of mowing the walks are recorded in definite sequences, the three days for the Head and New Vennel Walks being entered for 29 April, 15 May, 5 June, 10 July, 14 August, and 11 September, and the five-day sequences for the remaining walks listed on 22 May, 19 June, 17 July, 7 August and 4 September. Whilst the timings vary in frequency, the cutting seems to have been at three-to-five-week intervals, presumably depending on the rates of growth of the clover. An unusual task is recorded for 14 August 1756, when Hume and Graham were paid for 1½ days' work 'howing borders and taking of the hemlock of the Garding and ye Mount' (the 'Mount' here referring to the Bank). It would seem that the umbelliferous plants of Hemlock (*Conium maculatum* L., which can reach heights of 6 feet) were proving something of a nuisance that summer.

The purchase of a new 'bank beater' in April 1755 focuses attention on this operation of beating the bank. As already indicated, such bank beating was especially necessary after heavy rainfall and was presumably to counteract any slippage of soil. Usually two men were engaged on this vigorous exercise for one day at a time. These days are carefully documented:

1752: 23 May, 1 August
1753: 7 April
1754: 25 May, 6 July, 20 July, 31 August
1755: 16 April, 28 June, 16 August, 11 October
1756: 17 April, 5 June, 3 July, 13 October

Whether these operations record the effects of rain or excessive drying of the soil must remain speculative. A task listed on 26 October 1754 is worth quoting: Daniel Campbell and 'a soldier' were engaged for one day 'rolling the walks to sadden them', 'sadden' here meaning to make firm or hard.

Whilst the amenities of the Great Garden were the continuing concern of the Faculty, it was also valued as a source of income. James Loudon's appointment as gardener in 1722 brought a reduction of £72 in the returns on Great Garden tack, already reduced to £210 per annum by various developments with the walks and borders when some of the land available for tack had been reduced (p. 103). As already mentioned, the annual rents of the 'Coladj Yeards' in 1694 and 1695 in the name of Robert Robertsone (= Robinsone, Robisoun) were £255/6/8d and £293/19/4d respectively. Robertsone's 19-year tenure of the tack ended in 1709 and the next tackholder was John Allan, whose bid was successful at a public roup (= auction) held on 11 November 1709. John Allan had been Robertsone's sub-tenant and had occupied the gardener's houses in the Little Yard, dismantled in 1704 and moved on the establishment of the Physic Garden. Allan claimed for financial losses as a result in 1711 (p. 54). The terms of Allan's tack[72] (dated 9 February 1710) are similar in many respects to those drawn up for Robert Robertsone in 1690, but with additional features. The conditions regarding care of the trees and shrubs were identical with those required of Robertsone, as well as the rights of entry by the 'Masters & primarii'. Robertsone had been allowed use of the aforementioned house in the Blackfriars Wynd, which had the Little Yard at the back — the house he later sub-let to Allan. This house, after being moved and reconstructed, was now occupied by the gardener of the Physic Garden, John Hume. Allan, the principal tackholder, was joined by John Cochrane and William Johnstone. They were to be allowed use of: '... the whole Laighest storie of that Tenement lately builded by the said Universitie near the entrie to the said Great Yeard on the south side of that wynd called the Blackfriars with Two byres on the south side of said Tenement with the use of the Brewhouse for Brewing therin And of one of the highest roumes of the said Tenement for drying their seeds and onions until they are otherwise provyded for ...' The tenement is the 'gardeners house' which was under construction between 1708 and 1710, and to which reference has already been made (p. 43). The planting of any grain crops in the garden was forbidden, nor was any pasturing of beasts allowed. Only the Masters and their families were allowed to hang out their washing along the walks, at any time between September and the following May, but not during the summer months. It was also laid down that the transportation of dung should be effected 'in such ways that the walks and the suard be not spoiled'. The tackholders were to be responsible for mowing the walks: the grass so obtained was to be theirs for sale. The widths of the walks were to be maintained at 15 feet, with a further 3 feet to be left clear on either side. The annual rent was 307 merks (£204/13/4d). The full time of the tack was to be 19 years.

Three sub-tacks between John Allan and other gardeners were found in the bundle of documents containing Allan's tack. The three were for Alexander Miller (1712), James Stewart (1718) and John McArter (= McArthur) (1720) (Figure 4.5). The terms of Miller's sub-tack were equally as detailed and verbose as Allan's 1710 tack, but do give us a valuable insight into the conditions set for sub-letting in the Great Garden. Miller was the principal sub-tackholder in association with Mathew Allason, a skinner. For an annual rental of 112½ merks (£75/3/8d), payable in two instalments at Lammas and Candlemas, they were entitled to 'a just and equall half of the southmost half of the said Great Yeard and Orchyeard belonging to ye Colledge, with the just and equall half of the back walk on the south east thereof'. With this went a proportionate share of the byres and brewhouses of the tenement 'recently builded' by the University and particularly mentioned in John Allan's tack. The sub-tackholder shared the responsibility for the care of the fruit trees and other trees and shrubs in the part of the garden which was his, and Miller's right to half of the southeast walk was an entitlement to the grass cuttings after mowing. The other half of this walk was in the possession of James Nicoll, the sub-tackholder of the other half of the 'southmost half' of the Great Garden. The times of cutting the grass on the southeast walk are also specified: at least three mowings had to be made in the summer months, before 26 May, 26 June and 26 July. Nicoll and Miller were also required to mow the walks in the northernmost half of the garden belonging to James Allan, and even the times of cutting were specified. Between them they were required to mow these walks in five 'proportions', before 12, 16, 20, 24, and 26 May and then before the same days in June, July and August. All the cuttings, however, were to be the property of John Allan for subsequent sale. The conditions of transportation of manure applied also to the sub-tacksmen. In addition they were required to leave 'six elnes [= ells] of land in breadth and length' near the 'Meikle Yeatt' (= main gate) of the garden for a 'Middensteed' (= dunghill), and to allow Allan access across their ground for transportation of manure to his land. James Stewart (also Stuart), who became a sub-tenant of Allan in 1718, was given the 'equall half of the northmost half of the Great Yeard' under similar

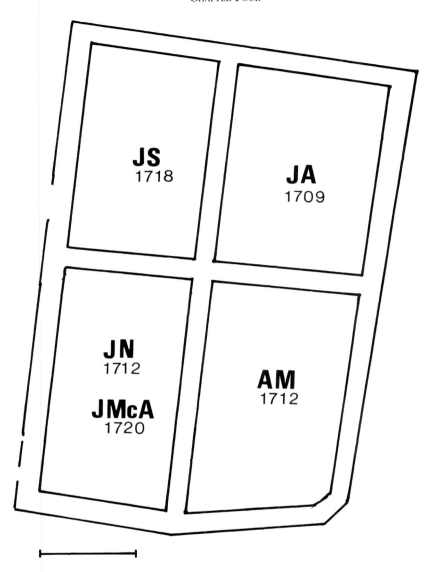

Figure 4.5. John Allan's sub-tackholders and their 'plots'

JA = John Allan (1709) **AM** = Alexander   uncertain) **JMcA** = John McArthur (1720)
Miller (1712) **JN** = James Nicoll (date   **JS** = James Stewart (1718)

Scale line: 150 feet

conditions to those for Miller; the garden was now subdivided, with a tacksman in each quarter.

John Allan would have received £225/11/- Scots in tack money from his three tenants. The outlays of the principal tackholders via Allan were £204/13/4d in annual rent and £40 per annum for rent of the tenement building. They were also responsible for maintenance of the building and of some features of the garden, so that any profit made would have to come from sale of grass and fruit; but, with three sub-tenants, Allan's fruit- and grass-sale returns would have been from one-quarter of the garden. The conditions laid down for the sub-tack of John McArthur in 1720 were similar to those forerunning but with an additional clause that, whilst he had to take his share of mowing Allan's walks, Allan would have to supply him with a new scythe every two years (attention has already been drawn in Table 4.1 to the prodigious purchasing of scythes over the years by the College). Allan, Stewart, Miller and McArthur are the four tacksmen to whom earlier reference has been made (p. 103) where the losses from their plots of land after enlargement of the walks and borders were assessed by William Galbraith and James Loudon in 1723. From this we can conclude that John McArthur replaced James Nicoll as sub-tenant of an 'equall half of the southmost half' of the garden.

The bundle of documents with the substances of Allan's tack conditions and those of his sub-tenants also contain two relevant legal papers. One is a bond which was drawn up on 8 August 1723 between Allan and eight persons who were prepared to act as his cautioners for the annual tack duty of 307 merks. These eight were John Cochrane (maltman); Alexander Sayers ('suggarboiler'); James Stewart, John McArthur and James Loudon (all gardeners); John Alexander (wright); James Lawrie (cordener); and Alexander Tamfrey (merchant). Two of Allan's sub-tenants were thus prepared to act as his cautioners. All eight signees of the bond agreed each to pay one-eighth of the 307 merks tack should the College at any time so require. To what extent John Allan's affairs were going so awry that he was in need of financial backing remains unknown. Allan died in late 1723, and in January 1724 the eight cautioners entered into a formal discharge with the University, withdrawing any claim referable to Allan's tack.

Earlier in this chapter, reference was made to the appointment in 1722 of James Loudon as gardener with responsibility for the hedges and general upkeep of the Great Garden. This is the same James Loudon who was prepared to act as cautioner for James Allan — the signatures on the bond and on the several relevant precepts for the Great Garden are identical. Both Alexander Miller and John McArthur were employed in work in the Great Garden in 1728 (Table 4.3). Whether the Alexander Miller of the sub-tack was the senior or junior one is not known.

With the death of John Allan, the tack of the Great Garden could again be offered for public roup. On 20 January 1724,[73] the Faculty laid down a revised set of conditions under which the tack could be offered for auction. As previously offered, both the 'College Great Yeard and the gardeners house with the conveniency of the byres and brew houses' were to be included, at a rental of £40 Scots per annum. This refers to the same tenement as in Allan's 1710 tack. The whole garden was available for lease, excluding the walks and the border along the north wall and the piece of ground at the back of the Common Hall (Figure 4.2). The tack would be chargeable per acre and would go to the highest bidder. The full tenure of the tack was again to be for 19 years, with the right for either side to be released on the Whitsunday after five years. If the arrangement was to continue beyond this, a second mutual release could be obtained on the Whitsunday of the eleventh year, and if not then the tack was to run full term. The tacksman could not sub-let any part of the garden without the permission of the Faculty.

The tacksman was responsible for the upkeep of the house except for the roof slates, which were the responsibility of the College. Two rulings referred to crops, viz.: 'That the tacksman shall have no claim to the Grass of the Walks nor he be obliged to cut them' and 'with respect to the planting of fruit trees, it is also provyded that, where yr are any vacant ground whom such have ought to be planted that the Faculty will give orders to ye own Gardiners to sett trees in such ground when they shall think fitt, which trees as planted at the ffacultys expence shall later ye use of ye present tacksman to be taken care of by him'. The main differences here with John Allan's 1710 tack conditions are that the Faculty was now assuming responsibility for the maintenance of the walks and for the replanting of any trees. The tacksman would still have the grass of the main plots for sale, and the fruit from the trees, which he would still have to maintain and prune. It seems evident that all previous tacks were a means by which the Faculty could maintain the general appearance of the walks and the grounds by the simple method of letting the garden to tenants who could make as much profit as they might from sale of certain produce, but who in return not only paid an annual rental but were expected to serve as gardeners for the general upkeep of the grounds. The change signalled in the 1724 conditions of tack fit into the pattern of events already described (p. 102) when, in 1722, the Faculty set course on a series of changes for the 'better ordering and beautifying of the Great Garden'. To bring about the necessary changes effectively, the first full-time gardener for the Great Garden was appointed (James Loudon) and the subsequent hiring of labour for the general maintenance of the walks and hedges became an annual event.

The members of Faculty were well aware of the need for adequate manuring to keep the ground in good heart, but they were not in favour of their shoes being soiled by such a necessity. Hence the following ruling in the 1724 conditions, more specific than in earlier ones:

Next ye Gardiners house in order to get and for preventing spoiling the walks and the walk from the Great Gate Causeway is to be laid att ye Colledge expence, and no Dung is to be carried from ye SW to any other of ye quarters but by hand barrows, under the penalty of ten lib for any transgression

Hence the dung could be unloaded on a causeway outside the College Gate and only wheelbarrows could be used for its transportation. The likely siting of the causeway is shown in Figure 4.2. Just who became the tacksman in 1724 is not known. Whoever it was seems to have held the tack for five years only, as the conditions and letting came up for revision again in 1730.[74] The terms of the tack was now reduced to nine years and only the grass and fruit trees within the hedges and walks were available for let, '... but that part within the hedges which used to be delved is excluded from the tack'. This last condition would suggest that in previous tacks part of the ground could be cultivated separately. The new tackholder was not permitted to 'open ground in any other part of the garden', i.e. not to dig over any other ground. The College was to be responsible for the removal of the 'useless' fruit trees bordering the Head Walk (with one exception) and would replace them. No wheeled carriages or wheelbarrows would henceforth be allowed in the Great Garden — except the latter in times of frost. The question of how manure could be transported was left unanswered. Yet among the tackholder's duties was the following:

That they shall dung the garden the third and seventh years, and that the quantity and quality of the dung shall be determined by two skilled men, one to be chosen by the College and one by the tacksman, and these two shall have power to choose an overman in case they cannot agree

The 'overman' would presumably have the final word. The importance of the proportion of straw to organic matter in the manure was a problem obviously recognised at the time (and it still is). No breakage of hedges was permitted on the part of the tackholder or anyone employed by him 'on pains of law for breaking over enclosures'. The tack duty was to be £17 sterling (£204 Scots) payable in two instalments, at Martinmas and Whitsunday. The keys of the garden went with the tack, and if required the College house belonging to the garden with the named exception of the one occupied by William Galbraith. Faculty still retained the right to expand the walks if they so required.

These conditions had been verbally agreed to by John Alexander, merchant, and John McArter (McArthur), the gardener already met with as a sub-tackholder of John Allan. John Sym, the College writer (= lawyer), was duly instructed to draw up the tack. It was subsequently reported to Faculty that Alexander and McArthur had withdrawn from the arrangement and so, early in April 1730,[75] the Faculty decreed that the tack should again be offered by public roup. The relevant committee was able to report towards the end of April[76] that three men, James Coulie (cordiner), Archibald Robb and William McLea (both maltmen), had been awarded the tack. The tack duty had meantime been advanced to £17/10/- sterling and the responsible committee had to take into account an objection by the three potential tacksmen regarding the increase of 10/- in the tack duty. John Sym, the writer, had also complained about the size of his fee ('instrument money'). A meeting was then called between all the parties, and one result was that the 10/- increase was removed. On 28 April 1730, 'two fair copies of the Tack of the large garden upon stamped paper' were read before Faculty and the tacksmen. Both parties then signed the two copies before witnesses, one copy being given to the tacksmen and one 'laid up in the Charter chest'.[77]

Coulie, Robb and McLea duly took possession of the Great Garden on 3 May 1730 (at Beltane, an old Scots Quarter Day). Their tenure of the garden tack did not meet with success, however. In the search through documents for the present book, a small scrap of paper was found caught up in the folds of the 1710 tack for John Allan. This states:

> Receivd from the Masters of the College a Tack of the College Gardens sett to James Coulie & partners dated the 28 Aprile 1730 in order to do Diligence agst them for the tack duty, and yrfore I oblige myself to Return an Extract yrof, written and signed att the College of Glasgow the 29 Novr 1731 years by
>
> [signature illegible]
>
> present
> Principal
> Mr Forbes
> Mr Loudon
> Rob. Simson

It would seem that Coulie and his associates had failed to meet their Martinmas payment and the Faculty, through a suitable committee, was applying a 'diligence' — a legal means of enforcing payment. Things seem to have gone from bad to worse for the unfortunate tackholders. At some time early in 1732 they were forced to write an apologetic letter[78] to Faculty, declaring that they, '... young and inexperienced men Did rashly And inadvisedly offer for the Grass and fruit foresaid'. Their returns for the current year would yield less than half the required annual rent of £17 sterling, and they then asked to be released from the tack. Evidently the Faculty refused to accept this informal letter and the three were required to make a more formal application, which then followed in a letter dated 31 July 1732.[79] In this it was acknowledged that the College had entered into the agreement fairly and above board, but that they had been 'pushed on to it By their own youthful rashness and ignorance of any such matter'. Whilst recognising that this was no excuse, nor any basis for an argument in law, they further pointed out 'that by the barrenness and sterility of the soill and great plenty of Clover grass and cheapness thereof about the City The foresd subject sett to us is not worth the half of the rent foresd wee are obliged to pay for it. And the fruit of the sd yeard is scarce with gathering'. (Note the reference to 'clover grass', the result of the mixture of rye-grass and Red Clover sowings as described in earlier pages.) The three tacksmen placed some emphasis on the poor condition of the soil as being a contributory factor to their failure, but their problems may well have arisen from too intensive a cropping, possibly allied with a summer drought, and undoubtedly their own lack of experience (one shoemaker and two maltsters). In their first letter they had concluded with the supplication 'And Knowing that you Honours will be favourable unto us And not Suffer us to be great losers or even ruined by the foresaid tack'. The second formal letter concluded: 'In respect of which we crave that out of your wonted generosity you would be pleased to quit us of the foresd tack And wee shall submitt to you what wee shall pay for the two years of our possession which if you do It shall all be remembered with a grateful acknowledgement by us and our Great hurt yrby prevented'.

The minutes of Faculty meetings over the period make no mention of the difficulties with the three tackholders, but from some evidence to be quoted later it seems that they were discharged from the agreement. A later tack drawn up between the College and Alexander Johnson,[80] a carrier, in 1738 shows only minor differences from those already described. The tack duty was now reduced to £156 Scots, which is probably a reflection of more land being taken over by the College. Whilst Johnson was given the fruit harvest, all replacements of trees and their cultivation and pruning remained the work of the College's appointed gardeners. He was to manure the ground after six years and was permitted to re-seed with rye-grass when necessary, but no other seeding was permitted. As previously, the same rules applied to the use of any wheeled carriages for transporting the manure, so perhaps the tacksmen had to resort to the laborious task of transportation by buckets since any sledge-like apparatus would have been equally damaging to the ground.

In addition to the tack duties, the College could occasionally raise money from other sources in the Great Garden. A few documents from the 1730s are available. One submitted by John Loudon, already mentioned as one of the Faculty who had assumed responsibility for overseeing the garden costings, takes the form of a balance sheet,[81] with 'debts' being the money he held on behalf of the College and 'contra' for his own cash outlays. The sale of 300 holly plants from the College nursery raised 5/- sterling. Whilst the plants were valued at 3/- per hundred, of the 9/- received, 4/- was owed to James Loudon, the gardener, for some reason. Then 4/4d was obtained '. . . what was got from ye grasse of ye first cutting off ye ½ rood taken from ye tacksmen for laying ye earth on which was wheeled out of ye parterre but of this 4d was paid to a carter for carrying it to ye Gorbals where it was sold, ye Govan Lands doing so not their grasse = 0:4:0 ye second cropt sold to Mr Dunlop's set. for 0:0:8'.

This is the first mention of a parterre — a levelled area for entirely decorative effects, usually with a lawn or ornamental plants — in the garden. The earth removed in its creation was placed on half a rood of ground taken back from the tackholders, but first of all the grass on the half-rood was cut and sold. On the 'debt' side of his balance sheet Loudon listed £6/9/8d: the additional £6 was in the nature of a 'float' provided by the College, the total then being £6/9/8d with the proceeds from the sale of holly plants and grass. For the same period Loudon then listed his own ('contra') outlays:

By workmen's wages beginning 8 Febr and ending 7 Nov 1731
a particular accot.   15 : 14 : 8
By ye price of 4 long sythes bought from James Mitchel for
ye use of ye garden at 2sh 3d   0 : 09 : 0
½ lib Turnep seeds to sow on ye top of
  ye Bank   0 : 02 : 0
2 spades got on 25 Apr at 3 sh   0 : 06 : 0
2 shafts fr them at 4d   0 : 00 : 8   0 : 08 : 8
By 2 Cent Birch stobs purchased at Langside wood for railing
in ye two plots of ye parterre, including 1 sh of expences
wi ye wood cutters at bargaining   0 : 14 : 4
By 12 lib White Clover of ye Dwarf kind got ye preceding spring,
part of it sown on ye bare places of ye walks, ye rest used
at sowing ye parterre this season. wt ye charges of a bag
for carrying it, for Wm Miller junior his Acct discharged   0 : 07 : 6
To David Rob as what he paid his son Archibald one of ye
Tacksmen of ye Garden for ½ rood of Grasse taken this year for
laying ye earth on which was wheel'd out of ye parterre, ye
Tacksmen refucing to lett any else than ½ rood, nor that at
a lower price than 10 sh per ½ rood, alledging they paid no less
for it to ye College.   0 : 10 : 0
By an accot of morning drinks at mowing ye walks & some
Extraordinary work beyond their stated hours, including too
what was given ye Masons at different times at building ye
wall of ye parterre re a discharge accot pd. to
Marion Shearer   0 : 14 : 6

                                 £18 : 8 : 8

From the difference between the 'debt' and 'contra' accounts, Loudon was able to show that the College owed him £12/9/- sterling.

Loudon's balance sheet includes the payments made to men maintaining the garden walks and hedges, a sum equal to £186/16/- Scots. Langside Wood was evidently a good source of birch branches of varying sizes. The parterre was enclosed within a stone wall and subdivided into smaller plots by birch railings. Nowhere in the accounts or records of the time is there information on the precise location of the parterre. Clearly the Faculty had some difficulty in wresting the half-rood of ground from the tacksmen, who grudgingly gave over the plot but charged the College a repayment of £6 Scots for the loss. Noticeably, the need to maintain the clover covering to the walks was a continuing problem, and the sowing of turnip seeds on the top of the bank would hardly be decorative. Once again there are payments to Marion Shearer for morning drinks, but seemingly separate from those earlier described (p. 122).

More sales from the nursery were recorded in 1732 and 1733.[82] These were for young trees of beech, hornbeam and holly, bringing in £79/16/- Scots. The customers included John Simson, a sword-cutler in Edinburgh, who purchased 1,050 beech trees for £3/3/- sterling; and John Cameron, merchant in Glasgow, who paid £1/16/- for 1,200 hollies 'in danger of spoiling'. A Major Stuart of Torrance near Glasgow bought 500 hornbeams for £1/10/-, his gardener being paid a 'fee' of 1/- 'as is said to be usual, at his receiving and paying them'. 'Mr Rosse Professor of Humanity' received 50 hornbeams for 3/- and 50 holly plants 'not in danger of spoiling' for 2/-, the good quality plants being valued at 1/- per hundred more than those of poorer quality; presumably the trees were for Ross's private garden.

Echoes of the episode involving the three inexperienced and rash young men, Coulie, Robb and McLea, are to be found in another of Loudon's accounts for 1732.[83] 'To ye whole of ye Grasse of sd. garden (except ye private walk let this year by ye Principal) received by ye Compter for Do Grasse cropt being a very bad one that year & being left in great Disorder by ye former Tacksmen fo. a particular accot. 6 : 13 : 6'. The three unsuccessful tacksmen had complained about the poor harvest. Loudon reported that he had sold 11/- worth of apples and pears to McLea, who had also paid 9d for 'half a sleik of bad pears' (a sleik or sleek was a fruit container of unknown capacity). Some labour costs from June 1732 to June 1733 came to £7/17/11d sterling; spades and scythes cost 11/4d and a payment to Marion Shearer for morning drinks for the mowers and to the 'people employed to gather ye fruit' came to 10/4d. These accounts show that maintenance of the Great Garden for 1731–3 came to £281/11/- Scots overall.

A statement prepared by John Loudon in 1733 gives further information on the letting of land, summarised under the heading 'Intromissions wi the grasse of the large garden ye College of Glasgow cropt 1733':[84]

for ye Grasse in ye upper pt of ye garden from Mr Dunlop
for his rood £8 Scots   0 : 13 : 4
from Patrick Mitchel & Wm Baird for ye rest of ye upper
part except ye rood next ye south beech hedge   2 : 01 : 8
        = £25 Scots
from ye Principal for Do one rood, next ye south Beech
hedge   0 : 13 : 4
In ye corner part of ye garden from Agnes & Margaret
Parks for 2 rood next ye South Beech hedge ye agreed
price = 10 sh pr rood   1 : 00 : 0
The two roods next ye former let to John Moir at £7 Scots
p. rood got   1 : 03 : 4
The rood next Do lett to Elizabeth Winning spouse
to Andrew Watson at Do Price, but tho often craved and promised
never received + N.B. ye above John Moir & Elizabeth Winning
had added to ye Do Roods ye small quantity of grasse
betwixt ye two Hornbeam hedges
From Wm Mason and John Howie for all ye grasse betwixt ye
North Hornbeam and ye North Beech hedge let to them at
£27 Scots got   2 : 05 : 0
The outer walls of ye private Walk had been this year broke down
& common road made thro' it yt nobody was found to offer more
for it this year than 2 sh which was got for it from
John Howie   0 : 02 : 0

These are monthly payments of the annual rents for the small plots in various parts of the garden, and some defaulting and appropriation of land seems to have occurred. Why Principal Carmichael and Alexander Dunlop, Professor of Greek, rented some land is not explained.

The Molendinar Burn was the east boundary of the Great Garden and beyond this lay the Dowhill or Dovehill land, of some 13 acres, granted by Queen Mary in 1562[85] to a far from prosperous University (Figure 4.1). The land was finally enclosed in 1755. A smaller parcel of ground, the Muir Butts, also owned by the University, lay east of the Dovehill (Figure 4.6). On occasions a representative party from the Faculty was required to 'perambulate the Dovehill lands'. One result of such a perambulation was recorded in the Faculty minutes for 4 November 1729,[86] when it was decreed that a piece of land opposite the East Walk of the Great Garden was to be 'staked out at the sight of the Masters as a bleaching field place for the use of the College' and so was to be excluded from any future tack. The tack of the Dovehill land and appurtenances was put to public auction at 3 p.m. on 17 May 1730,[87] following the tenancy of Walter Boyd and his sub-tenants Robert Wilson and William Stewart. The period of letting was to be for either nine or 19 years, with entry to the land on the following Martinmas and to the house the next Whitsunday. Reference is made

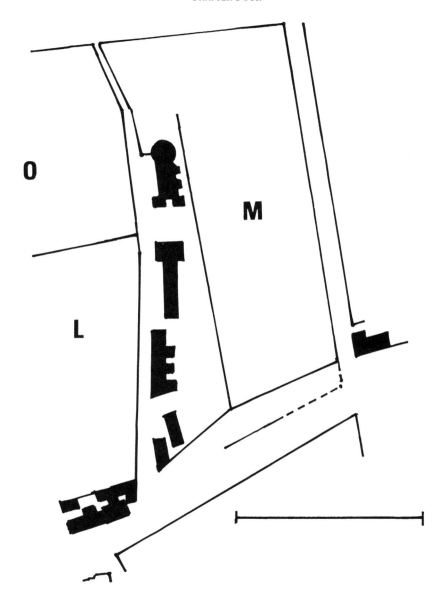

Figure 4.6. The College land called the Muir Butts, which lay east of the Dovehill

0 = Observatory Park **M** = Muir Butts **L** = land south of park

Scale line: 300 feet

to the exclusion of the ground taken for the bleaching field, but that the tenant was to have the benefit of the 'five furlets bear' payable by the town of Glasgow for the use of the bleaching rig, 'which the tenant is obliged to keep be for their use as formerly'. The rig possibly refers to the vessels containing the bleaching agent in which the cloth was steeped. A house and barns were included in the tack, and the College agreed to ensure that the house was 'wind and watertight and in good tenantable condition'. Whilst the tenant was required to maintain the house in good condition, the College would supply all 'stone and greet [= grained] timber'. The tiends payable on the land were the responsibility of the tenant, who was also to supply annually to St Nicholas's hospital (an almshouse founded by Bishop Andrew Muirhead at some time during 1455–73) three bolls of 'victuals'.[88] The College withheld the right to enclose the land if they so desired 'in whole or in part', whence the tenant could then be freed from the terms of the tack or could continue paying extra for the enclosed land, as would be determined by Faculty. The tenant was required to 'dung sufficiently and keep the lands in good condition towards the end both of the nine and nineteen years'.

The conditions attending the public auction were also defined: 'The lands to be let up at the roup at Twenty bolls bear and twenty two pound Scots for the house, barn and yards, and that the persons who bid at the roup shall advance at each bidding at least half a boll of bear'. 'Bear' here refers to barley, usually meaning the four-row-headed or six-row-headed type. The result was that Robert Wilson, a maltsterman, outbid his competitors by offering 'Twenty Nine bolls bear and a half for the land and twenty two pound Scots for the house barn and yard'. A Robert Wilson was named as a sub-tenant of the previous tackholder. One condition laid down was that previous sub-tenants would be allowed to apply for the tack only with special permission of the Faculty.

Reference to the Faculty deciding to take part of the Dovehill land for a bleaching field, and to the presence of a 'bleaching rig', raises the question of motivation. In 1729, the bleaching process was a protracted and uncertain one.[89] The cloth had first to be treated for eight days with a ley prepared from vegetable ashes, then washed with black soap and steeped for seven to eight days in the bleaching agent (butter-milk at the time). Then, after a further washing with black soap, the treated cloth was spread on the grass of the bleaching field and left for two to three weeks and regularly sprinkled with water. The whole process might have to be repeated two or three times before cloth of the right quality was obtained. The apparent generosity of the University in allowing part of its land to be used as a bleaching field is more understandable when it is appreciated that the Board of Manufacturers, set up in 1727 to promote the fisheries and various industries in Scotland, granted liberal rewards to persons or institutions which established bleaching fields. Presumably the College became one of the beneficiaries.

Possession of land outside the boundary of the Great Garden sometimes brought problems regarding rights of way. In May 1749 the Principal received a letter from a William Fogo,[90] occupier of some land abutting onto the Dovehill:

> Revd Sir
>   No doubt you have heard how your gardiner undermined our dykes for which I raised process against him before dean of gild and as a friendly meeting wi the masters was proposed and delayed: and now out of revenge he gott souldiers and a rable and this day stopt Francis reid our tennant from carting his dung up from the butts in by the head of your new dyke, he was leading the same road he was carting on and he loused his cart so that the poor man has 3 sh to pay the carter for his days work. Its certain we have been in possession of that road past memory and I need not tell you a servitude so well known that where any his land a way to it must be to prevent any reflections before I take legall recourse I apply to you and faculty to order a road according to use & wont and punish the fellow for abusing our man your anger shall wait till Monday 11 a cloack as the man must have his dung off the street agst tuesday
>   I am Sir Your most humble sevtt
> 6 May 1749   William ffogo

It is not clear which College gardener was taking his revenge on the unfortunate Francis Reid, who suffered the two indignities of having transportation of his manure prevented and having his cart 'loused', i.e. someone pulled out the metal rod holding the body of the cart onto the shafts with the result that it was upended and the load deposited on the ground. The carter still claimed his day's fee. Fogo's letter was accompanied by a formal declaration:

> These are declaring that Francis Reid my tennant Carting dung by the butts to his land throu the Colledge land for this season shall by no means be plead ane instance in my process after this for the servitude of a cart road, and that I might preach in terms of the act of parliament wiout regiard to this season
>   William ffogo

The legal implications of the term 'servitude' as used here entail some form of obligation regarding property, either limiting the owner's use or allowing others some specific rights. We can only presume that Mr Fogo obtained some satisfactory settlement with the Faculty. No reference to the affair is to be found in the Faculty minutes.

Enclosure of the Dovehill lands was commenced in 1753. In March of that year John Gardner, the tenant, presented an account[91] detailing the costs of 'enclosing the lands of the Dovhill'. The list includes 'stabs, rafters, timber for the yats, padlocks, and double and single flooring nails'. The quantities indicate that a sizeable area was being enclosed. In addition to the wood fencing (stobs, rafters and yats [= gates]), some 4,000 thorns were also bought, planted and manured. All told, the fencing and attendant features (wrights, gardeners, manure) came to £120/5/- Scots. There are no indications as to what part of the 13 acres of the Dovehill was enclosed. Care and maintenance of the hedges was to be Gardner's responsibility, although he was able to charge the relevant expenses to the Faculty. In a precept covering three years, 1753–6,[92] several men were engaged at digging and weeding the hedge — usually seven or eight days in spring and autumn each year. Three hundred thorns were purchased on 15 November 1754 (£1/16/- Scots) and 'One hundred and Seventy Alm Trees' on 22 April 1756 (£8/10/- Scots). According to the statement in the precept, all the elm trees were planted in a single day by one man. As with the hedges etc. in the Great Garden, the annual upkeep of the hedges on the Dovehill can be traced in a series of yearly precepts in Gardner's name up to 1762, all following similar patterns of weeding, clipping the hedges, digging and manuring them and mending the ditches as required. The purchase of stobs continued for 'stabbing the vacant parts', and on 20 March 1757[93] 400 thorn plants were required to fill spaces in the hedges. In a submission to Faculty at some time in 1761,[94] Gardner pointed out that the benches and ladders available for him for hedge-cutting were 'old and unfit for the purpose on account of the great Height of the hedge'. He included estimates for a new bench (6 feet high, 10/6d) and a 'short ladder' (in fact, one 11 feet in length and costing 5/6d). The note ends: 'He begs the Meeting would either allow him the Bench or Ladder or order in what way the Hedge is to be drest', which rather implies that this was not for the first time of asking. He was allowed the bench and ladder. A precept for fruit trees was presented on 16 October 1760:[95]

	£	s	d
To 70 Aple & Pear Trees at 1 sh each	3	10	0
To 97 Cherry trees att 8d each	3	4	8
To 6 Fine Plume Trees at 2 shills sterl each		12	0

On this same precept a claim for losses was also submitted:

To the profets of the rod to the Observatory from March 6 1760 to March 6 1761	7	10
To ground taken for the Observatory crop 1759 & crop 1760	17	0

The claims were for compensation due to loss of profits from land being taken for a road to the new Observatory, and for the loss of crops due to land being taken over for its construction.

The Observatory was erected on the southeast corner of the Dovehill. The foundation stone was laid in 1757, [96] and the overall cost of building came to £400 Scots. A valuable collection of astronomical instruments had been left to the University in the will of Alexander Macfarlane, a one-time student and later a merchant in Jamaica, whose own observatory there had been equipped with the best instruments available. Transportation of the instruments by sea cost £10 sterling; repairs for damage due to 'sea air', carried out by James Watt, cost another £5. To ensure clear observation additional land on the Dovehill and Butts was purchased for £500, and the Town Council gifted a third plot. Under the terms of transfer of the latter, the University agreed to construct a turnpike road between the Gallowgate and the Drygate,[97] but this lay outside the Dovehill. The Observatory was completed in 1760. The new road was hedged in the vicinity of the Butts for 'Fourty Shillings sterling' by William Findlay,[98] who in turn submitted a claim for losses incurred following the new road's construction:[99]

To onions, turneeps, Cabbage & green kell computed to be	£1 : 11 : 10
To profits arising from the grounds during the remainder of the tack being 14 years	7 : 0 : 0
To one boll of corn wi foder	13 : 4
	£9 : 5 : 2

John Gardner submitted annual claims for his loss of profits up to 1762.[100] Tenants of College land in other parts of the town also submitted claims with regard to upkeep of hedges. Between 1752 and 1760 a number were submitted by a George Craig for men 'clipen, diging and hoing the Hag' ('Hag' = hedge),[101] and on occasions for cartloads of manure and for thorns for 'mending the Hag'. Craig was tenant of some 7 acres and 3 roods of land near the Broomielaw,[102] part of some 10 acres owned by the College.

Patrick Stevenson, gardener in the Physic Garden, is rarely mentioned in the College Accounts over the period of his employment, nor are many precepts available. He was responsible for supervising the maintenance of the Great Garden. One account details work for the seven months from May to November 1759:[103]

To mowing and Rolling the Walks Six Rounds	£5 : 10 : 8
for sharping stone	1 : 0
for four sythes	8 : 0
for Sharping the Scythe	1 : 0
Six Bissoms for Sweeping the Walks	1 : 0
for clipping of the Hedges and Dressing of the Borders of ye same	2 : 0 : 0
Digging the borders Round the wall and Dressing the same	10 : 0
	£8 : 11 : 8

The overall expenditure (in sterling) was equivalent to £103 Scots, similar in amount to the payments made in earlier years. For the next year's work, however, Stevenson submitted an identical account to the Faculty,[104] and this seems to have been settled without any questions asked. A clue to the unreliability of Stevenson's timekeeping is to be found in a precept issued in his name by the Bedellus John Bryce for the period May to November 1758:[105]

> To Moeing Walks: Cliping Hedges and Digging Borders etc from
> May 1 1758 to Nov 1 1758 in the College Large Garden   £8 : 4 : 4
> [Under the above, an additional note was appended by Bryce:]
> As Patrick Stivenson kept no regular Accot of the Above Last Year :
> The Above is the exact medium for some years past which I paid

It would seem that Stevenson was not too efficient a timekeeper, and for 1758 had to be helped out by Bryce. This may also explain the more complete record given in for 1759, but one is left wondering whether the identical 1760 account was in part a cover-up for another lapse.

Routine maintenance of garden equipment continued, as shown in an account presented by George Jardine in 1756.[106] This included 'mending a frame for the rolling stone' (2/-); 'iron work to 3 wheel barrows' (4/11½); followed by 'more iron work for the wheel barrows' (2/3½); a 'shod for a shovel' (6d); a 'spinel for a Gardener's Reel' (6d); and '2 hooks for Cleaning the hedges' (1/-). The 'shod' was a metal tip for a wooden shovel and the 'spinel' the spindle for the reel (Table 4.1).

At some time in the 1760–1 academic session, Stevenson left the employment of the University and was replaced by Alexander Adams. The change would most likely have been on a Quarter Day, but in the College Accounts the two names are included as sharing the annual salary of £72 Scots. With the appointment of Adams, the point in time had been reached where it was found convenient to end the previous chapter, and for the same reason this chapter can be drawn to a close at this point. Whilst much of the available information is episodic and desultory, some sort of picture emerges of the management and working of the Great Garden. The principal change over the years was the gradual transition from a garden in which the tackholders were responsible for upkeep of the hedges, borders and walks, including replacement of trees or shrubs where necessary, to one in which the Faculty came to exercise a more direct control of all aspects of maintenance through its own gardeners. At some time in the 1750s, the gardener having charge of the Physic Garden became an overseer of the maintenance of the Great Garden — but without extra pay.

The name of James Loudon has made a frequent appearance in this chapter. One final reference is worth including. The whole story is explained in a petition to the Faculty presented by him in 1734:[107]

Unto the principall &. Remanent Members of faculty in ye

University of Glasgow The representation petition of James Loudon for himself & John Stark and Company Showeth that the Representers Entered into a Tack wi the Faculty in April 1710 for a little bit of ground of Little or no Use to ye College adjacent to the Garden wall at ye South east Corner Thereof, on which they built a Stillhouse

The Tack was for Nineteen years & if they desired they were to have ye sd Tack renewed for orther two Nineteen years upon paying fifty merks of Gresham at ye end of ye first Nineteen years as if ye Said Tack Dated 19 April 1710 more fully Bears. The plenty & Low price of forreign Spirits Obliged the Representers to give over ye work in 1714 to their no Small loss.

And Now having Disposed of their stills and Utensils They resolve also to Dispose of ye Tack wi consent of the Faculty wi Such as may have use for the House & are inclinable to purchase a little longer Tack.

But being informed that ye Smoke of ye Said House incommodes ye Garden & yt it would be more agreeable to ye Masters to have said House quite taken away & ye Garden Wall repaired & put in good condition like ye rest of ye wall as it was before & give up the said Tack & refer to ye faculty which part of yt 50 Mk they shall pay in ye above case of a New Tack if it had been desired for two other 19 years May it therefore please ye Faculty in consideration of ye premises to give Liberty to remove ye sd House in above terms. And the rather because ye sd House is become Ruinous & a party to every vagrant person to steall away ye Stines & Slaitts many of which are already taken away

The 'spirits' are whisky, and 'foreign' could mean that coming from sources south of the border. It has been estimated that in 1708 some 50,844 gallons of spirits were produced by distilleries in Scotland.[108] Following the Act of Union in 1707 a Board of Excise was created, and, although numerous illicit stills were to be the concern of the Board for many years to come, an operation so obvious as the one established on College land would not have been able to escape paying the necessary duty. We must assume that the failure of the joint venture was through a combination of duty payable and the factor of competition from 'forreign spirits'. The members of Faculty apparently found the fumes from the distillery unpleasant whilst they walked in the garden, and possibly harmful to nearby plants as well, so that the petition by Loudon and his associates would probably have been settled without great difficulty.

Robert Simson was one of the more distinguished members of the University. He was appointed to the Chair of Mathematics in 1711, and held the appointment until his retirement in 1761, dying in 1768 at 81 years of age. He was a much-respected teacher who by his researches brought to light Euclidean Geometry and helped establish it as a fundamental aspect of mathematics. A bachelor, his whole life was bound up with the College. One of his main outside enthusiasms was the Anderston Club, which he founded in 1748.[109] Its members met early on Saturday afternoons in a hostelry in the village of Anderston a few miles west of the College, and the main course of their meal was a 'hen soup' — a chicken soup thickened with black bean and black pepper. Simson is said to have regularly counted his paces to the hostelry and back and to have similarly enumerated his steps when strolling the walks of the Great Garden.[110] His appreciation of the walks caused him to write a letter of protest to the Faculty at some time in 1757[111] (the letter is undated but the contents indicate the year):

Robert Simson Protests in his own name and in the name of all who shall adhere to this protest against the resolution of turning the walk in the garden next the College into a gravel walk [Here Simson refers to the Head Walk constructed in 1727],

First because the only advantage it can be of it to afford a walk in such days in the winter whereon the weather is fair, but the grass is wet, which are very few; and in there the same advantage may be had by making a gravel walk within the hedge parallel to the walk now prepared to be altered, or by making one round the four sides of the parterre either of which would be sufficient for the desire proposed, and the first of them better than the altering of the walk into a gravel one, as it may be made larger than it, by carrying it down to the stone seat.

2ndly because the alteration proposed would be a deformity instead of a beauty to garden.

3rdly But supposing the alteration proposed was eligible, the doing of it this summer is most unreasonable, when the College has two very expensive works on hand, the building of the Principal's house, and on the Observatory and it seems to be quite unreasonable to load the revenue with so much expense in one and the same year, especially as it would put out of the College power to allow of some more necessary developments which contribute more immediately to the promoting of learning. Such as assisting the Professor of Botany and Anatomy in purchasing some things very necessary to his teaching etc. Some machines and preparations for teaching Anatomy and the putting the Physic Garden into good order and furnishing it with plants which it very much needs, as also the purchase of the Orery bought by Mr Dick; all these things which are of publick utility must give way to this project which at best is only for the convenience of a very few members.

4thly Because the majority of members were they present would be against this project; and therefore I protest that if the majority shall think fit to cause this walk after it has been turned into gravel be again reduced to its present state of being entirely in grass, that the expenses of turning it into gravel, and then back again into grass shall be chargeable upon those members who voted for such a change.

Simson's letter can be dated approximately in 1757 by its reference to the commencement of the building of the Observatory. His indignation at the 'grassed' Head Walk being gravelled, with the attendant discomfort to his feet, expresses the feelings of one who regularly used the garden walks as his principal form of exercise.[112] It also illustrates the depth of feeling such relatively small internal matters could arouse, and lengthy letters were invariably the way of giving vent to one's opposition. Noticeably, Simson enlisted the support of the Professor of Botany and Anatomy, probably the newly appointed Thomas Hamilton, by referring to the poor condition of the Physic Garden. Coming just three years after Robert Hamilton and William Cullen's strictures on the same topic we are justified in concluding that the Physic Garden was in decline, probably through the poor management of Archibald Graham, Patrick Stevenson having just succeeded him in 1757. It seems that Simson was able to convince the Faculty. It has been suggested that other members of Faculty, including Adam Smith, Professor of Moral Philosophy from 1752 to 64, and his successor Thomas Reid (1764–98), also regularly paced the walks whilst in pensive mood.[113] The gardens and perambulating Professors were also described in a poem entitled 'Elegiac Lines on an aged Elm which fell in Glasgow College 1st September 1799'.[114] McUre, writing in 1736,[115] described the 'large fine Garden, with broad pleasant Walks for the use of the Masters and students to walk in consisting of Seven acres of Ground well furnished with Fruit Trees and Pot Herbs'. As already shown, however, student access to the garden was limited to the privileged few.

The most romantic reference to the Great Garden is that provided by Sir Walter Scott, who, in *Rob Roy*,[116] used it as the setting for the duel between the cousins Frank and Rashleigh Osbaldistone, describing a remote region of the garden — a sort of wilderness with statues. The duel, stopped in the nick of time by the outlaw, and the preceding pensive wandering of Frank Osbaldistone through the quadrangles and other parts of the garden fit the story line to perfection. It would seem churlish, therefore, to point out that none of the characters would have gained admittance — at the time of the setting of the novel — without having been given a key by one of the masters. Since none was either a scholar or a son of a nobleman of high enough degree, no keys would have been forthcoming. The *Rob Roy* episode probably resulted from Scott's visit to the Garden in July 1817. Before then, however, changes were taking place in the Physic Garden and Great Garden which would have produced further irate letters from Robert Simson had he been alive. By 1760–1 we have reached a point when the Physic Garden was giving cause for concern whilst the

Great Garden appeared to be flourishing. Alexander Adam's entry on the scene is relevant to both gardens, and his contribution will be considered next.

Notes

1. CA, 1702–3: 26623, p. 45.
2. GUAA 45496.
3. GUAA 45568.
4. GUAA 8258.
5. GUAA 42339.
6. GUAA 42653.
7. College Revenue Book.
8. FM, 29 June 1722: 26634, p. 65.
9. FM, 6 December 1722: 26634, p. 81.
10. GUAA 42660.
11. GUAA 37210.
12. GUAA 37208.
13. GUAA 37209.
14. GUAA 42616.
15. GUAA 42619.
16. CA, 1722–3: 26624.
17. GUAA 42772-42786; 42811.
18. GUAA 42787-42793.
19. GUAA 42704; 42794-42798; 42800-42812; 42816.
20. GUAA 45296.
21. GUAA 39869; 39870.
22. GUAA 39871-39878.
23. GUAA 39870.
24. GUAA 39870.
25. GUAA 39873.
26. GUAA 39876.
27. GUAA 39881.
28. GUAA 42815.
29. GUAA 42816.
30. GUAA 42813.
31. GUAA 39861.
32. FM, 25 May 1727: 26634, p. 30.
33. GUAA 39995; 39996; 39999.
34. GUAA 39994.
35. GUAA 39994.
36. GUAA 39994.
37. GUAA 39996.
38. GUAA 39996.
39. GUAA 39996.
40. GUAA 39999.
41. GUAA 39999.
42. GUAA 39998.
43. CA, 1726–7: 26624.
44. FM, 10 December 1728: 26635, p. 76.
45. GUAA 40077.
46. GUAA 40077.
47. GUAA 40073.
48. GUAA 40078.
49. FM, 17 June 1729: 26635, p. 117.
50. FM, 11 May 1730: 26635, p. 173.
51. FM, 19 May 1730: 26635, pp. 174–5.
52. FM, 27 May 1730: 26635, p. 180.
53. FM, 17 March 1730: 26635, p. 162.
54. GUAA 40685.
55. GUAA 40588.
56. CA, 1727–8: 26624.
57. GUAA 40681.
58. GUAA 40690; 40691.
59. GUAA 40689.
60. GUAA 40686.
61. GUAA 40692.
62. GUAA 40772.
63. GUAA 40773; 40774.
64. GUAA 40773.
65. GUAA 40930; 40931.
66. FM, 26 March 1742: 266481, p. 118.
67. GUAA 26308 (undated draft re 'Garding locks').
68. GUAA 9269.
69. FM, 1 June 1748: 26639, p. 244.
70. CA, 1744–5.
71. GUAA 58257-58260.
72. GUAA 58023.
73. FM, 20 January 1724: 26634, p. 121.
74. FM, 24 February 1730: 26635, p. 159.

75. FM, 6 April 1730: 26635, p. 167.

76. FM, 24 April 1730: 26635, p. 168.

77. FM, 28 April 1730: 26635, p. 168–9.

78. GUAA 417.

79. GUAA 532.

80. GUAA 29046.

81. GUAA 40575.

82. GUAA 40678.

83. GUAA 40576.

84. GUAA 40688.

85. J. Coutts, 1909. *History of the University of Glasgow 1451–1909* (J. Maclehose & Son, Glasgow), p. 52.

86. FM, 4 November 1729: 26635, p. 130.

87. FM, 17 May 1730: 26635, pp. 174–7.

88. J.D. Marwick 1911. *Early Glasgow* (James Maclehose & Son, Glasgow), p. 43.

89. D. Bremner, 1969. *The Industries of Scotland* (David & Charles Reprints), pp. 261–2.

90. GUAA 431.

91. GUAA 58257.

92. GUAA 58259.

93. GUAA 58260.

94. GUAA 58062.

95. GUAA 58246.

96. J. Coutts, 1909. *History of the University of Glasgow*, pp. 229–30.

97. GUAA 58440.

98. GUAA 58246.

99. GUAA 58244.

100. GUAA 58247.

101. GUAA 58258; 58259; 58246.

102. GUAA 58023.

103. GUAA 58244.

104. GUAA 58246.

105. GUAA 58243.

106. GUAA 58259.

107. GUAA 58023.

108. D. Bremner, 1969, *The Industries of Scotland*, p. 445.

109. R. Griffin, 1856. *Glasgow and its Clubs* (J. Strang & R. Griffin, London & Glasgow), p. 2, pp. 20–3.

110. D.M. Mallock, 1913. *A Book of Glasgow Anecdotes* (T.N. Foulds, London & Edinburgh), p. 253.

111. GUAA 31124.

112. D.M. Mallock, 1913. *A Book of Glasgow Anecdotes*, p. 11.

113. D. Murray, 1927. *Memories of the Old College of Glasgow* (Jackson, Wylie & Co., Glasgow), pp. 416–17.

114. A. Molleson, 1801. *A Poem, and A few Miscellaneous Poems* (Chapman and Lang, Glasgow), p. 64.

115. ——— McUre, 1736. *View of the City of Glasgow*, p. 216.

116. W. Scott. *Rob Roy*, chapter 25.

'...Being Well Satisfied with the Ability & Care of Alex^R Adams...'

'...BEING WELL SATISFIED WITH THE ABILITY & CARE OF ALEX^R ADAMS...'

Alexander Adams was the ninth gardener in succession appointed with responsibility for the Physic Garden (Table 3.1; Figure 3.2). The Principals and Professors of the University, often men of considerable intellectual stature and renowed nationally and internationally, are rightfully remembered by their writings, portraits and by their involvement in University affairs, as recorded in their letters, memorials and in the minutes of Faculty meetings. Whilst lesser mortals make but transient impressions on the records of the University's history, they are very much part of it. The gardeners were regularly recorded in the College Accounts Books, either regarding their annual salaries or for various garden transactions. Their names rarely appear in the minutes of Faculty meetings. John Kennedy is not mentioned. John Hume served the University for 13 years without mention. His successor, James Nichol, died within a few months of being appointed, working so short a time that the University forgot to pay him; his only appearance in official records was when his unfortunate widow claimed for the missing money, which the University paid about twelve months after his death. Nichol's successor, William Craig, achieved notoriety in the Faculty minutes by being under notice of dismissal, then falling out with one of the Professors, destroying plants in revenge, behaving in an obscene manner when remonstrated with and being summarily sacked by the Principal as a result. William Galbraith served the University for 28 years as gardener, but so far as the Faculty records are concerned he was non-existent. William Hume, son of John Hume, followed Galbraith for a short period and was succeeded by Archibald Graham. No direct mention of Graham can be found in the Faculty records, but he is referred to by implication in the memorial presented to the Faculty in 1754 by Robert Hamilton and William Cullen, in which they complained about the state of the Physic Garden and the need to get a 'good gardener'. Patrick Stevenson, who followed Graham, receives an occasional mention in the College Accounts, as with his predecessors.

Alexander Adams differs from all the preceding gardeners in being named in the Faculty minutes soon after his appointment, and thereafter his name makes numerous appearances. The first such is in the minutes of the Faculty meeting on 4 February 1762:[1]

> A proposal in writing for improving the Great Garden having been given in some time ago by Alexander Adams Gardner in the Physick Garden and sent round to all the Masters for their perusal, was this day taken into Consideration, and Mr Clow and Mr Hamilton are appointed to draw up a scroll of a proposed minute for putting it into Execution & are asked to lay it before the next meeting

There is no record of the proposals put forward by Adams, and the two Assessors appointed to draw up the scroll did not report to the next Faculty meeting. At the meeting held on 8 April 1762,[2] however, some pertinent resolutions were passed regarding the Great Garden:

> The Meeting having taken the state of the College Garden into consideration, Find, That the rent does very little more than pay the expenses of keeping it in order, & that the Grass in the Plots is almost worn out by constant cutting without manure being laid on the ground; Considering further that £6 is too small an Allowance for a Gardner of Skill & Diligence to keep the Physick Garden without any emolument & being well satisfied with the Ability & Care of Alex^r Adams the present Gardiner for his better encouragement they agree to set him the College garden, Rent free, upon the following conditions:
> 1mo That he shall continue to manage the Physick Garden to the Satisfaction of the Faculty and particularly the Professor of Botany 2do. That He shall keep the College Garden in good order to the Satisfaction of the Faculty without any expence to the University 3to That he shall trench the Plots gradually & both put the ground and keep it in good Heart 4to That he shall cut down and carry off from the Garden whatever Trees shall upon examination by found Rotten or otherwise rendered useless 5to That he shall take care through the whole year that the Garden is not spoiled by Students or others. And by this Minute he is Authorized to seize and bring before the Principal the Person or Persons offending or to give up their Names in Writing. And Considering that the carrying off the Leaves & other Rubbish of the Garden is necessary for keeping it clean & may be attended with some expence to the Gardiner. The Meeting allow him the Dunghill of his & Mr Pettigrew's house for keeping the said Rubbish & he shall be obliged to carry it off from the Garden at his own expence.

From the several examples quoted in the previous chapter, it is evident that the steady reduction in the garden tack duty over the years, caused by the tackholders' loss of ground following the improvements commissioned by the Faculty, had brought the income down to the level at which it hardly balanced the outgoings to cover the work necessary for annual maintenance. The Faculty continued to have responsibility for the replacement of trees and shrubs, hence the statement in the preamble to the new arrangements proposed at the meeting of 8 April 1762. It is clear that the Faculty valued Adams, both for his work and for his advice, and for the first time in 58 years was prepared to give some additional emoluments to the gardener's annual salary of £72 Scots. The Faculty minute implies that Adams was to have the garden rent free, and that any supplementation of his salary would have to come from the profits he made, either from sub-letting or from the sale of grass and fruit. Sub-letting the plots would have reduced his own sales of grass and fruit and since the Faculty was finding it difficult to pay for the annual garden maintenance from the garden rents it would have been difficult for Adams to gain from such an arrangement. He was expected to keep the garden in good order, i.e. to mow the walks, weed and dig the borders, to cut and shape the trees and shrubs, prune the fruit trees and attend to all replanting, without any charge to the Faculty, and these operations would probably have required extra labour. The new financial arrangement is, however, clarified by an entry in the College Accounts for 1764–5, which states that £240 Scots was to be allowed to Adams 'for his pains and expences in keeping the walks' — a payment made for a two-year period. Hence, Adams was paid an additional £120 Scots per year to cover the labour costs of general garden maintenance. His additional emoluments would then have come from any profits he might make from the Great Garden.

The requirement to double trench the plots (possibly with extra labour) and to 'put the ground and keep it in good heart' probably means to render the soil in a satisfactory condition by manuring and cultivation. As already pointed out, the College was still to be responsible for replacing any dead or decaying trees or shrubs that it was Adams's duty to remove. The rulings of earlier years regarding the exclusion of students and the prevention of trespass from outside the College now became part of his duties, he having to act as a sort of policeman, either to bring offenders before the Principal or to take their names if the former proved difficult. He was also to receive some return for cleaning the grounds of leaves and other vegetational debris by being allowed this waste for his compost heap, and to incorporate that of his (presumed) neighbour if necessary.

Attention was drawn in a previous chapter to the seemingly limited expenditure on the Physic Garden during Thomas Hamilton's tenure of the Professorship of Botany and Anatomy (1757–81), the years which also cover most of the period of employment of Adams. Whilst the relevant precepts may have been lost with time, no evidence of a great deal of expenditure is to be found in the various College Accounts for the period, although these become rather muddled after 1776. Adams was clearly much valued by the Faculty for his first year's work in the Physic Garden. A capable gardener would be able to maintain his plant stocks by propagation methods and the conservation of seeds, so that the lack of expensive plant purchases over the years may well be an expression of Adams's efficiency as a gardener. The permanent trees and shrubs would by now be well established. One precept in his name and relevant to the Physic Garden charges for the period 1765–8 (£2/10/5d sterling) for the cartage of manure and bark, together with two scythes (2/6d), hoes (3/-) and 'Mending the Glass in the Hot House & ye Bark beds, 7/3d'.[3] The reference to the hothouse (= greenhouse) is the first mention of one in the garden. Cartage of bark and the bark beds refers to a form of hot-bed (see also p. 78). A further precept regarding the greenhouse is dated 10 May 1765[4] and is one for Alexander Buchanan: 'for Reparing Hot hous and Hot Beads for years 1763 & 1764 & 1765 To Wood Work Glas Neals and Whiting the above in fisick garden £0 = 15 = 9'. It is possible that the greenhouse was erected at the instigation of Thomas Hamilton. Whether the work of George Nisbet in 1760 (p. 93) actually referred to a 'hothouse' and not just a 'hot-bed' has been questioned in earlier pages. Note that 'whiting' or whitewashing the glass to prevent excessive irradiation of the plants was then a recognised practice.

Over the years, Adams was to submit numerous accounts for labour, materials and plants, mainly for the Great Garden and for the College land beyond the Molendinar Burn. In these accounts there are occasional references to the Physic Garden, mostly regarding implements — scythes, scythe stones, spades, Dutch Hoes and rakes (see Table 4.1). Plants in the Physic Garden are rarely mentioned; on two occasions, 10 May 1773[5] and 12 June 1779,[6] nails were purchased for 'nailing the mulberries and the vines in the Physick Garden'. An entry for 7 May 1771[7] gives the cost of purchasing 'stobs, nails, lock, hanges, cork and painting the Box of the Pluviometer that stands in the Physick Garden' (4/2d sterling). This rain gauge is also mentioned in an entry for 5 December 1778:[8] 'To Tarr for tarring the stobs which support the Pluviometer, To Cork and a Gage Stick, 2/2d'. Whoever was responsible for the routine rainfall measurements and for whom is not known. The only reference to a rain gauge in the University precincts is to that owned by John Anderson.[9] Having fallen out with all his colleagues, Anderson's parting shot was to instruct his executors to ensure that after his death all additional features which he had paid for in his University house were to be removed unless the Faculty immediately agreed to buy them. A rain gauge was one of the additional features in the roof of his house. Since Anderson was so quarrelsome, it is unlikely that even the sociable Thomas Hamilton would have allowed him the use of another one in the Physic Garden.

In the first years of his employment, and before the revised arrangements of April 1762, Adams kept a meticulous record of the employment of men for the routine annual maintenance of the Great Garden, a record in marked contrast to that of his erratic predecessor. In 1761–2 the bredd gardeners were paid 15/- Scots per day for mowing the walks, trimming the hedges and pruning the trees and shrubs. The workmen (now at 12/- Scots per day) were required for rolling the walks, weeding and digging the borders and clearing away the hedge and tree clippings. The labour costs for the period Whitsunday 1761 to Martinmas 1762 amounted to £120 Scots. Principal Leechman's authorisation to pay this sum to Adams (as £10 sterling) is dated 6 January 1763. Since the payments to gardeners and workmen were from Whitsunday 1761 to Martinmas 1762, and since, as already shown, the casual labour was paid weekly, the University's debt to Adams was almost double his annual salary at the time. Just how these weekly payments were made remains a mystery. In the 1722–9 period when James Loudon was gardener, precepts were issued weekly and he became the means by which cash was handed over; he never carried the level of debt apparently borne by Adams. In August 1762 Adams purchased a bench and ladder for cutting the hedges, costing 16/8d sterling. The precept[10] was drawn up by Joseph Black, who signed himself 'Cl. Univ.', having succeeded Robert Simson as Clerk to Faculty in 1762. The relevant entry in the Faculty minutes,[11] acknowledging and granting Adams's request, concludes '. . . and he is allowed to provide himself with them in the best and cheapest manner'.

The meticulous accounts submitted by Adams from 1764 on are concerned mainly with works in the Great Garden and the Dovehill and adjacent land. Whilst the Faculty had given Adams the overseeing of the Great Garden work programmes, its members still exercised some control, as shown in a minute of a meeting held in June 1763:[12]

> The Principal, Dr Trail, Dr Smith, Dr Wilson, Mr Muirhead and Mr Anderson are appointed a Committee to see the Holly Hedge in the Garden rooted out, & the Gate of the New Court repaired & to continue the Hedge across the north end of the three parallel walks

A committee of six to supervise such relatively simple jobs would seem overweighted, unless the inclusion of the quarrelsome Anderson may have called for counter measures. The presence of Adam Smith in the Committee is a rare event. The three parallel walks would have been the Head, Middle and Foot Walks, and the actual work was duly recorded in a precept dated 28 May 1764:[13]

> Accompt of the College of Glasgow to Alex^r Adams Gardiner for Labourers Wages Employed during the following work in the Grate Garden 1 Feb 1764

To Removing Lime Trees & planting them across
the end of the Walk North side of the Garden   £1 . 11 . 6
To Digging out Old Decayed Holly Hedges   2 . 1 . 4
To Sloping, throwing back & forming the Mount   1 . 16 . 8
To Leveling & Making a New Walk top of the bank   1 . 3 . 11½
To enlarging and raising the two side walks   1 . 8 . 5
3 June 1764
To 1¾ Bolls of Rye Grass seed at 11 sh per
Boll for sowing the said Walks and Mount   19 . 3

                                      9 . 1 . 1½

To Alexr Adams Gardiner for Attending the
Labourers & Work extraordinary   3 . 0 . 0
To Oak Stakes and Nails for the end of the side walk
south side of garden   3 . 4
To one day of two labourers nailing up the said stakes
and rolling the new walks   1 . 0

                                   12 . 5 . 5½

The Mount (Mound or Bank) will be remembered from the previous chapter, in which there are frequent references to 'beating the bank'. The establishment of a new walk on the top of the Bank is a noted departure from growing turnips on it as in a previous year. The price of rye-grass seed had only slightly increased in a 36-year interval, from 7/6d Scots per peck in 1728 to 8/3d in 1764 (see p. 116). Note that the 'labourers' were paid 6d sterling per day, compared with 1/- per day for the 'workmen' in the garden and 1/3d per day for the bredd gardeners. About this time all accounts and precepts were being given in sterling, and in 1765 the College Accounts went over completely to 'sterling money'; the previous (sometimes confusing) mixture of Scots and sterling money no longer appears. Similarly, any sums of money mentioned from here onwards will be in sterling, except when comparisons with earlier years are made.

The location of the parterre built in 1731 was not disclosed in any of the relevant accounts or precepts. A small precept issued on 4 December 1764,[14] however, refers to Adams being paid £7/1/11d for 'covering the Parterre behind the Common Hall & the Entry to the Laboratory with Gravell'. This points to the parterre being situated in the rectangular plot between the Common Hall and the Head Walk (Figure 5.1). According to the College Accounts, Adams was also paid £13 Scots (£1/1/8d sterling) for gravelling the New Court at some time in 1764. A further extension of his range of supervision is to be seen in work described on 29 November 1764,[15] when men were employed on improving the Molendinar Burn within the University grounds:

To Widning & dressig out the burn   1 . 16 . 0

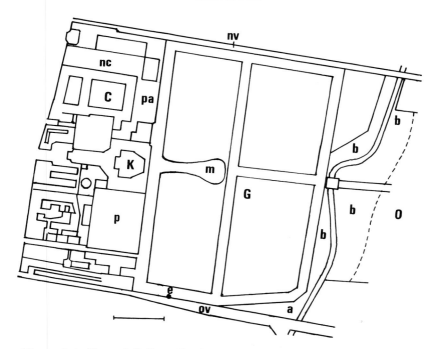

Figure 5.1. Plan of College Garden with main features involving work of Alexander Adams over the years

C = College Buildings K = Blackfriars Kirk G = College Garden 0 = Observatory Park (previously Dowhill or Dovehill) nv = New Vennel nc = New Court pa = site of parterre p = Physic Garden m = Mount or Bank e = elm tree in wall ov = Old Vennel a = the angle-foot region b = the burnside walks region

Scale line: 150 feet

To leveling & sowing the Banks of ye said burn	16 . 0
To rye grass seed to sow ditto	3 . 6

The decision to clean out the burn and rebuild the banks had been taken by a Faculty committee of four (George Muirhead, Patrick Cumin, Alexander Wilson and John Anderson). Their memorial to the Faculty carried further recommendations:[16]

> The Committee having examined Mr Adams accompt of work done at the Molendinar Burn amounting to £2 . 15 . 6 sterl. Find that it is exact that the work is judiciously executed and that Mr Adams is entitled to some Consideration for his own work and inspection
> The Committee appointed to survey the Molendinar Burn Report
> 1 That the small Timber Bridge near the Dye House ought to be

159

taken down and rebuilt which appears as estimate will cost for stonework 3sh 4d ster.

2 That the Arch in the Stone Wall may be widned which as appears by Estimate will cost £2 . 0 . 0 without any College Stones

3 That the Burn ought regularly to be cleaned every Summer with cost only the Labour of two men for a few days

4 That if these things are done the stagnation of the Burn will be entirely owing the Bridges and Dams below, and in no Degree to the College Banks, Bridges or Walls

N.B. If the Brae was to be secured by a Stone Wall, the Expence as appears by an Estimate would be about Eight Pounds supposing the College gave no stones

It appears that in the summer the slow-flowing burn was becoming stagnant and fouled enough to be offensive even to the hardy nostrils of those times. The Faculty appears to have been sensitive to outside criticism, and the committee was quick to point out that any future problems regarding flow rates would now lie outside the College grounds. The proposal that there should be a regular annual cleaning out of the burn resulted in further supervisory work by Adams and included a number of other activities all concerned with maintaining the attractiveness of the burn and its banks. References to payments for men cleaning out the burn are to be found regularly in the accounts submitted by Adams over the years — especially for the removal of gravel. For example, in the summer of 1775 this work occupied three men over twelve days at a cost of £1/16/-.[17] Overtime was required, and this was paid for with 8/6d worth of 'Ale an Whiskie'. In September 1780, two men were engaged over three days at clearing out from the burn 'dead dogs, dead cats, brushwood and other nausances'.[18] Nothing was wasted which could be used. The gravel cleaned from the burn annually was saved and used somewhere in the gardens; any large quantities of brushwood were dried and sold. As recorded in 1775,[19] '... For men's wages cleaning the Burn of Gravel etc. £1 . 16 . 0, To Ditto For men's wages making a Walk of said Gravel on the West Bank of said Burn Above the Bridge to the Observatory, 16/3d'. In other years, more gravel from the burn was used to construct a walk between the Bridge and the Old Vennel. The replacement of the bridge over the burn recommended by the committee was commenced some three years later. Early in 1768, Adams supervised four men over 11½ days in 'picking out and carting the Found for the Landstools of the New Bridge to Observatory, daming the burn taking out dams Ramming earth to back of West Landstool'.[20] The 'Found' would have referred to the soil dug from banks of the burn to make way for the landstools, the latter being the stone foundations of the bridge. Some reference was also make to working on the 'Haucks' of the new bridge — probably the level ground on the banks of the burn. At some stage it had been necessary to dam the burn to help in the construction of the landstools.

Care of the banks of the burn was always necessary. In the summer of 1772,[21] three men were engaged over 11½ days in 'facing up the sides of the said Burn from the New Bridge to the foot of the Old Vennal with stones in order to raise a Bank to prevent the floods from coming into the College Garden'. The floods in the burn which at times spilled over into the Great Garden were also occasions for cleaning out the gravel and sand. At such times the workmen so engaged were usually rewarded with buns, ale and sometimes whisky for literally working in the burn, and probably getting wet through in the process. The work of facing up the burn banks mentioned above was associated with '2 men 6½ days each at 1 sh per day wheeling earth and clay to raise the walk top of the Arch betwixt the Ledges of the Bridge to the Observatory and drawing up sand and gravel from below the said Bridge to cover earth and clay and prevent the water sinking down and spoiling the Arch'. From this we can assume that the arch of the bridge was of wood and rested on the two stone landstools. Ivy was planted on the two sides of the bridge on 17 March 1773.[22] Further reconstruction of the banks on the southeast side of the burn was carried out in 1776.[23] In early February 1776, four men worked for 59 days (at 10d per day each) '... sloping and making up the Banks to the North & South side of the Bridge leading to the Observatory and making under Drains with the old Willows that grew on the said Banks to Drain of the underwater in order to prepare the said Banks for planting trees, shrubs, etc. £9/16/8d. To a horse and cart 8 days at 3 shillings per Day £1/4/- Carting earth from Different places and at Different times off the said Bank'. With the waterlogged soil of the banks in need of drainage, branches of the willow bushes previously growing there were laid in trenches to speed up the draining process.

Later, on 3 May 1776, Adams reported that '40 Large Elms, 100 Beeches, 30 Different exotick plants' had been planted on the Dovehill side of the burn, and that the four men so engaged were also 'Levelling and making a Walk round the said Banks and sowing and raking them with Rye Grass and Dwarf Clover'. The rye-grass seed was priced at 9/- per boll (compared with 10/- in 1728 and 9/- in 1764; the dwarf-clover seed had changed little in price since 1727, then costing 1/3½ per pound whilst in 1776 it was 10d). The 100 beech trees were all about 5 feet in height. Also planted were '2 large Larickes [= larches] and 2 Birches'. Purchase of the elm trees is not mentioned, so they may have come from stocks within the garden. The 'exoticks' are not listed. More of these were purchased in 1776 and 1778 from a Charles Ross of Paisley: 130 different kinds of 'exoticks' were planted in 1778 'in place of those that were dead'.[24] A further 40 exotic plants and flowering shrubs were required for this area of the bank in the spring of 1779, 'in place of those broke by the old Elm tree & others that were dead'.[25] The Elm tree had been blown down and its wood was sold for 11/6d. This planting of 'exoticks' between 1776 and 1779 originated in some suggestions put to the Faculty by Adams in November 1775.[26] The Faculty then formed a committee to consider the 'representations of Alexr Adams to make such improvements to the Observatory Gardens as might be required'. As a result of the committee's findings, it was decreed in February 1776 that 'Alexander Adam Gardiner is appointed to provide flowering shrubs for planting on the Bank on the east side of the Molendinar Burn within the Observatory Garden'.[27] Hence Adams had suggested improving the appearance of the Dovehill grounds and the burn banks opposite the Great Garden. For the first time official records were talking of the 'Observatory Garden', probably regarding it as an extension of the Great Garden.

Supervision of the annual cultivation of the garden trees occupied a good deal of Adams's time. Any trees that had been blown down, or had to be felled, were always offered for sale, an event which was always well organised:[28]

Glasgow May 7th 1768

	£	s	d
Accot. College of Glasgow to Alex^r Adams for the following work viz:			
To 4 men 13 days at 10d per day Cutting down the dead and decayed trees on the Burn side	2	3	4
To 5 men 9¾ days at 10d per day Cutting down the trees in the Old Vennal & Cross Cutting the same for measuring and dressing the remaining trees that stand	2	0	7½
To 14 Young Elms at 2d pr tree & planting them		4	10
To 24 Dozen Stobs at 1/- pr Dozen & 2 Dozen hoops at 1d each and cartage for stobs & hoops	1	7	8
To 300 nails at 8d pr 100 with driving the stobs and nailing them around the young Trees	0	5	0
To Ale at Sundrie Times to the men that assisted in letting down the trees with ropes to save the Garden Wall of houses in the Old Vennal	0	12	6
To Deacon Thomson for measuring the wood	0	7	0
To 2 advertisements for at 3/6d each	0	7	0
To a Towns Officer for calling the roup	0	2	6
To Punch, Ale and Paper at the roup	0	2	4½
	£7	12	10

In the following November 1768, [29] two men each worked half a day 'cutting and sawing an old Plane Tree Blowen down in the Privet Walk — 2/6d, To measuring the tree, 1/6d' ('Privet', as will be shown later, is a misspelling of 'Private'). The Gardens Committee of the Faculty on occasions inspected the garden trees and then gave orders regarding their subsequent felling where necessary. At a meeting in June 1771 it was decided that 'all the trees marked by the Committee are ordered to be sold to the highest bidder'.[30] In the following October, the committee reported that '10 Elm trees, 2 Ash and 1 Plain tree' had been sold to David Girdwood and Gavin Allen for £19/5/- sterling.[31]

The routine of cutting the trunk and counting ('measuring') the annual rings obviously played an important role in valuation. Numerous examples of the practice are to be found in the many accounts presented by Adams. On 2 February 1772, 6/6d was paid for men 'cross cutting and measuring the Elm Tree blown down by the High Wind', followed on 27 March by a man working for four days 'digging out and cutting to pieces the root of the Elm Tree blown down by the wind & planting a young Elm in its place'.[32] Occasionally a large tree needed felling, as described in an entry for 9 March 1779[33] when four men took three days to cut down and cross cut an old Elm tree at the foot of the Great Garden. A Mr Thomson (Deacon Thomson as above) was then paid 2/6d for 'measuring' it. In February 1782,[34] we find the members of Faculty giving consideration to a representation from Adams 'concerning the blown down tree'. The Gardens Committee were then ordered to deal with selling the wood and replacing the tree. An entry in one of Adams's many accounts duly reports for the following 25 March: 'To 5 large Elm trees 4d each and 2 men 1 day planting them in place of 4 dead on the burnside, and one for the old one blown down by the high wind — 3/8d'.[35] We may wonder whether Adams's 'representation' was a means of speeding up a process being unnecessarily protracted.

Where a number of trees were offered for sale the public roup (or auction) seems to have been a convivial affair. Evidently newly planted young trees were protected by rings of stobs held in place by metal hoops. Some of the old trees in the Great Garden seem to have been especially prized. In July 1769, three men worked for a day 'setting in large Whin stones to Preserve the Elm tree & wall in the Old Vennal'.[36] In December 1776, two men were engaged for three days on an identical task involving the 'old Elm tree' by the Old Vennel. The need had arisen as a result of the 'towns Causayers' having been 'Causaying' (= paving) the Old Vennel, and in so doing having lowered the level of the road and underpinned the wall and the old Elm tree.[37] McArthur's drawing of the Old College grounds in his 1778 plan of Glasgow (see p. 35) shows this tree in a prominent position *in* the wall between the Old Vennel and the College Garden (Figure 5.1; see also Figure 1.2 and p. 19). In 1779 Adams was organising workmen to 'pin the roots' of this tree with soil and turves. The December 1776 entry in the accounts states that 32 carts of earth and rubbish 'left by the Causeymen on the side of the Garden Wall' had to be removed. Hence we can visualise the 'causeymen' shovelling up the rubbish and earth from their paving work in the Old Vennel and then throwing it over the wall into the College Garden. Whilst cartage of the 'causeymen's' debris cost 5/-, some use would have been found for it. For example, on 29 July 1772, 10/6d was paid for 2½ days' use of a horse and cart 'at moving into the garden the earth and mason rubbish from the outside of the new wall foot of the Old Vennal'.[38] On the following 18 August, two men were paid for 'trenching down the said rubbish to raise the ground betwixt the walls and levelling it to prepare it for the young trees'. Planting and 'dressing' the young trees in the raised area followed in the autumn, when '31 large young Elm trees, 11 large young Lime trees, 11 large young Beech trees and 160 Thorns' were installed. This small plantation was established in the southeast corner of the Great Garden, in what was to become known as the 'angle-foot' between the Old Vennel and the Molendinar Burn (Figure 5.1). The development of this 'angle-foot' amenity continued in May 1773, when Adams engaged a man for 'wheeling off the rubbish of the Garden Wall that fell down and burying it to raise the walk thro' the young trees foot of the Old Vennal'. At the same time 4/10d worth of rye-grass and dwarf-clover seed was sown between the young trees. The summer of 1773 turned out to be an exceptionally hot one, and in late autumn two men were employed planting '11 large Elms and 6 Limes' in the angle-foot plantation 'in place of those dead by the great drought of last summer'.[39] A further five young tree replacements were necessary in November 1774.[40] The angle-foot plantation seems to have been much valued. From 1774[41] until 1782[42] when Adams's last account was presented, men were engaged each year in February and March 'pruning and dressing up the old and young trees on the side of the burn private walk and in the Angle of the Vennal'.

Some tree transplantations were ordered by the Faculty Gardens Committee in April 1776,[43] when it decreed that 'The Lyme Trees in the Garden opposite to the Professors Houses No 10th and 11th are ordered to be transplanted to the sides of the Middle Walk of the Garden in the places of such trees as are dead'. Adams recorded this operation in an account entry dated 28 December in the same year, when two men worked for twelve days (at the rate of 1/- each per day) 'Digging out 6 Large Lime Trees at the back of Dr Muir and Mr Clows Houses and planting 6 Large Flowering shrubs in their place Likeways digging out 6 Lime trees was dead in the row towards the south end of the Middle Walk and planting 6 Lime trees in their place'.[44] It sounds as if the large trees were blocking the light reaching the windows of the two houses, and that flowering shrubs would have been both less incommodious and more attractive. Tree-transplanting would have been a major operation in those days. No mention is made of any special apparatus being used, although a machine for transportation and erecting trees was available at the time (Figure 5.2). From the timing of the operation it is likely that each tree required two days' work for uprooting and transplantation. Sometimes extra assistance was necessary, as in November 1768 when a number of men were repaid in ale for 'assisting in transplanting the Large Elm Tree to the foot of the Bridge stairs'.[45] The bridge was the one over the Molendinar Burn.

Figure 5.2. Tree-transplanting in the eighteenth century

The term 'Dovehill Garden' (also the 'Observatory Garden') appears in Adams's accounts in the late 1770s, as on 30 January 1777 when a man was engaged for 11½ days at 'cleaning and cutting the old and young Hedges around the Dovehill Garden and likeways dressing up the old & young Elms on the side of the Burn private walk'.[46] The angle-foot region received some attention in April of the same year when it was planted with 60 large thorns and one young Lime tree.

Adams was always ready to remind the Faculty of a state of affairs in the garden if necessary — as if not prepared to wait for the deliberations of the Gardens Committee. In October 1779 he made representation to the Faculty regarding the state of hedges to the walks in parts of the Great Garden:[47]

The Representation of Alex[r] Adams
Sheweth
That the Hedges in the College Garden are very much decayed, especially for these two or three years past. For recovering of which I would recommend the following method viz.
To lop off the inside branches this year closely to the bogles, and take out the dead wood, which is the occasion of its decaying so fast, and to take about two or three feet off the top of it on account of many of the tops being entirely decayed; and, two or three years hence, when the young growth on the inside is well up The Hedge will be quite thick: and then the outside may be one in the same manner, if you think proper. Thus the figure of the Hedge may still be preserved agreeable to the eye, and the hedge in a great measure

renewed, and made to stand for many years. And if this, or some other method, be not fallen upon, it will be past recovery.

The Gardens Committee, seemingly having deliberated the matter at some length, set in progress the work advised as shown by an account entry by Adams for 17 February 1780,[48] when two men were reported as having worked for 25 days (each at 10d per day) '... cutting and loping the High hedges around the College Garden and taking out all the decayed and dead ones likewise Digging out the two decayed hedges Mid Walk lower part of the gardens and dressing those that were left for standards'. It then took ten days in early March to remove all the 'dead and brushwood' that was lying about after the cutting-out process described above, and then in mid-March the replacements were planted in the hedges:

140 beech trees at 1d each
120 beech trees at ½d each
260 lime trees at 2d each

At the same time, three shrubs ('1 large Buckthorn, 1 large Barberry, 1 large Newfoundland Dogwood'), each costing 6d, were purchased and planted opposite the back of the New Court. The beeches and limes were planted in the vacant hedge spaces by two men working for seven days (each at 11/- per day). This initial replacement planting seems not to have been too successful. In December 1780,[49] Adams records that 250 beeches (at ½d each) and 23 limes (2d each) were planted 'in the gaps of the hedge round the College Garden in place of those that failed'. Since this occupied two men for five days, it rather suggests that small trees were used. In the same month 86 different shrubs (costing 13/6d) were planted on 'the two banks of the burn Observatory Park in place of those dead by the severity of the former winter'. The Observatory Park — also called the Observatory or Dovehill Gardens on occasions — was that area of the Dovehill lying immediately east of the Molendinar Burn. Tree replacements for 1781 included eight young elms (4/- worth) being planted in place of 'dead old Plane trees' on the garden side of the burn in the spring, and this took two men six days at the workmen's rate of 1/- per day.[50] For the same wage, two men were engaged for ten days in March 1782 'lopping trees on the south end of the Middle Walk in the College Garden and carrying off the branches'. It required two men for a further three days to clear away the resulting 'small brushwood', which in due course was sold. In March 1782,[51] Adams recorded that two men took three days to remove '6 Large Lime Trees' from the angle-foot region by the Old Vennel and to transplant them in place of dead ones lining the Middle Walk. From the amount of work involved, one suspects that 'large' is used as compared with more juvenile trees. In the same month Adams had to buy 300 elms (£4/6/-) for 'supplying the gaps in the Beech

Hedges, College Garden', and 60 lime trees (12/6d) for the hedge at the 'foot of the garden'. Elms and limes were seemingly being used in preference to beeches or planes. In April 1782, 170 different flowering shrubs (£1/5/10d) were planted 'to thicken the two Banks above and below the Bridge leading to the Observatory'. If only we had some idea of the variety of shrubs used and some picture of their layout on the banks of the burn; but, whilst Adams was meticulous in accounting for the timekeeping of his workmen and the other expenses, nowhere has he left us any plan of the new plantings which he supervised.

Reference was made in the previous chapter to the building of the Observatory in the Dovehill land. The instruments left to the University by Alexander Macfarlane were installed in 1760. The building proved to be rather damp, and various attempts were made to counteract this defect and prevent damage to the instruments; work which included painting the walls with linseed oil and digging drainage ditches around the basement.[52] Adams became involved in supervising work around the Observatory from the spring of 1768, when he organised four men working for six days (wages of 10d per day) 'digging and casting out a drain round Observatory and through Deacon Gardner's garden to carry off the underwater'.[53] Was this a further manifestation of clay-soil drainage problems as already described for the Great Garden or had the Observatory been sited on a natural spring? Each year thereafter, usually at some time in the autumn, two men were engaged '... cleaning out the drain that takes water from the Observatory several times'. In May 1775, two men spent 2½ days 'sloping back the sides of the drain that takes water from the Observatory'.[54] In the late 1760s a similar drain had been built from the New Court in the College Garden — and once again Adams had to organise the annual clearance of this drain, often several times in a year. All these clearances are recorded in his accounts.

Further work around the Observatory was commenced in May 1768,[55] with four men 'wheeling off the Green Sward round the Observatory and levelling the slope round the side of said drain'. This was followed by 'wheeling off the earth and levelling the border for a hedge, planting and laying dung round sd hedge', the hedge itself consisting of '200 Crabs and 1100 Thorns'; and every two years thereafter, for as long as Adams kept records, three or four cartloads of manure were applied to the hedge each autumn to 'strengthen' it. Between the Observatory and its surrounding hedge 167 cartloads of gravel were 'levelled, rammed and rolled', possibly another attempt to offset the drainage problems. The gravel was obtained from some point in the River Clyde, and each cartload coming to the College grounds had to pay a ½d toll at the Gallowgate. The Observatory hedge was also surrounded by a wood fence of 'stobs and rafters'. This required regular maintenance, and any stobs which were broken or decayed, either from here or from any other part of the garden, were used for the Observatory fire. A final development regarding the Observatory was the establishment of a bank sloping down onto the Dovehill. Two men ('beaters') were supplied with an oak plank for 'beating the banks', and this operation was followed by the sowing of rye-grass seed and dwarf-clover seed. Another drain was dug down this bank and the five men so employed were also paid for 'raming stones in the spouting place at the bottom of the slope'. Thenceforth further annual exercises became necessary, as described for 21 October 1769[56] when two men were employed for six days 'weeding & rolling the gravel, cutting the hedge and mowing the banks around the Observatory'. Sale of grass cuttings from the Observatory banks regularly raised small sums as income (5/6d-11/6d) and all of these were recorded as credits in the Adams accounts. Weeding, raking and rolling of the gravelled New Court were also recorded at regular intervals. We can perhaps understand Robert Simson's objections to gravelling the Head Walk (p. 149): he could probably foresee the state it might get into, especially with the implied innefficiencies at the time of the two gardeners Graham and Stevenson. It would also seem that his strong arguments must have worked, since had the Head Walk been gravelled we would have seen some records of its cleaning in Adams's accounting.

The banks of the Molendinar Burn were constantly in need of repair. A minute in the Faculty meeting records for 10 June 1771 states:[57]

The Burn at the North End of the bleaching field is ordered to be embanked with large stones and the stair to be condemned. The Bank of the Burn within the Garden is ordered to be faced with stones where most necessary as far as the stones upon the ground will go and the Channels of the Burn to be cleaned out

The distinction made between that part of the burn abutting onto the bleachfield and the 'Bank of the Burn within the Garden' (i.e. between the New and Old Vennels) points to the bleachfield being in that part of the Dovehill ground to the north of the Great Garden (Figure 5.3). This concern for the state of the banks was linked with the occasional flooding of part of the Great Garden when the burn was in spate after heavy rains. One causative factor is apparent in a petition submitted to the Sheriff Depute of Lanark by the Principal and Faculty on 8 February 1772.[58] This claims that 'Messrs Robertson and Campbell, merchants in Glasgow, sometime ago erected a dam upon the Molendinar Burn for steeping of hides, which was made to high that it laid part of your petitioners Garden under water always when there was any rain whereby your petrs Garden has been greatly damaged'. Robertson and Campbell were proprietors of a tannery. In McArthur's 1778 plan of Glasgow, a tannery is shown situated on part of the Dovehill land just above the point where the Old Vennel bridges the burn (Figure 5.4). A later accounts entry by Adams's successor refers to 'the burnside opposite the Tanworks', which rather confirms the site

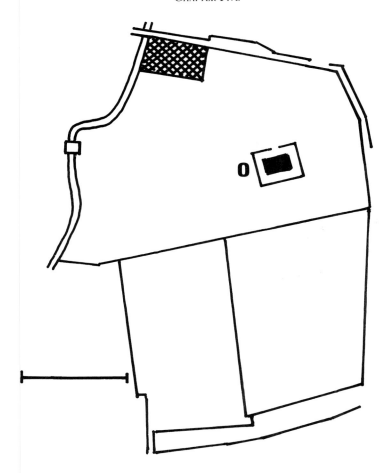

Figure 5.3. Probable site of bleachfield, so far as can be determined from records. Area not known

0 = Observatory
The bleachfield is indicated by cross-hatching.

Scale line: 300 feet

on McArthur's plan. A recent detailed study of the development of the city shows (for about the time under discussion) a tannery just south of the Old Vennel bridge, with two more further downstream.[59] The dam must have been close to the tanworks: the entrapped water was used to soak the hides to remove hair and fat. The Faculty petition continued with the information that on the previous day (7 February 1772) the

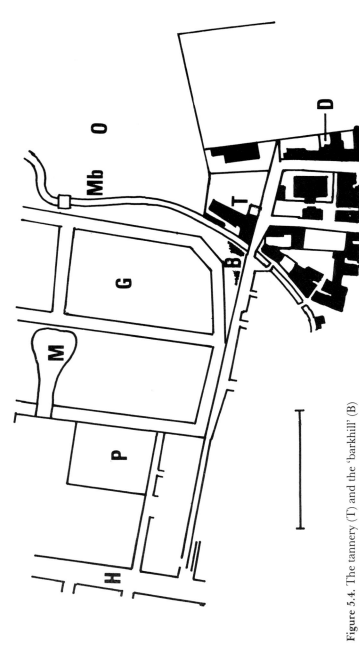

Figure 5.4. The tannery (T) and the 'barkhill' (B)

H = High Street P = Physic garden M = Molendinar Burn O = Observatory Park D = Mound or Bank G = College Garden Mb = Dr Moore's Garden

Scale line: 300 feet

dam had broken under pressure of an increased flow rate due to heavy rains, and that the tannery proprietors had decided to rebuild it. The Faculty had heard that the new dam would be larger, and expressed concern that as a result any flooding in the future 'will utterly destroy the lower part of your petitioners Garden'. Faculty asked that the Sheriff Depute place an injunction on any further dam construction, and apparently won their case. This affair came again under consideration in the following March:[60]

> Mr Anderson, Mr Hamilton and Dr Wilson are appointed a Committee, two being a Quorum, to meet with the People at the Foot of the New Vennal and the Proprietors of the Tan Work below the College Garden in order to examine the Propriety of erecting a Dam or Sluice upon the Molendinar Burn and report.

Reference to the inhabitants of the *New* Vennel being consulted is probably an error, since all indications are that the flooding, when it occurred, was on the southeastern region of the Great Garden, and both the dam and the tannery were situated close to the Old Vennel. Adams became involved in the following June when he supervised the reconstruction of the banks of the burn:[61]

> 6 June 1772 To 3 men 16½ days work at 1/- per day wdning the Burn & casting out the found for faceing up the side of the said Burn from the New Bridge to the foot of the Old Vennel with stones in order to raise a Bank to prevent the floods from coming into the College Garden £2 . 9 . 6
> To 2 men 3 days each at 1/- per day digging up the old stones on the Waste ground opposite the College & carrying them to the street for facing the said Burn 6/- To Ale for the said men 6d 0 . 6 . 6
> To Carting down 49 carts of the said stones at 4d per cart 0 . 16 . 4
> 20 June To 3 men 8 days each, at 1/- pr day, making up the bank on the side of the burn with a walk on top of it 1 . 4 . 0
> 27 June To 4 men 3 days each, at 1/- pr day wheeling and levelling the ground betwixt the said walk and the Garden Wall 1 . 0 . 0
> To Rye Grass Seed 6/3 dwarf Clover 1/- 0 . 7 . 3
> For Ale to the men when Widning and dressing out the bottom of the Burn it being extraordinary work 0 . 1 . 10
> To 2 men 3½ days each at 1/- pr day mowing, rolling and beating the Banks and Walks on the side of the said Burn above and below the Bridge betwixt the Old & New Vennals at different times 0 . 7 . 0

No report seems to have been forthcoming from the consultative committee mentioned above, and references to flooding of the garden do not appear in subsequent years, so we can assume that a satisfactory compromise was reached between Faculty, the Old Vennel inhabitants and Messrs Robertson and Campbell over the siting and height of the proposed new dam. It is not until July 1778 that Adams again mentions floods in his accounts,[62] when he refers to 'setting up wooden Grates on the Burn for time of floods foot of the Old and New Venneal, wi two padlocks for holding sd Gates' — presumably describing sluice gates.

Frequently in Adams's garden accounts there are entries for rebuilding walls, especially in the Dovehill land. Often the work is that of 'goffing' or 'gouffing' — the process of underpining or reinforcing existing walls, or coping, with the latter sometimes effected with turves. In May 1772, a Faculty committee reported that they had inquired into the expense of building a new wall 'to enclose ground upon the South side of the College Garden'.[63] The Faculty promptly appointed a different committee (Mr Anderson, Dr Wilson and Mr Cumin) to oversee the erection of a wall 6 feet in height and 'to order the Top of the said wall to be covered with lime stuck full of broken bottles'. Once again Adams was called in to accompany a mason, Deacon Paul, in the process of surveying and estimating the overall cost of the wall. Adams reported that it would cost £19/5/-.[64] The wall extended from the foot of the Old Vennel towards the bridge over the burn, as if to enclose further the angle-foot region.

The dual spelling of 'privet' and 'private' in some entries, with the two words in the same sentence on occasions, was mentioned earlier with reference to certain 'Privet' walks. So far as can be interpreted from diverse accounts over the years, this private area eventually consisted of walks in the angle-foot region and along the raised banks of the burn on either side, later extending into that planted area of the Dovehill (or Observatory) Garden opposite the Great Garden. It was another of Adams's responsibilities to supervise the maintenance of these gravelled walks and to extend them on occasions, utilising gravel dredged from the burn whenever possible. We must assume that the privacy of the walks was for the Principal and Professors, although the proximity of the tannery to the angle-foot part of the garden must have afforded a constant reminder to the strolling academics of the biological processes involved in leather manufacture. Another, more useful, by-product of the tannery is recorded by Adams when he describes a 'barkhill' which lay in the area to be the angle-foot plantation. This was the accumulation of waste bark (oak or birch) which in its fresh ground-up condition was used in the tanning process. On one previous occasion (p. 156) there was mention of a 'barkbed' (a form of hot-bed) in the Physic Garden. In November 1768 Adams described how three men over 4½ days worked at 'Trenching down bark and rubbish from the barkhill to the private walk to clear the barkhill ground and raise the said walk to keep the burn out of the gardens. Cutting out Found for a wall at the said barkhill picking up rubbish and cart to West End of Do'.[65] No payment is mentioned for the bark, so perhaps the tannery was permitted to deposit the bark residues on the College land for the use of the College gardeners as required. In July 1769[66] Adams reported that a further 130 cartloads of bark had been carted in to help make up the private walk, and in December of the same year two men were employed 'nailing stobbs and Thorns and casting Ditches to stope the roads in the Privet walk foot of the Old Vennal'. 'Roads' probably means 'inroads', as if outsiders were trying to penetrate into the private region in the angle-foot (the plantation on this site was not fully established until 1772). 'Dressing up' the old and young trees in the private walks on the burnside was still being carried out in July 1781.[67]

A more pertinent reminder of the need to maintain the privacy of the angle-foot plantation and associated walks comes in April 1780, when Adams reported that an outlay of 8/10d had been made for 'stobs, rafters, nails for enclosing the Angle foot of the College Garden to prevent students from going into same and over into the Private Walk'.[68] This simple statement raises the question of student access to the Gardens, the implication being that students were now permitted to enter the Great Garden. It will be remembered that all earlier references stated clearly that students were not permitted to use the gardens, with the exception of those who were sons of noblemen, and students studying Botany who were admitted to the Physic Garden, and that in 1742 even the aristocratic privileged number was denied admission. We find an answer to this student-access question in a memorial of George Jardine,[69] Professor of Logic and Rhetoric from 1787 to 1827:

Memo[1] taken down from Professor Jardines diction
In the year seventeen hundred threty when I first came to the College students were never allowed into the Garden but by 1770 a gradual relaxation had commenced & the students got admission by Keys till at last after they had been in the habit of lending their keys and some of them getting keys made for themselves the garden had become quite a public one it was allowed to continue open but there was no formal opening & it was originally that to them
Geo. Jardine
Glasg. 15 January 1827

From the dates mentioned above we may well question Jardine's memory of when he entered the University, but the implication in his memorial is that student access to the Great Garden from about 1770 onwards seems to have been achieved almost by default, with no formal cognisance from Principal Leechman and the Faculty — which is all the more surprising with someone like John Anderson a member of Faculty. The problem highlighted by Jardine was that once some keys had been obtained by students they could be multiplied rapidly by the co-operation of local blacksmiths, a problem not unknown to the College authorities from earlier years. With a sufficient number of duplicate keys available, the public would soon have taken advantage. The public was admitted to the Great Garden on special occasions, as on the accession of George III in October 1760 when there was a bonfire and fireworks display in the College grounds, together with an exhibition of paintings in the inner quadrangle of the College.[70] Public admissions had been permitted also on some summer evenings when bands played in the College grounds, but in May 1773 the Faculty withdrew this privilege:[71]

> The Meeting ordered that no band of music shall play in the Garden in the Summer which has been the case formerly, as they have found that the Trees have become hurt and other Inconveniences have arisen from the crowds assembled on these occasions. The Faculty observing that the Door which was opened from the back part of Dr Moor's house into the Garden has produced several inconveniences therefore orders the said Door to be built up and that no linen shall be dried or bleached in the College Garden and the Servants are to take care that these Orders shall be put into execution.

Dr Moor (Moore or Muir) owned a sizeable garden abutting onto the southwest region of the Dovehill (Figure 5.4), and any door or gate from his land would allow direct entry onto the Dovehill and into the Great Garden. The ruling regarding the drying or bleaching of linen goes counter to an earlier one that permitted the servants of the Professors to dry the clothes of the families along the walks from September to May.

While official openings of the grounds seem to have presented problems, even more so were those arising from unofficial entries. This is well expressed in an undated letter from Adams:[72]

> Unto the Rector Dean of Faculty Principal and professors of the University of Glasgow
> Gentlemen I beg leave to Acquaint you that the Garden is now so crowded with all Sorts of people and is quite common to the greatest prejudice of Trees, Hedges and Walks and it is not in my power to help it except the Tron Gate is kept Closed & the keys supprest as they grow so numerous
> Gentlemen your Humblest Servant
Alex^r Adams

The letter requires no further comment, and the strong feeling of Adams on the matter was emphasised by his address being to *all* the senior members of the University. On the back of this letter there are some notes and comments written in a different hand, which suggest both in their style and in their penmanship that they are the notes taken down by a scribe at a Faculty meeting:

> The College Gardiner represented to the Meeting that unless he is allowed to padlock the Garden doors it will be impossible for him to preserve the Walks, Trees & Hedges, and it is well known to many of the Members of the Meeting that the College and Gardens is often infested with Crowds of low People particularly that during on Sunday last, the Meeting therefore allows twenty shillings to be laid out upon a Man who is to assist the College Servants in keeping Improper Persons out of the Garden and College & Anderson Wilson & Reid are appointed a Committee any two being a Quorum with Power to padlock the Doors when they shall think it requisite, and with Power to lay out the above sum in the best manner & with Power to give orders to the Gardiner & College Servants.

The outcome of Adams's urgent letter is contained in a Faculty minute of 10 June 1775:[73]

> As the College Garden has of late been much infested with improper and disorderly persons, the Gardiner is ordered to prosecute them before the Sheriff at the expence of the College and the College Servants and hereby ordered to prevent such persons from going about the College and to prosecute them before the Sheriff

One can imagine the feeling of Adams at such an edict. Whilst it was one thing for Faculty to agree to cover the expense of bringing the malefactors before the Sheriff, it still left Adams the physical problems of bringing such 'improper and disorderly' persons to justice. Perhaps he could have enlisted the help of other College servants. It is true that this policing duty had been laid down in the revised conditions of his employment in April 1762, but it is apparent from the tone of his letter that the problem had become unmanageable. In 1769 Thomas Patoun was employed as 'Keeper of the Garden Gate' during the summer months, receiving 30/- for 30 days' guardianship[74] — a temporary appointment. In later years, 1784–5, one David Morton was paid £1/16/- per month as Keeper of Court and Garden.[75] The trespassers were apparently gaining entry via the Dovehill land. It would have been inevitable that Adams would have had to patrol the grounds during the lighter evenings and at weekends: the Sabbath was not sacrosanct to 'improper and disorderly' persons.

The principal sources of Adams's overall salary have been enumerated earlier. His Physic Garden salary of £6 remained unchanged, and in due course his successor was to receive the same. He was allowed £10 to cover the costs of annual maintenance of the Great Garden, and any profits would have had to come from his sales of grass cuttings and fruit. He sought extra land from the College in June 1774:[76]

> Unto the Revernd Principal & other Members of the Faculty of the College of Glasgow
> Gentlemen
>   as the Dovehill ground round the Observatory is out of Tack at present & if you think it proper to have it laid out in grass, I will give £3/10/- per Acre, to have a Tack equal in time to the rest of the Tennants, & that odd ridge betwixt McNairs ground & the New Turnpike which I would lay out in the Nursery way; as to the Fences the sloping of the roads will be sufficient & that is absolutely necessary whatever way the ground may be employed
> Gentlemen your very humble
& Obliged servt
Alex^r Adams

Faculty moved slowly in this matter, and not until March 1775[77] did it decide that a committee (Mr Clow, Dr Wilson and Dr Reid) was to exchange missives with Adams for a 19-years' tack at the rate per acre as suggested in the letter. The arrangements were to be made without delay (!) — '... as the time of labouring the ground is now come'. A later submission by Adams[78] (undated, but by the nature of its contents about 1776–7) pointed out that at the time of exchanging the missives he had 'Verbally agreed' to take into the Observatory Garden the barkhill, then in 'such bad order', and to ensure that it would be 'equally as good as the rest'. For this he sought some consideration from the Faculty regarding the increase in rent which would now be necessary, and at the same time claimed for some 'extraordinary expence':

To filling large hollows, leveling and Carrying the stones	£2 .	7 .	7
To 370 Carts of Earth at 3 halfpence pr Cart	2 .	6 .	3
To 33 Carts of Dung Wheeling and Cartage at 1sh 4p pr cart	2 .	4 .	0
	£6 .	17 .	10

NB It will take three or four years before it be properly cultivated and will cost about thirty shillings yearly in extraordinary expence

Seemingly the plan was to incorporate a now redundant barkhill (not in the angle-foot) into the Observatory Garden, although it would take some years to reach a similar state of cultivation. The exact position of the barkhill is not described, but was probably somewhere on the southern side of the Dovehill land.

Adams presented a further petition[79] to the Principal and Faculty in March 1778:

The Petition of Alex[r] Adams College Gardener
Humbly Sheweth
 That the Hon[abl] Board of Trustees for improving the
Manufacturers in Scotland have impowered Mr Andrew Stirling
Mercht in Glasgow to make a trial of an acre of ground in this
country for Raising Madder — The sd Mr Stirling has been pleased
to apply to your petitioner to find ground for, and manage the same
under his direction for three years, being the time limited for sd.
experiment — your petitioner is of opinion that an Acre could be
taken off the south-side of the Observatory Garden, next to Dr
Moore's Garden which will be very little observed from the Walk to
the Observatory, and would, he thinks, be very fit for said
experiment, whereby the sd. Ground would be very much improved
for grass there after
May it therefore please your Hon[rs] to consider this Petition and if
agreeable to grant leave to your Petitioner to make trial of said
experiment (which, if successful, must be of very great utility to the
Public) and your Petitioner shall be
Alex[r] Adams

Roots of the Madder (*Rubia tinctorum* L.), a climbing plant, were the
source of the dye Turkey Red, used for dyeing cotton. At the time of
Adams's petition it was cultivated mainly in France and Holland.
Production of the dye in Glasgow commenced in 1785,[80] and a
successful method of dyeing cloth with Turkey Red was introduced
into the city at about the same time.[81] In the mid- and late 1800s, one of
the larger dye works was that belonging to William Stirling & Sons
near the village of Renton in Dunbartonshire. Adams's petition was a
carefully structured one, stressing the public (and national) good which
might follow such an experiment, and the benefit that the soil would
obtain over the three-year period. The records of Faculty meetings
contain no reference to the petition or to the subsequent decisions
taken, but in the light of the intellectual climate then prevailing in
Scotland under the influence of the Enlightenment it seems very likely
that permission would have been granted. Adams may therefore have
played a role in an important development for the dye industry in
Glasgow — and in Scotland. (Figure 5.5)
 In October 1769, Adams made the following entry on one of his
accounts sheets:[82] '11 October to 3 men $3\frac{1}{2}$ days each at 1 sh pr day
leveling the Earth & Rubbish around the Type Foundry 7/6d, to 24
Carts Gravel at 5d Cart 10/-. to wheeling levelling the said Gravel
round the said Type foundry 3/7d to make it passable for the men'. On
the face of it this was just one more of the numerous supervisions that
were Adams's lot over the years. The type foundry had been erected in
University grounds in 1762,[83] following the request of Alexander
Wilson, Professor of Practical Astronomy from 1760. Prior to that, in
1750, he had been appointed type founder to the University, this being

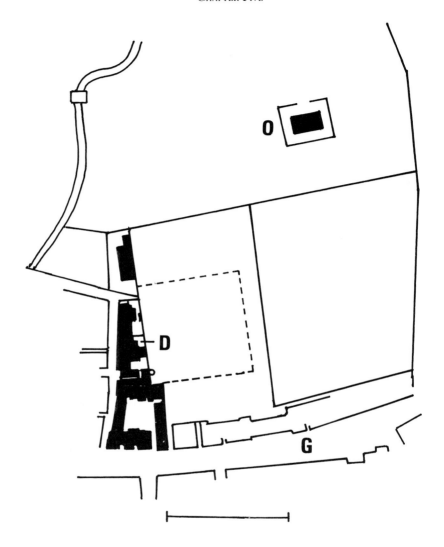

Figure 5.5. Probable site of Alexander Adams's trial plot for growing Madder (outline with broken line)

O = Observatory **G** = Gallowgate **D** = Dr Moore's garden

Scale line: 300 feet

his main livelihood. Wilson's petition of 23 March 1762 pointed out that his type-foundry business had now become closely bound up with the University's printing requirements and, since he would soon be resident in the College, it would be of greater convenience if a type foundry could be erected in the College grounds. His estimated cost of the project was £39/8/-. The foundry was built in a small garden close to the Physic Garden at a cost of £59, and for which Wilson paid an annual rent of £3/15/- (Figure 5.6). In time it became necessary to expand the foundry and permission for this was given by Faculty in 1769. The work described by Adams was a clearing-up operation after the extension had been built. In time, however, the foundry was to loom large in the history of the Physic Garden and in a manner with which Adams would have disapproved. This aspect will be described in a later chapter.

With such a record of multifarious supervisory duties in all parts of the Great Garden and Dovehill lands over the 23 years of his employment, it is very easy to lose sight of the fact that Adams was originally appointed as gardener to the Physic Garden. Attention has already been drawn to the seeming lack of information on the running of the Physic Garden over this time, although it was his efficiency in his first year in the Physic Garden that so impressed the Faculty. The only plan of the Physic Garden for that period is that drawn from memory (without a scale) by John Hope, one-time student at Glasgow and later Professor of Botany and Medicine at Edinburgh. Hope's drawing depicts the garden in about 1770,[84] at a time when Adams was fully in charge. It shows a rectangular garden divided into six plots with intersecting paths (Figure 5.7); one plot containing two greenhouses, one of which is orientated to be south-facing. From Hope's outline drawing it seems reasonable to assume that the garden left a fair impression, more so than would a badly run or depauperate area. As suggested earlier, lack of information in precepts and accounts may be a measure of Adams's efficiency as a gardener. Outside of the Physic Garden there seems to have been no part of the College grounds with which he was not in some way involved over the years. In addition to the routine maintenance of the Great Garden — for which the preceding chapter gives a full account of the type of work involved — it was under Adams's supervision that the area to become known as the Observatory Garden was developed, with its plantations of trees and flowering shrubs, walks and grassed areas. Wall-building and reconstruction in various parts of the Dovehill and neighbouring land was also to be his responsibility. In December 1778, he was paid £6/17/- for 'improving the Butts'.[85] One puzzling aspect of his accounts over the years, however, is that repayments to him were invariably in arrears, and on occasions he could be owed over £50 for work going back over two years. From all available sources, it is estimated that the expenditure handled by Adams on behalf of the Great Garden and Dovehill land was about £325 over 21 years — not evenly spread and

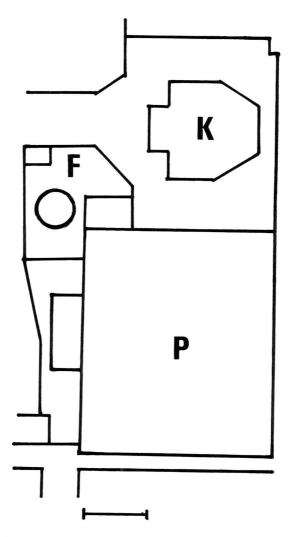

Figure 5.6. Position of the type foundry built in 1762

F = type foundry K = Blackfriars Kirk P = Physic Garden.

Scale line: 50 feet

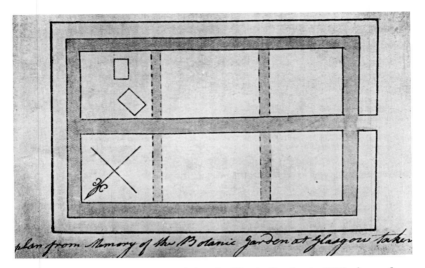

Figure 5.7. Plan of the Glasgow University Physic Garden in 1770, drawn from memory by John Hope. An 1807 plan shows four plots (Fleming's map)

for the main part covering wages of casual workmen. A somewhat anxious note is to be found at the foot of an undated precept for some garden tools:[86]

> N.B. Be pleased to give me a preceipt for nine or ten pounds for to help to pay the Labourers that has and is to be employed in doing the different works that are ordered belonging to the College as I pay the said Laborers once a week

Suffice to say that this prepayment of £9 is duly recorded as a credit in his account for 1775, when the sum owed to him was £58/8/2d. Repayment of this sum was carried out on a precept dated 13 January 1776.[87] There is no evidence of any other prepayments. Knowing his sources of income, we are left wondering whether these debts on behalf of the College were sustained by Adams from his profits on the Great Garden and those parts of the Observatory Garden for which he became tackholder. Perhaps he regarded these annual debts as a means of forced saving, bringing a welcome reimbursement at the end of the year. Noticeably, the College paid no interest on the moneys it owed.

The impression Adams leaves is of an energetic and highly intelligent individual who rarely waited for instructions and more often foresaw the necessary actions and informed Faculty or the relevant committee what would be the best solution. He became a member of the Incorporation of Gardeners (as a 'near-hand' or local man) on 17 September 1766.[88] His wife ran a small shop in their house in the

Blackfriar's Wynd, selling 'medical herbs of all kinds, with distilled waters such as Cinnamon, Peppermint, Pennyroyal, Mint, Hysop and others and Herb Ale during the season' (from an advertisement in the *Glasgow Advertiser* for 27 January 1783).[89] It would seem that Adams had permission to dispense some of the products of the Physic Garden. Adams has left us a record of meticulously kept accounts, all written in his copperplate hand. The last reference to him, in the minutes of Faculty meeting of 16 December 1783, is of the briefest:[90]

> A Meeting is Appointed to be held here on Monday next at 12 o'clock to consider the state of the College Garden and to appoint a Gardener in room of Alexander Adams, deceased.

And for all the contributions he made over the years, there is a sad footnote in the Faculty minutes for 10 June 1784:[91]

> Faculty agree to allow Mrs Adams, widow of the late Gardener, now in great distress, the sum of £5 sterling

The last years of Alexander Adams were also those of change in higher spheres in the University. In February 1781,[92] a letter from Thomas Hamilton describing his current ill-health, and proposing his son William as his successor, was read to Faculty. William Hamilton was already teaching in the University whilst deputising for his father, but the events which followed the reading of his father's letter brought him into much closer association with the University's gardens. William Hamilton's contributions to Botany in the University are considered in the next chapter.

Notes

1. FM, 4 February 1762: 266421, p. 121.
2. FM, 8 April 1762: 26642, pp. 133–4.
3. GUAA 43417.
4. GUAA 58251.
5. GUAA 58283.
6. GUAA 58186.
7. GUAA 58281.
8. GUAA 28756.
9. D. Murray, 1927. *Memories of the Old College of Glasgow* (Jackson, Wylie & Co., Glasgow), p. 116.
10. GUAA 28248.
11. FM, 13 August 1762: 26642, p. 165.
12. FM, 26 June 1763: 26643, p. 4.
13. GUAA 58249.
14. GUAA 58180.
15. GUAA 58249.
16. GUAA 43408.
17. GUAA 58285.
18. GUAA 58280.
19. GUAA 58285.
20. GUAA 43417.
21. GUAA 58282.
22. GUAA 58276.
23. GUAA 58285.
24. GUAA 58274.
25. GUAA 28756.
26. FM, 9 November 1775: 26690. p. 335.

27. FM, 27 February 1776: 26690, p. 370.

28. GUAA 43417.

29. GUAA 58261.

30. FM, 10 June 1771: 26690, p. 34.

31. FM, 26 October 1779: 26691, p. 293.

32. GUAA 58276.

33. GUAA 28756.

34. FM, 20 February 1782: 26692. p. 161.

35. GUAA 58280.

36. GUAA 58261.

37. GUAA 58285.

38. GUAA 58283.

39. GUAA 58284.

40. GUAA 58284.

41. GUAA 58284.

42. GUAA 58280.

43. FM, 17 April 1776: 26691, p. 8.

44. GUAA 58274.

45. GUAA 43417.

46. GUAA 58274.

47. GUAA 43371.

48. GUAA 58196.

49. GUAA 58280.

50. GUAA 58280.

51. GUAA 58280.

52. J. Coutts, 1909. *History of the University of Glasgow 1451–1909* (James Maclehose & Son, Glasgow), p. 229.

53. GUAA 43417.

54. GUAA 58284.

55. GUAA 43417.

56. GUAA 58261.

57. FM, 10 June 1771: 26690, p. 34.

58. GUAA 17937.

59. A. Gibb, 1983. *Glasgow: the making of a city* (Croom Helm, London), p. 47, fig. 3ii.

60. FM, 17 March 1772: 26690, p. 59.

61. GUAA 58282.

62. GUAA 28756.

63. FM, 15 May 1772: 26690, p. 68.

64. GUAA 43403.

65. GUAA 43417.

66. GUAA 58261.

67. GUAA 58280.

68. GUAA 58196.

69. GUAA 47965.

70. D. Daiches, P. Jones and J. Jones (eds.), 1986. *A Hotbed of Genius — The Scottish Enlightenment 1730–1790*, see cover picture and notes.

71. FM, 13 May 1773: 26690, p. 159.

72. GUAA 43370.

73. FM, 10 June 1775: 26690, p. 321.

74. GUAA 58255.

75. GUAA 58262.

76. GUAA 43369.

77. FM, 4 March 1775: 26690, p. 286.

78. GUAA 58276.

79. GUAA 84816.

80. A. Gibb, 1983. *Glasgow*, p. 90.

81. D. Bremner, 1969. *The Industries of Scotland* (David & Charles Reprints), pp. 297–9.

82. GUAA 58261.

83. GUAA 43409.

84. F.O. Bower, 1903. Notes on Botany in the University of Glasgow in the 18th century. *Transactions of the Natural History Society of Glasgow*, vol. 7, pp. 121–36.

85. FM, 14 December 1778: 26691, p. 226.

86. GUAA 43409.

87. GUAA 58285.

88. P.B. McNab, 1903. *The History of the Incorporation of Gardeners of Glasgow* (J. Smith & Son, Glasgow), p. 197.

89. D. Murray, 1927. *Memories of the Old College of Glasgow*, pp. 419–20.

90. FM, 16 December 1783: 26692, p. 317.

91. FM, 10 June 1784: 26693, p. 14.

92. FM, 13 February 1781: 26692, pp. 68–9.

'A PERSON MOST FIT AND WELL QUALIFIED...'

Thomas Hamilton had been burdened with ill-health from 1777, and in October 1780 had obtained the permission of the Faculty to enlist the help of his son William for the ensuing teaching programme. On 13 February 1781,[1] the Clerk to Faculty read the following letter from Thomas Hamilton to the assembled meeting:

> It is well known to all of you that in the month of August 1777 I had the misfortune to be struck with a palsy, and although I bless God I have since recovered sufficient to attend to and perform several parts of my Chirurgical character yet from the first day to the present I have uniformly experienced not only a Difficulty but almost an incapability to perform my duties as Dissector and Professor of Anatomy. Unwilling that my class should suffer by my Misfortunes, I beg leave to propose my son William for my Successor in the Professorship of Botany and Anatomy if you shall judge him fit for these Offices. He is known to you all while passing a regular course of lectures in this University, where he likewise attended the Lectures on Anatomy and Medicine. After this he studied Anatomy, Botany and Medicine in its different Branches at Edinb[r] & next went to London where he continued three years under the justly celebrated Dr William Hunter attending the ablest teachers there in the other Branches of Surgery and Medicine. This year the University was pleased to nominate him to teach my class which, I am happy to hear, he does with Credit and Reputation. May I be forgiven to beg the favour of you, my Colleagues, to write in a proper representation to the Crown, to Procure my Office for my son, which I hereby promise to resign. And it would greatly enhance the Obligation & favour if you would do this with all convenient speed, As you are sensible of the very precarious situation of my health. To prevent possible Misunderstanding in this matter, I beg leave to add

that when I resign my Office in this College I mean to reserve my present House, but that no person may have reason to complain, shall willingly agree that my son shall have no Claim whatsoever to any College House during my life, or 'till I may find it proper to resign that House which I now possess.

Some further details can be added to William Hamilton's *curriculum vitae*.[2] In 1781 he was 23 years of age, having entered Glasgow University in 1770 and graduated MA in 1776. After two years of study at Edinburgh University, he was awarded his MD in 1779. His period of study with William Hunter in London brought him into contact with all contemporary developments in anatomical knowledge. He lodged with Hunter and took charge of the dissecting room. Hunter's opinion of the young Hamilton was well expressed in a letter to James Graham, third Duke of Montrose, and Chancellor of Glasgow University, regarding the proposed succession to Thomas Hamilton: '... it is in the best interest of Glasgow to <u>give him</u> rather than solicit the appointment'.

Thomas Hamilton's letter was duly considered by the Faculty at their meeting of 20 February 1781:[3]

Faculty judged the desire of the same highly reasonable and unanimously resolved to recommend Mr William Hamilton to the Secretary of State as a person most fit and well qualified to succeed his father in the Office of Professor of Botany and Anatomy, and the Principal, Mr Clow, Mr Anderson, Mr Millar and Dr Reid, or any three of them, are appointed a Committee to draw up a scroll of recommendation & Petition to the Secretary of State to that effect and report.

The subsequent arrangements seem to have been made with commendable speed. Some of the behind-the-scenes activity is indicated by Hunter's letter to the Duke of Montrose. William Hamilton's Commission of appointment was issued under the Privy Seal of Scotland at Edinburgh on 8 March 1781. This Commission was read before Faculty on 6 April.[4] It was then decreed that he should present a 'discourse' on *De Vasorum asborbentum natura et usu* (On the nature and use of absorbent vessels), 'as proof of his qualifications for office', on Tuesday 10 April at 12 noon. Hamilton, on the day and time appointed, having taken the Oath of Allegiance to the Government and 'Subscribed the confession of Faith before the Presbytery', then read his discourse, with which the Faculty 'declared themselves well satisfyd'. He then took the oath *de fideli* and was 'solemnly admitted & entitled to all the priviledges and emoluments of a Professor of Botany and Anatomy in the College'.

The procedural steps in Hamilton's appointment were to remain virtually unchanged for all his successors until near the end of the nineteenth century. The nature of his discourse rather implies that greater emphasis was being placed on the medical aspects of his dual Chair, for which by prior experience he was well prepared. His father's letter of recommendation had, however, stressed his son's botanical expertise. We may well look back askance at the nepotism which ensured the dynastic succession of another Hamilton, so keeping the joint Chair in the Hamilton family for some 40 years. We may equally wonder at the terms of Thomas Hamilton's letter, not only proposing his son as his successor, but insisting that he himself should continue to occupy his University house, although demitting office. William Hamilton had also written a letter to the Faculty before his appointment stating that, if appointed, he would make no claim to a University house 'whilst my Father possesses a Professors house'. Thomas Hamilton died early in 1782; his house then becoming vacant, there followed a series of moves between houses on the part of certain of the Professors (the usual procedure once a house became vacant) with the result that house number 5 became available for William Hamilton in June 1783,[5] five months before his marriage to Elizabeth Stirling.

The suggestion made earlier that emphasis might have been placed on the medical aspects of the joint Chair is underlined by the appointment of a Faculty committee 'to receive the Apparatus of Anatomy and Midwifery the property of the College from Mr Thomas. Hamilton and to deliver the same by Inventory to Mr Wm. Hamilton and to take his Receipt for the same'.[6] In June 1781, however, Hamilton represented to Faculty 'that one Scythe and some other tools are wanted in the Botanic garden amounting to 7s 6d. The Meeting agreed to grant the sum for this purpose'.[7] Compared with his predecessors, Hamilton was taking an early and direct interest in the Physic Garden (here and in later entries usually described as the Botanic or Botanical Garden). The result of this representation was duly recorded by Alexander Adams in one of his accounts, with an entry dated 20 June 1871,[8] 'to 1 Sythe & 4 Sythe Stones 2/8, 1 Dutch hoe 1/2 and a shaft to Do. 4d, a spade 3/10 for the Physic garden, — . 8 — .'. As described in the previous chapter, Adams meanwhile carried on with a variety of supervisory duties in the Great Garden and Observatory Garden, as well as continuing to cultivate the Physic Garden. A further Garden Committee of Faculty (Dr Wilson, Mr Richardson and Mr Young) had been appointed in May 1781 and was required to report back in due course.[9] The collaboration between Adams and Hamilton was to continue for 2½ years until the death of the gardener later in 1783.

We left the account of Alexander Adams at the end of the previous chapter with the Faculty proposal of 16 December 1783 to hold a meeting on the following Monday to appoint his successor. At this meeting, 'Mr Hamilton, Professor of Botany, having mentioned Robert Lang as a proper person for that office. Dr Wilson, Mr Miller, Mr

Young and Mr Hamilton are appointed a Committee to consider everything relative to the College Garden previous to an election and to report. And this day fortnight is appointed for the Election, at 12 o'clock noon'.[10] At this same meeting, another committee was formed 'to consider the state of Mr Hamilton's class rooms and report' (the necessary repairs were to come to £61/18/4d).[11] The Faculty meeting of 12 January 1784 minuted the conditions of Lang's appointment:[12]

> Robert Lang is appointed College Gardiner during the pleasure of Faculty, the Committee formerly appointed for the inspection of the Garden are from time to time to give him such directions as may be necessary for keeping the same in proper order. The said Robert Lang during the time of his incumbency is to have a salary of Ten pounds a year to commence from Candlemas next and to have a house rent free from the term of Whitsunday next. His Business is to take care of the Physick Garden and to keep in order the College Garden by cutting the walks and rolling them, clipping the Hedges, dressing the Borders etc. The said Gardiner is also to have the grass of the College Garden for which he is to pay Ten Pounds yearly as rent. And it is hereby declared that he is not to subset any part of the College Garden for the use of Grass nor to labour any part thereof, the borders excepted, without the express permission of the Faculty. And it is further declared that the Piece of Ground at the bottom of the Garden, and cut off from the same by a Hedge, does not fall under the possession of the Gardiner.

The differences between Lang's conditions of employment and those of Adams of 22 years before include the rent-free house for Lang. Adams had to pay rent, Mrs Adams being allowed to retain possession of the house until Whitsunday 1784. The time of her dispossession roughly coincides with the Faculty allowance to her of £5 for 'being in great distress' (p. 182). Lang was to be paid a salary of £10. Adams was allowed the same sum for the upkeep of the Great Garden, and any profits made from the grass sales were his. Lang was required to pay £10 annually to the College for the grass of the garden. In fact, the Faculty account of the conditions of Lang's appointment is incomplete. A precept of 24 May 1785[13] is for 'Robert Lang Keeper of the Physick Garden Six Pounds Sterling his salary for keeping that Garden from Candlemas 1784 to Candlemas 1785'. As with Adams, the £6 annual salary for the Physic Garden remained unchanged. The principal gain by Lang over Adams was to have the house rent-free. It is not clear whether Lang himself was to be responsible for mowing and rolling the walks and clipping and dressing the hedges. The hedged ground at the bottom of the garden excluded from Lang's use included the area of private walks, trees and shrubs laid down under Adams's supervision.

Within a few weeks of his appointment, Lang presented an account for 'utensils absolute necessary for the Physick Garden':[14]

To 1 Spead	£ — . 4 . —
1 Syth and Mounting	— . 4 . —
1 Syth Stone	— . 0 . 3
1 Reel and Line	— . 3 . —
1 Dutch howe and handle	—. 2 . —
1 Large hand do	— . 1 . 6
1 small do	— . 1 . —
1 Wattring Can	— . 3 . 6
1 Wheel Barrow	— . 12 . 6
1 Grap	— . 2 . 6
1 Weeding Iron	— . — . 8
1 Large Iron Rake	— . 3 . —
1 small do	— . 2 . —

£1 . 19 . 11

The above utensils are necessary   Wm Hamilton

The 'Grap' (also 'Graip') describes an iron pronged fork, a term still used at the present day. Whilst the utensils are normal requirements, we once again see the responsible Professor countersigning the order, a procedure last practised in the early years of the century during the time of Thomas Brisbane. The above account was not settled by the College until 23 June 1785.

In November 1784, Hamilton recommended to Faculty that '40 cartloads of dung' be ordered for the Physic Garden.[15] This was delivered on 13 December, as shown by the relevant precept:[16]

To 40 Carts Dung @ 1/2	£2 : 6 : 8
To Wheeling out to the street 2d	6 : 8
To Cartage to the Garden 5d	16 : 8

£3 : 10 : 0

William Hamilton

Coll. Glasgow 14 Dec[br] 1784
To Mr Morthland College Factor
Pay to Robert Lang College Gardner three Pounds and ten Shillings Sterling which he has paid for Dung to the Physick Garden and take his Receipt on Stamped Paper

Will. Leechman

Lang's receipt, on stamped paper, is dated 15 December 1784, so that repayment this time was rapidly accomplished. With the surface area of the garden being about 0.7 Imperial acres, this would seem to have been a sizeable dressing and must have been a memorable event for all those in the near vicinity, even allowing for the natural 'odour levels' of their everyday existence. A further development close to the Physic Garden was permitted by Faculty, as minuted for 22 March 1785,[17] when it was agreed that an additional 'Type house' or foundry could be built beside the two already existing.

Maintenance of the walls of the College grounds was a continuing problem. The kirkyard wall on the north side of the Physic Garden came under Faculty's scrutiny in October 1786:[18]

> The Wall of the College Kirkyard where it is bound by the Physick Garden belonging to the College being ruinous, and those who have burial places upon the wall having agreed to pay half the expence of rebuilding, the Faculty upon their part likewise agree to pay the other half of the expence: and whereas the wall at present is too low upon the side of the Church Yard by means of which the Physick Garden received material hurt, the Faculty further order the said wall to be raised a foot higher than at present at the sole expence of the College, and for the same reasons they order two feet to be added to the height of a small part of the West Wall, at the head of Castlepens Close, extending about ten feet in length, at the expence of the College. According to the Estimates given in the Expence of the Preparation and Addition to the wall first mentioned is less than ten Pounds, and the expence of additions to the other walls is less than five pounds

The 'material hurt' received by the gardens can be well imagined, with the wall low enough to allow trespassers to enter and help themselves to fruit, flowers and plants. The ready acceptance by Faculty of the need for these repairs was probably a result of some effective lobbying by Hamilton.

Lang approached Faculty in April 1787 with a request for compensation for land he had lost owing to some improvements in the Great Garden. The inevitable committee was appointed and reported back at the meeting on 5 June 1787.[19] Lang had lost 'the Rood at the north end of the foot of the Garden' and 'all that ground along the Molendinar Burn which is now planted with young trees'. The committee proposed that Lang be compensated at £2 for each area of ground that he had lost. Faculty deferred a decision on these proposed rates until 11 June:[20]

> The meeting resumed consideration of the compensation of Mr Robert Lang College Gardener ... and agree to allow him Forty Shillings yearly for the loss he sustained by the articles reported by the Committee and likewise agree to allow him forty shillings yearly during pleasure upon account of extraordinary labour and trouble which Mr Hamilton represents the said Robert Lang must now have in attending the Botany Garden.
> The Professor of Botany having represented that it is quite necessary for rendering the botanical Garden useful that there be some fresh earth and clay carted into it and laid upon the surface and some new

Physical plants bought for it, the Faculty appoint the Garden Committee to cause the same to be done at an expence not exceeding five pounds sterling for this current year.

Faculty was prepared to allow Lang half the sum proposed by the committee in compensation for lost land, but then added another £2 for the extra work involved in the Physic Garden — again evidence of pressure by Hamilton. The requirement for fresh earth and clay to be brought into the garden was a new departure. In the following August Lang submitted an account[21] for 40 carts of earth (10/-), together with 19 days' labour by Francis Gilleanders, a bredd gardener paid at the rate of 15d per day (£1/3/9d), who helped in the general refurbishing and in spreading the soil. Payment was authorised in the following October.[22] At the Faculty meeting on 11 June 1787, Hamilton was allowed £5 to purchase 'Physical plants'. A repayment of £3/12/9d was authorised on 10 December in the same year,[23] although this bill was for plants and implements supplied much earlier in the year:[24]

Professor Hamilton for the Physic Garden
Glasgow 1787   Rd. of McAlan & Austins

Jany. 31st	To 1 Garden spade	£ — . 3 . 6
	115 Poplars 3/6 Flower Seeds 1/-	— . 3 . 10
Feby 6	Fruit Trees for the Walls	— . 6 . 3
May 3	1 Garden Line	— . 1 . 2
	Sundrie plants for ye Garden	1 . 0 . 0
7	Do.	1 . 1 . 0
June 11	Do.	— . 16 . 0
		£3 . 11 . 9

There seems to have been some error in the accounting on the part of the suppliers regarding the poplars and flower seeds sent on 31 January. The Faculty authorisation for the relevant precept gives the sum as £3/12/9d, which would suggest that 1/4d worth of seeds was obtained. The supply of 115 poplars is a puzzling feature for such a relatively small garden, unless they were really intended for the Great Garden. Once again, the lack of information on the actual seeds and plants obtained is a major loss.

On 11 March 1788,[25] Hamilton again asked for a grant of £5 to cover 'bringing in fresh earth and dung into the Botanical Garden, and also for furnishing some plants'. Most of the available money had been spent by the end of April, when Hamilton reported that Lang was owed £4/4/- 'for bringing in fresh earth, lime and dung into the Physick Garden, and also for furnishing some plants to the said Garden'.[26] Of this sum, only the account for lime and manure is available:[27]

Mr William Hamilton
1788   To Robert Lang
March To 4 carts of Lime shells for Botany Garden
            @ 5/-   £1 . — . —
        Paid for Carring Watter to Slackning the same
        and Turning   — . 1 . 6
        Paid a man for 2 days assistance in Wheeling
        in manure to Botany Garden   — . 2 . 4
        10 carts Dung ditto @ 1/3   — . 12 . 6
        Wheeling Do. @ 2d   — . 1 . 8
        Cartage of do. @ 5d   — . 4 . 2
                                                            _____
                                                            2 . 2 . 2
                        Received the within
                                                William Hamilton

According to Hamilton's submission to the Faculty at the end of April, £4/4/- was claimed; therefore a further £2/1/10d would have been spent on plants, but the relevant account is missing. Most of the remaining sum allowed to Hamilton had been spent by the end of April:[28]

Apriel 6 1788
    The College to = Robert Lang
    To 3 Carts of Good Earth to Botany Garden   £0 . 3 . 6
Apriel 16 to 6 Carts of Dung to Botany Garden at 1/4 per
    cart at dunghill whilling to street 2d per
    cart Cartage 4 per cart   0 . 11 . 0
                                                      _____
July 9 By Cash to 14=6 Robert Lang   0 . 14 . 6

The above account is of particular interest, being the only one available entirely in Lang's hand, all others being written out for him, although he signed all the receipts. This sum was repaid to Lang on a precept authorised by Faculty on 6 August 1788.[29]

In the summer of 1788, Hamilton managed to persuade his colleagues on Faculty that Lang was underpaid. The relevant minute is in the record of the 7 June meeting:[30]

It being represented by Mr William Hamilton that Robert Lang College Gardener has now a great deal of additional labour by the improvements now carrying on in the Botanical Garden, the Faculty agree to add to his present wages for this year Two Pounds Sterling and impower the Principal to give him a precept on the College Factor for payment of the same.

The additional £2 brought Lang's Physic Garden salary to £8, and to this must be added some additional emoluments and allowances as already mentioned. 'Sundry jobs' (unspecified) by Lang in both the Physic Garden and the Great Garden between May and November came to £3/11/10d. Hamilton was not associated with this claim, and a Faculty committee of two was appointed to examine it and report back.[31] Permission to pay the money was given on 2 January 1789.

Hamilton's efforts to improve Lang's financial status were even more successful in January 1789,[32] when the following decision was taken:

> The Meeting considering that the necessary employment for a Gardener in the Botanical Garden and in various other work in the College Garden such as cleaning, pruning and dressing young trees and taking care of pailing is much increased of late times, and that there will be full Employment now for a Gardener for every day during the whole year they judge that it will be for the interest of the College to have the present Gardiner Robert Lang to be constantly employed in the different branches of work aforementioned, and in general for keeping all the gardens and Observatory Park in proper order. Therefore the meeting did and hereby do engage the said Robert Lang for one year commencing at Martinmas last at the yearly wages of seventeen Pounds sterling and the Grass of the College Garden valued at Eight Pounds Sterling together with One Pound sterling more yearly for buying and upholding all his tools, making in all twenty six pounds sterling and they further agree to allow him to possess his present dwelling house for the said year free of charge : and it is hereby expressly declared that no accompts whatever are to be received from or paid to Robert Lang excepting for nails, pailing and other materials bought by him, by the express orders of the Gardens Committee, and that no wages will be paid to Labourers, or to other assistants employed by him unless he shall produce a written order from the Garden Committee for employing them

Lang's annual emoluments were to show a marked improvement over those of earlier years. It should be noted that not all the money from the University was to be in cash. Part of the sum was still to be dependent on Lang's annual grass sales in the town, and we know from an earlier example that such a venture could go badly awry at times (p. 138). There were, however, material gains for Lang in the new arrangement, and the rent-free house was still included. The Faculty had by now recognised the need for a full-time gardener, but with this there was a clear understanding that most of the workload was to fall on Lang's shoulders, and the hiring of extra labour would require special permission from the Gardens Committee. It should also be remembered that the Observatory Garden was now part of his responsibility, in addition to the Great Garden and the Physic Garden.

Lang's improved financial status had been made possible by the diligence of Alexander Adams in the early 1760s, the continuing support he obtained from William Hamilton, together with his own abilities.

So far in our account of the Physic Garden it has been very difficult to assess fully its role in the teaching of botany at the University over the years. There is plenty of evidence for the value placed on the garden by the members of the Faculty. William Hamilton's active interest in the garden shows that he was more involved in its management than any of his predecessors. From a number of contemporary accounts, it is also evident that he was a conscientious physician and teacher. Of all the eighteenth-century Professors of Botany and Anatomy, William Hamilton is the only one who has left a record of his lecture syllabus in Botany (Table 6.1).[33] In 1902 this invaluable record (in the form of a bound booklet) came from an unknown source into the hands of Isaac Bayley Balfour, Regius Professor of Botany in the University of Edinburgh. Balfour sent the booklet to F.O. Bower, then Regius Professor of Botany at Glasgow University. In a note appended to the letter which Balfour enclosed with the syllabus, Bower wrote 'It seems uncertain which Professor Hamilton this was', listing below the succession of Hamiltons from 1742 to 1790. Neither Bower nor Balfour had access to documents bearing the handwriting of the above. A comparison of the three hands (Fig. 6.1) confirms that the lecture syllabus was that of William Hamilton. F.O. Bower gave an outline account of this lecture syllabus in an article published in 1903,[34] on eighteenth-century Botany at Glasgow University.

The syllabus of the 58 lectures shows that Hamilton's Botany course was first and foremost a general botanical one and not heavily biased towards medical aspects. Some 48 per cent of the lectures were devoted to the classification of plants and based on the Linnaean system. Recognition of genera and species would be of value in the identification of plants of medicinal value, and it is possible that some bias would have been given to 'physical plants', at least from the point of view of demonstrations to students. Only the last lecture of the series was concerned with plants of medicinal value, especially those indigenous species which could be substituted for foreign plants. The role of demonstrations in the course can be visualised from lectures 53-6 on 'Crytogamia', viz. '... An examination of the Cryptogamia - Their parts - flowers & their genera & species from specimens'. Such demonstrations (ferns, mosses, liverworts, algae and fungi) were probably incorporated in the lectures. Since the lectures were given some 100 years after the publication of Grew's *Anatomy of Plants* (1682) and the volume of Malpighi's *Anatome Plantarum* (1671–9),[35] knowledge of the cellular structure of plants was well established.

Whilst the general botanical scope of the lectures is of interest, knowing of Hamilton's evident enthusiasm for the Physic Garden it

Table 6.1. Syllabus of lectures on Botany given by William Hamilton (as far as possible the original titles are given; some have been abbreviated for spatial reasons)

1. Introductory
2. History of Botany
3. Plants as distinct from animals and fossils
4. Anatomy of seeds
5. Structure of the Root
6. Uses[a] of the Root
7. Parts of Root
8. Uses of Bark
9. Uses of Wood
10. Trunks
11. Bark — structure of Cuticle
12. Structure of True Bark
13. Structure of Wood
14. On the Growth of Plants in Breadth
15. Growth of Plants in Length
16. Structure of Leaves
17. Examination of the effects Plants produce on air
18. The power plants have in fouling air
19. Some effects on Leaves
20. Observations on Soil: observations on manures
21. Motions of sap explained
22. Examination of the flower

23. Parts of the Flower
24. An Examination whether there are sexes in plants
25. Same subject
26. Classification: An Explanation of Linneus's Arrangement
27. Same subject
28. Same subject
29.–33. Explanation of terms from the genera
34.–43. Reducing plants to their genera
44.–46. Explanation of terms
47.–50. Reducing plants to their species
51. Different Systems of Botany
52. On Natural Arrangements
53.–56. An Examination of the Cryptogamia
57. Uses of the Knowledge of Vegetation in Gardening
58. Plants in this country capable of being substituted in medicine for foreign plants on the indigenous plants that may be used as manufactures

Note: a. 'Uses' as interpreted in the lectures were really 'functions'

would seem expedient to examine the series more closely for any indications that materials from and methods used in the garden could have been drawn into the lectures. From the outline summaries it is possible to pick out 20 lectures which included some reference to the gardening topic. At the beginning, seed germination ('causes of vegetation in seeds') was discussed. Lectures on the branching of roots and their uses (= functions) included references to root hairs ('fibres on surface') and 'some observations on the choice of soil necessary for trees'. The study of trunks (= stems) included annuals, biennials and perennials, and extensive discourses on wood dealt with the 'vessels', 'wood formed from inner bark', 'production of layers of wood — some observations on engrafting'. Lectures on the 'fluids of plants' included reference to 'water not the nourishing fluid but the vehicle',

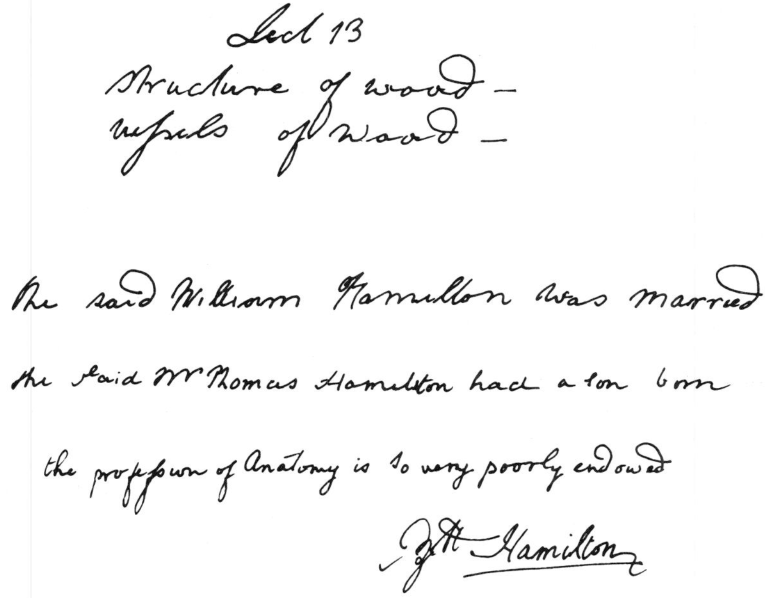

Lect 13

Structure of wood —
uses of wood —

The said William Hamilton was married

the said Mr Thomas Hamilton had a son born

the profepsion of Anatomy is so very poorly endowed

Wm Hamilton

Figure 6.1. Part of the 'Hamilton' syllabus of Botany lectures, with (below) examples of the handwritings of William Hamilton, Thomas Hamilton and Robert Hamilton

'observations on soil', 'observations on manure — do all plants live on the same nourishment — that the fluid is changed by the vessels in different parts of the plant — properties of sap — motion of sap in the vessels — motions from root upwards and from leaves downwards — Is there a circulation in plants?'. From these many topics it is possible to visualise the use of plant material and possibly associated demonstrations in the garden. Practical illustrations would surely have accompanied the three lectures on 'examination of a flower — are there sexes in plants? — observations on male plants'. Lecture 57, 'Use of knowledge of plants in gardening', is the only one specifically linked with horticulture. Physiological aspects discussed included leaf structure and 'Effects of plants on air — the power they have in making the air pure. Attempt to prove that this arises from the air being taken into the sap vessels for the nourishment of the plant, where the noxious parts are left and the air is thrown out pure'. Also included were discussions on 'the power plants have in fouling the air' and 'perspiration'. The role of plants in gaseous exchange and the participation of the leaves in the process was well known, but the process of photosynthesis remained unknown at the time.

It is especially fortunate that a complete set of notes taken from Hamilton's lectures is available.[36] These belonged to Robert Cowan, who attended Glasgow University and studied under Hamilton in 1787 and 1788. This is the same Robert Cowan mentioned earlier (p. 49) as the great-grandson of Henry Marshall, brother of John Marshall who was the first Overseer of the Physical Garden. The notes are handwritten on pages 11 × 19.5 cm, covering 137 sides; the whole set is bound and forms a personal text-book, a common practice in those days. (It was not unknown for the less scrupulous to try and publish their Professor's lecture notes, all too often without his permission.) As was also typical of the time, the notes take the form of verbatim records of Hamilton's dictated lectures. As a 'time capsule' of views on contemporary Botany as taught in Glasgow University in the late eighteenth century, the notes have a particular value. Nevertheless, for our particular purpose it is necessary to seek out that information which emphasises the likely participation of the Physic Garden in the lecture course. Whilst the notes adhere closely to the scheme of lectures outlined in Table 6.1, they do not include every item. It is not known in what year Hamilton noted down his syllabus, and he could be forgiven for varying its content on occasions. Nor can we be certain that Cowan obtained a complete record of all the lectures: it is especially to be noted that the last lecture in Hamilton's syllabus, on those indigenous plants which could be substituted for foreign ones for medical purposes, is not included in Cowan's notes — a particularly unfortunate exclusion!

The first lecture was introductory. Hamilton's opening statement was: 'The term Botany is applied to our knowledge of everything respecting plants'. (Note that the current definition in the Oxford English Dictionary is 'Botany is the science which treats of plants'.) Quite early on in the lecture the basis of a plant classification was described, with the comment that 'the Linnean system has carried the division into greatest perfection'. The discussion on the uses of plants was prefaced by the comment 'The vegetable kingdom is perhaps more necessary to our existence than any other work of nature'. Following the enumeration of the various uses of plants, the lecture continued '... Besides this they supply us with our most valuable medicine as a proof of which we need only mention Bark, Opium, Impechuana, Aloes, Jallap etc. — Nor is the store yet exhausted for every year is adding something valuable to our Materia Medica'. In this sentence we see a listing by a practising late-eighteenth-century physician of some of the sovereign remedies of the time: Bark or Peruvian Bark (*Cinchona*), the natural source of quinine, for the treatment of agues; Opium as a soporific; Impecacuana for the treatment of phlegm; and Aloes and Jalap, both purgatives. The structures and anatomy of plants was a necessary item of study, 'for this part of the course likewise underlines the affairs of life. For the principles of gardening depend on it, by examining a plant we often know what soil is best for it. Thus with regard to trees according as the roots creep along the surface or shoot deep into the soil we know whether they require shallow or deep soil &

also what distance from each other they should be planted'. Books recommended for reading by the students included Grew's *Anatomy of Plants*, and reference was made to Malpighi's volumes. Attention was also drawn to the publications of du Hamel (H.L. du Hamel due Monceau) and to Stephen Hales, whose *Vegetable Staticks* had also been much valued by William Cullen when teaching Botany at Glasgow in the 1740s. The works of Joseph Priestley and Jan Ingen-Housz were also commended. Linnaeus's *Philosophia Botanica Genera Plantarum* were regarded as fundamental for the lectures on plants classification.

Hamilton's lecture on the history of botany placed emphasis on the close link with medicine, viz. 'The Botany of the Ancients ... was chiefly what now goes by the name of Materia Medica & hence the history of Botany & medicine is nearly the same. Botany in this sense is as ancient as medicine'. The 'Botany of the Ancients' listed the numbers of plants described by Hippocrates, Theophrastus and Dioscorides, all concerned with Materia Medica. The institution of a 'Botanical professor and garden at Padua in 1540' was regarded as a major 'step towards improvement' in botany. A lengthy list of botanists which followed shows one notable exclusion. Although a reference was made to the flora of the Leiden Physic Garden, Boerhaave's name is not mentioned. The views of Charles Alston, King's Botanist and Professor of Botany at Edinburgh from 1738 to 1760, on the 'nourishment of plants and animals' were included in the lecture on the differences between plants, animals and fossils.

In the lecture on seeds and germination there is evidence from Cowan's notes that some practical work was involved, e.g. '... We will examine the seed of the Bean macerated in water which is convenient for its size'. The 'parts of the young plant' were the 'Radical ... that forms the root', and 'The Plume ... when examined by a Microscope is found whenever this the appearance of stems and leaves tho' very small'. The significance of uptake of water by the seed through 'a small hole' prior to germination was described, with an experiment to demonstrate that the exclusion of water would prevent seed germination. The need for air was emphasised by quoting the failure of seeds planted too deeply in the earth or if kept in 'an exhausted receiver of an air pump'. The development of roots from the 'Radical' was described, and that a root when growing '... uniformly goes down into the earth as is proved by different experiments. This does not arise from the earth being the source of nourishment for the nourished from above it takes the same direction'. This last sentence, although inaccurately written down, hints at the geotropic curvature of roots. Hamilton distinguished between 'spindle roots' which 'strike directly down into the earth and send off no branches for a long time' and 'Creeping roots which send off a number of branches & spreading along the surface of the ground ... According as plants have one or other of these Roots they ought to be placed at a greater or less distance and in a deeper or shallower soil.' The 'Villi' (the small lateral roots) '...

increase the quantity of surface to which nourishment is supplied ... The number of Villi differ according to the nature of the soil. They are less numerous in Barren than in a rich soil ... The Root absorbs water which however is only the medium in which other substances more nourishing are dissolved conveyed to the plant ... Their true nourishment seems to be putrid animal and vegetable matter ... A soil formed of animal & vegetable substances is best for growth of plants — and after plants have been raised for some time in such a place as this the soil is exhausted and they do not grow well'. Many of the points discussed could have been subject to demonstrations in the garden, or of material supplied from it. In the same way demonstrations of rooted cuttings could have been used for '... A slip of any plant being put into the ground, one end of it becomes the root and the other the stem'. The process of 'layering' (though not called as such) was described for the propagation of willows.

The lectures on the internal cellular structure of roots and stems were comprehensive. There was much speculation on the origins of the annual growth rings in plant stems ('trunks') — the 'measuring' of trunks after the felling of trees in the College Garden will be remembered from the previous chapter. The role of the 'inner bark' in wood formation was described. The term 'cambium' is not used, although it was originally coined by Grew, who recognised the function of the 'slimy' layer between the wood and the bark; he never saw its cellular structure, his microscope not being good enough. Proof that the wood was formed from the 'inner bark' was offered by describing some 'remarkable experiments'. In one, a sheet of lead was introduced between the wood and the bark of a tree branch by means of a longitudinal incision in the bark, which was then resealed with tar. After several years it was found that the lead sheet had become enclosed by layers of wood formed on its outer surface, with the layers of new wood of the same thickness as those formed elsewhere in the branch during the period of experiment. Hamilton's point was that if new wood had been formed from that already present the lead sheet would have remained between the bark and the outermost wood layer. Another experiment described had been carried out 'In the Botany Garden at Edin^r'. Part of a branch had been split longitudinally and as much as possible of the wood removed without damaging the bark. The bark had then been closed and sealed with pitch. After several years it was found that this region of bark had produced new wood. Whilst these were experiments carried out elsewhere, mention that annual growth rings were observable in thin stem sections rather implies that Hamilton's students may have carried out some practical work. The significance of spring and autumn wood formation was also recognised in the lectures. In his account of longitudinal growths of the stem, Hamilton again placed much emphasis on the essential role of the 'inner bark'; apical growing points were not mentioned. In his concluding sentence to the lectures on plant growth, Hamilton had dictated:

From what has been said it is evident that the bark alone induces more to vegtation than any other part of the plant so far as discoveries have yet been made

In the lecture on leaf structure, Cowan's notes contain references to the 'parenchymatous substance' (mesophyll cells) and 'spindular fibres containing sap and air vessels'. The 'air vessels' (also mentioned in describing the cell structure of the stem) were the large xylem vessels, which were assumed to play a role in the internal conduction of air and also in gaseous exchange by the plants. This feature of gaseous exchange was given pride of place in discussing the uses (functions) of leaves:

> The drawing in the air with its effluvia in an impure state & throwing it out in a pure state devoid of animal and vegetable principles & the phlogiston with which it is impregnated

Here Hamilton was drawing on the earlier work by Stephen Hales and Joseph Priestley. It was the latter who discovered the release of oxygen by plant leaves in sunlight. The reference to phlogiston is a reminder that in the later 1780s this supposed component of the combustion process, first described by Georg Ernst Stahl in the early years of the century, was still regarded as a genuine fact. Any substance on combustion released this 'inflammable principle' or phlogiston. Priestley, on observing that the 'air' produced by green plants in sunlight (and that produced by the decomposition of some metallic oxides) supported vigorous combustion, called the gas 'dephlogisticated air' — air lacking phlogiston, which was why it allowed materials to burn so vigorously. Antoine Laurent Lavoisier's refutations of this obsolete interpretation of combustion were not published until 1787, the year in which Cowan attended Hamilton's lectures; the name oxygen dates from about the same time. Hamilton drew an analogy between this gaseous exchange in leaves and respiration in animals:

> Respiration in Animals being allowed to induce greatly to that heat observable in them when they respire. Some like manner this similar property of the leaves is said to produce the equal heat which exists in them summer & winter — The heat of trees thus never descending below the freezing point in winter not rising much higher in the summer. Hence the reason why a country covered with trees is cool in summer and warm in winter

The reasoning here is rather obscure, unless he was referring to tropical areas. If based on local situations, no account seems to have been taken of leaf fall. The leaves were also responsible for the discharge of 'noxious substances', so ridding the plant of 'all injurious and malignant particles'. A point of horticultural significance was then made: 'Hence the reason why some plants growing under the cover of trees decay whilst others flourish in the same place'. Here Hamilton seems to be describing allelopathic interactions between plants, a phenomenon not unknown to gardeners. The ability of some leaves to discharge water (guttation) was discussed, along with the suggestion that such leaves could equally well absorb water when necessary. Leaves were also able to 'perspire' (transpire) and Hamilton here made reference to a well-known experiment, viz., 'Mr Hales found that the Sunflower perspires nearly $2/3$ of its weight in a day'. The link between water-vapour loss from the leaves and the entry of water 'with nutritive particles' into the roots was fully appreciated, as was the fact that 'perspiration' was greatest in June and less in July and August. The tendency for plants to 'foul the air' at night with 'impure vapour' was linked with the 'perspiration' process, and the following intriguing sentence regarding such nightly emissions was duly noted down by Cowan:

This is the reason why people exposed to the noxious air of vegetables by sleeping out at night contract many dangerous diseases

The lectures then turned to light absorption by leaves, which 'seems necessary for plants for the preservation of the colour of their leaves. Plants excluded from the light are white instead of green'. Whilst the causes of etiolation were appreciated, the role of the 'green colour' was essentially regarded as providing the plant with its natural appearance, although it was also suggested that the leaves, by virtue of their colour, helped to shade the plants. The ability of plants to orientate themselves towards light was also described, and, regarding etiolation, 'A common tansy has been found growing in the bottom of a coal pit & so changed that it could not be known. It had broad leaves instead of narrow ones & was likewise different in its lustre & colour from common'. Many of the features described in these lectures lend themselves to practical demonstrations. We may wonder whether Hamilton made use of suitable garden material to emphasise the points in his lectures.

Particular attention seems to have been paid to the condition of the soil and plant growth. Water and air were regarded as 'two proper vehicles for the nourishment of plants'. Hamilton referred to some authorities who considered that water alone was sufficient, and that 'a plant placed in mere sand grows by the application of water'. With this he disagreed: 'But it would appear that putrid animal and vegetable substances is necessary otherwise the soil would never run out while it had plenty of water. A plant that grows in water deprives it of its putrefactive tendency from which it is plain that the plant did not subsist on water alone but having heterogenous particles mixt with it when it could reduce it to such pure state as to render it incapable of putrefaction'. We can appreciate the likely level of organic impurities in natural waters of that time. Hamilton's view was that such substances would be removed by the action of the plants for their nourishment and hence the water would be purified. The point was also made that distilled water would not so effectively support plant growth. The notes continue: 'Dung is made up of animal and vegetable substances. It continues to promote the growth of vegetables longer or shorter according to the particular degree of putrefaction it has undergone. Salt is another kind of manure. It does not seem to be proper for weak ground being little able to promote vegetation in itself as for strong ground containing a quantity of animal and vegetable substances unputrified. The salt promotes their putrefaction & consequently vegetation. Lime water is another kind of manure. It absorbs water in clay soil. It conduces to disunite the cohesion of the particles & allow the root of the plant to spread for nourishment — The burning of lime is of no use but that of rendering it to powder for when it lies on the ground for some time it becomes mild and in the state of Limp lime'. Hamilton clearly appreciated the use of lime for improving a clayey soil, and had the explanation right in terms of the improved working of a more friable soil after its application, so allowing better root growth. This keen interest in the soil and its conditioning is also borne out by Hamilton's concern for the soil of the Physic Garden: it will be recalled that one of his first contributions to its management was to order 40 cartloads of manure, and that all through his years of supervision he made frequent applications to Faculty for the purchase of manure, lime and fresh soil.

From the nature and treatment of soils there is a natural progression in the notes to 'the juices by which plants are nourished ... Some juices are however very injurious to one set of plants but promote the growth of others owing to the different structure of their parts'. Plants showed different response to light and heat. 'It is remarked that at the bottom of a mountain wheat grows best — oats higher up & above this, Heaths and Heather & still above this other kinds such as lichens'. An interesting experiment was described which purported to show that when camphor was introduced into plants 'The Roots smelled of it more than the upper bark, but it was impossible to make the flowers smell of it'. This was regarded as proof that water 'taken in by the roots is changed by the different vessels in the plant & not by the root & by the fruit and flowers more than by any other part of it'. No authority is quoted for the remarkable camphor experiment. Proof that 'sap ascends in the wood and descends in the bark' was also provided from an experimental source. 'If the bark of a plant is raised from the wood and divided it is plain that if the sap ascends in the wood and descends in the bark the under part will decay & the upper part will flourish which is found to be the case'. This seems to describe a 'bark-ringing' experiment, which could have been demonstrated with plants in the Physic Garden. Further proof that sap circulation was genuine was claimed from another experimental demonstration: '... let a tree that is planted between two others be unconnected with the earth but its branches folded over and incorporated with those of the other two in such a manner that it can receive no nourishment but from the other two in a retrograde direction. It will be found to flourish which is not the case if it did not receive the sap in a retrograde way from the other two'. The experiment so described seems to owe more to the imagination than to practical experience.

The part of the course devoted to plant classification was preceded by a discussion on the parts of a flower, or 'the fructification'. In this Hamilton first enumerated the various parts of the flower.

I Calyx 'The impalement of the flower cup ... a continuation of the cortex or outer bark ... It is generally of the same colour as the stalk'

II Corolla 'Foliation ... This is the termination of the Liber or Inner Bark ... It differs generally from the Calyx in colour — this is supposed to depend on the action of light'. Hamilton then went on to describe the arrangements of the 'leaves called Petals', whether they were a fused tubular structure and so monopetalous, or whether free from one another and polypetalous. Attention was drawn to the frequent presence of a 'Nectarium'.

III Stamina 'the male part of the flower ... each stamen consists of two parts

1 The Filament which supports the Anthera 2. The Anthera ... which is the essential part & contains the Pollen ... a form of Meal or Powder ... and destined for the impregnation of the Germen'.

IV Pistillum 'or female part is found in the Centre of the flower ... It consists of three parts

1 The Germen which is the rudiment of the fruit accompanying the flower and not yet arrived at maturity

2^d The Style which elevates the stigma

3^d The stigma which is the summit of the Pistillum & covered with a moisture for keeping the Pollen after the bursting of the Antherae

V The Pericarpium 'Seed vessels is the Germen mentioned above grown to maturity'. The notes then go on to enumerate, name and describe different types ('Capsule, Siliqua, Ligumen, Conceptaculum, Drupa, Pomum, Strobilus')

VI Semina 'the seeds'

VII Receptaculum 'the base that connects the six parts of the fructification'.

There is no evidence from Cowan's notes that these descriptions were accompanied by any demonstrations, yet with someone of Hamilton's stature and enthusiasm for botany it would seem likely that, with lectures given in the summer months and a nearby garden stocked with flowers, this survey of floral structure would have been accompanied by practical illustrations.

Hamilton's lecture on sexuality in plants was clearly based on his conviction that a true sexual process was involved. The pollen he recognised as being essential for 'the Propagation of the species'. He first quoted the work of Alston at Edinburgh, who earlier in the century had carried out experiments with species bearing unisexual flowers on different plants ('Hemp, Mercury [= Dog's Mercury] and Spinage are of this kind'). Alston had shown that isolated female plants of the spinach had been found to set seed. According to Cowan's notes, Hamilton had said 'Hence he concluded that there was no real existence of different sexes in plants as a contiguous and near position of male & female was not necessary in order to produce seed for vegetation'. Hamilton's counter argument was: 'In Answer to this it is supposed that these plants were hermaphrodite having both male and female parts, tho taken for one sex only'. Hamilton's explanation as quoted in Cowan's notes is not too clearly defined. It was known at the time that in the spinach staminate flowers could occasionally occur on pistillate plants. The lecture then went on to outline the ways in which pollen transport could take place: '... as the wind will disperse seeds, so this agency could also carry pollen from discharged anthers to the stigmatic surface of the pistillum ... Besides there are some insects that feed on the flower of particular plants & are constantly moving & carrying the generating particles from one flower to another, and in this manner the fruit is impregnated'. Later in the lecture he refers to the waterborne pollen of aquatic plants. Hamilton quoted the example of the Date Palm, in which 'male branches' have to be shaken over the female tree to enable fruit formation to take place. 'This experiment has been tried by a Palm Tree in the Leyden Garden with great success as it never produced fruit till a male branch was shaken over it — And when this was not done the tree was barren'. This example was underlined by an anecdote regarding Date Palms and an expedition by a Turkish army which 'cut down the male trees for some particular use, the consequence of which was that the female ones became barren and obliged the Army to drop their expedition for want of fruit to subsist on'.

For all Hamilton's convictions on sexuality in plants, he was in fact describing the key process of pollination as being essential for subsequent fruit and seed formation. To what extent he was familiar with G. Kolreuter's (1766) publications in plant sexuality, which followed the much earlier work of Camerarius published in 1694 in the obscure Transactions of the Tubingen Academy,[37] is not known. (From Hamilton's time, almost 100 years were to pass before the true nature of the fertilisation process in flowering plants was to be explained.) Hybridisation in flowering plants was also described. 'It is well known that variegated tulips can be produced by shaking the flowers of red ones about the time of their maturity on the flowers of white ones. This species can be called Mulio, being a production of two different kinds & partaking of the colour of both.' Hamilton concluded his lecture by an intriguing reference to what appears to be pollen tubes growing down a style, viz., 'A gentleman on the Continent says he observed the pollen growing down thro' certain fine ducts in the Pistillum to the Germen (with a fine microscope of his own making) in the Sunginisia which are all transparent. He sent both the Microscope and an account of his observations to London'.

Hamilton's conviction on the existence of sexuality in plants adds weight to the earlier speculation that on this part of the course there would have been demonstrations. Much the same viewpoint can be held regarding the remaining lectures, which were based entirely on the 24 Linnaean Classes,[38] in which, as he explains, 'All the Classes from the first to the 19th take their denomination from the number, proporation, situation and other circumstances of the stamina'. Hamilton was aware of the need for a 'Natural' system of plant classification and referred to this in his lectures. Cowan's notes give concise summaries of the 24 Linnaean Classes, ending with: '24th Cryptogamia this signifies concealment of marriage & includes such as conceal the flowers within the fruit or have them so small as to be imperceptible'.

Cowan's notes are the only available record of Hamilton's lectures, and indeed their content is the only known example of an eighteenth-century Botany course at Glasgow University. At the same time, John Hope, Professor of Botany at Edinburgh University, gave 65 lectures during the summer months. Lecture notes made by some of Hope's students are available for the years 1774–83.[39] There are striking similarities between the balance and contents of Hope's lectures and those of Hamilton. In both courses, about one-third of the lectures was devoted to plant anatomy and physiology. Both Professors recommended that their students read the works of Grew, Malpighi and Hales. Hope discussed sap movements at length, but was not convinced that a circulation process took place; Hamilton, after a similar lengthy discussion, came down in favour of a circulation process. Both gave up-to-date accounts (for their times) of gaseous exchange in leaves, although Hope's appears to have been more practically based. Hope gave more detailed accounts of plant movements, including accounts of his own experimental work. Both lecture courses follow similar pathways in discussing plant sexuality, although Hamilton seems to have more extensive references to pollination agencies. Hope included an account of his own experiments on rhubarb hybridisation. Finally, both sets of lectures give detailed accounts of the Linnaean system of classification. From the similarities between the two courses, we may conclude that Hamilton must have attended Hope's lectures when a student at Edinburgh University in 1778–9 before graduating MD. In fact, his father's letter of recommendation to the faculty at Glasgow regarding his son's succession to the Chair contains specific mention of his having studied Botany at Edinburgh. Both Hamilton's syllabus of lectures and

Cowan's notes have added value in illustrating the outlook of a one-time student of Hope, and of his later interpretation of how Botany should be taught. It is apparent that the main thrust of Hamilton's teaching was based on what he learned under Hope. It is all the more surprising, therefore, that, according to Cowan's notes, Hamilton made only one passing reference to his mentor, and then not regarding any significant botanical aspect despite the fact that he made references to experiments in the Edinburgh Botanic Garden. It is known that Hope included numerous demonstrations and illustrations in his courses. If Hamilton was taking full advantage of his training under Hope, it seems very likely that he would have used similar methods in supplementing his lecture discourses.

Having given due consideration to Hamilton's approaches to the teaching of Botany, we return now to discuss the final phase of his short tenure of the joint Chair. The last reference to Hamilton and the Physic Garden in the Faculty minutes is that for 10 June 1789,[40] when £2 worth of 'soil to the Botany Garden' was approved, with Hamilton and Dr Wilson appointed 'a Committee to overlook this'. The dual nature of the Professorship called for expertise in two branches of medical teaching, and from his earlier training it is clear that Hamilton would have been equally conscientious in his Anatomy course. In addition, he also lectured on Midwifery, as did his father. In partnership with James Towers (Waltonian Lecturer in Midwifery in the University from 1792 to 1815 and first Regius Professor from 1815 to 1820), Hamilton also ran an extensive consultative practice in Midwifery in the town. The outcome of many years of overwork of this nature is to be seen in the draft of a letter from Principal Davidson (undated, but from the nature of its contents and the reply to it probably written in the first week of March 1790), addressed to James Graham, third Duke of Montrose and Chancellor of the University:[41]

Mr Lord
I am extremely sorry to inform your lordship that Mr Hamilton our Professor of Anatomy is in a very dangerous state of health. As his Talents and his Virtues endeared him to the Publick at large and in a particular manner to his Colleagues, So the Event of that kind could occasion more General Concern or greater Anxiety about the filling up of his Place in the event of his Death. In this Situation I am desired and Authorized in a Conference held this day before your Lordsp our Humble and Earnest Hope is that no immediate Determination may be adopted for the Disposal of an Office of so much importance to the Society and that we may be indulged, of the Event shall render it necessary in submitting our views to your Lordship on what may be conducive to the Interests of the Medical School here.

Graham's letter (obviously, by comparison of the writing, dictated to a secretary but signed by himself) states in reply:[42]

London 16 March 1790

Sir

I have received the honour of your letter, written at the desire and by the authority of the Faculty — The University at large may depend on my not recommending hastily, the filling any Chair in the College, even when the vacancy exists — Great zeal & exertion has been made use of by the Candidates, to obtain what I have thought it my duty to withold — I shall be glad to hear from the Gentlemen of the University what they may individually think for the advantage of the Establishment, but a Government is always jealous of its Patronage. I would not recommend resolutions of the faculty on the subject —

I have the honour to be with great consideration & esteem Sir
your most obedient
humble Servant
Graham

Mr Principal

Graham's letter indicates some of the politicking behind the scenes which could accompany appointments to such 'Crown' Chairs. He would accept individual 'briefing', but regarded collective resolutions as being counterproductive. Between this exchange of letters, Hamilton died on 13 March at the early age of 32 years, as notified to the Faculty meeting on 19 March.[43] At the meeting of 1 May following, a letter was read to Faculty from 'Mr Hamiltons Trustees enclosing an Excerpt from his Settlement'.[44] This disposition and settlement was originally prepared in December 1788, and the letter disclosed that Hamilton wished to have his collection of preparations, the greenhouse in the Physic Garden, and 'all other things necessary for teaching Anatomy and Botany which shall belong to me at the time of my Death' to be valued by 'two medical gentlemen', one to be appointed by his wife and the other by the Faculty. If a mutually agreed figure was obtained, these items were to be offered for sale to the University. Failing this arrangement, the items were to be disposed of by his trustees 'in a way that may appear best to them'. Any books from his library chosen by the Principal and Professors were to be placed in the Public Library of the University. Hamilton also offered two legacies. The first was for £100, interest from which was to be for an annual prize for the 'best discourse on some subject in Anatomy'. The second of £200 was for the 'said College of Glasgow to be laid out in forming a Botanical Garden'. There were prior conditions before the two legacies became available to the College. These were that each sum would be paid to the College only 'in the event of the death of the whole of my said children before me and before marriage or majority, then if my said wife and Mother are also dead'. If all these conditions pertained at the time of his own death, all the teaching attributes previously mentioned would be given to the University without charge. The final clause was that 'these Legacies shall be paid two years after the death of me, my said Wife, Mother and Children, and no Sooner'. Faculty then decided to appoint Mr William Couper, Surgeon in Glasgow, to be their 'Valuator'.

On 26 May 1790,[45] Faculty was told the valuation agreed for Hamilton's anatomical preparations. These were valued at £200, but the greenhouse had not been assessed. Some difficulties arose here, and in June it was decided that the valuation of the garden equipment should be in the hands of a 'Tradesman'.[46] Five months later William Martin, wright and glazier, was appointed 'appreciator' by the Faculty.[47] In the following February 1791,[48] the trustees of Hamilton's estate declared their total valuation for all of Hamilton's effects to be £298. In reply the Faculty gave its valuation:

£200 for anatomical preparations and plants
£13 for surgical instruments
£15 for presses
£15 for hothouse

The total of £243 was 'the utmost length to which the College will go'. The time scale of the whole business was somewhat drawn out, largely by the protracted deliberations of Faculty, as if hoping that the longer they delayed the more likely the trustees of Hamilton's estate would come down in price. No agreement could be reached, however. The trustees then asked to be allowed to remove the several objects, including the greenhouse and plants. The Faculty agreed to the removal of the greenhouse and plants 'altho' the College thinks that in point of Law it might be considered their property'.[49] Removal was to be done carefully and without damage to the plants in the Physic Garden. According to a contemporary advertisement,[50] the sale of the greenhouse and effects was to take place in the Physic Garden, the sale to include 'the Hot-house, Hot-bed, Frame &c erected by Mr Hamilton, also a Collection of curious Exotic Plants, among which is a Banana or Bread Tree'.

Hamilton's death was a severe loss to the Glasgow medical school, and to medicine in Glasgow in general. The students held him in high regard, as stated in Latin on his memorial in the nave of Glasgow Cathedral.[51] The work of the gardens went on, as shown by the Faculty's authorisation of a precept for Robert Lang on 31 May 1790, when 17/6d was allowed for seeds and plants to the Botanic Garden.[52] The legacy for £200 for a new Physic Garden (although in fact the prior conditions were such that the money never did become available) raises again the question posed 36 years before by Robert Hamilton and William Cullen on the suitability of the site of the existing garden. The earlier Hamilton, with Cullen, had complained to the Faculty about the unsatisfactory nature of the soil, and the effects of the soot and smoke of the town on the plants. William Hamilton and Robert Lang had manured and limed the garden repeatedly over the years and frequently brought in cartloads of fresh soil, as well as purchasing seeds and 'physical plants'. Soil is a gardener's inheritance and, although being in this case of a clay nature, should after many years of cultivation have been of good tilth. An additional source of air pollution lay close to the Physic Garden. Alexander Wilson's type foundry, opened in 1762, had been expanded progressively over the years (his son carrying on the business), bringing it into closer proximity to the garden. Type-founding in the later years of the eighteenth century was a process of hand-casting involving the melting and re-melting of mixtures of lead, tin and antimony, with copper added for hardening.[53] Volatile products of such a mixture of metals would be toxic and accumulative; they could have proved harmful to plants in the near vicinity and may have affected the soil. It may be that Hamilton's frequent orders for manure, lime and soil were outward signs of an accumulating heavy-metal contamination of the soil close to the type foundry, to which a further building had been added in 1785.

With William Hamilton's death, the dynastic succession to the Chair of Botany and Anatomy came to an end. What at first sight seems to have been absolute nepotism on his appointment was in fact more than justified by the high standard of his subsequent service to the University. According to the Register kept by the University and into which the Professors entered details of their appointment, their marriage and birth of children (see Figure 6.1), William Hamilton married Elizabeth Stirling on 19 October 1783 and a daughter was born to them on 6 August 1784. A much later entry — made by his wife on 15 May 1807 — stated that a son, William Stirling, was born on 6 March 1788, and a second son, Thomas, on 4 January 1790. The survival of Hamilton's children meant that his legacy of £200 for a new Physic Garden was to remain unavailable. William Hamilton junior, later Sir William by male-line inheritance of another branch of the family, was a student first at Glasgow, then at Balliol College, Oxford, on a Snell Exhibition. He studied medicine, then became an Advocate and later Professor of Civil History at Edinburgh University (1821) and Professor of Logic and Metaphysics there in 1836. He died in 1856. Thomas Hamilton, also a student at Glasgow, was later commissioned in the Army, served in the Peninsular Campaign, and then became a writer in Edinburgh, contributing to Blackwood's Magazine. His novel *Cyril Thornton* included accounts of student life in the University and in the town in the early 1800s. The eldest child, the daughter, is known (without name) only from the Register entry.

Principal Davidson's letter to the Duke of Montrose at the time of Hamilton's last illness set in train a series of events which came to fruition on 18 May 1790,[54] when a Royal Commission was read in favour of James Jeffray as successor in the Chief of Botany and

Anatomy. Jeffray's admission to office following the reading of his trial discourse (*De Hernia Crurali* — 'On Hernia of the Leg'), and all the procedural requirements (as described for William Hamilton) having been fulfilled, took place on 18 May 1790.[55] With Jeffray's appointment we enter another phase in the history of the Physic Garden and Botany in the University, and this warrants separate consideration. William Hamilton's busy life, with all its commitments to the Physic Garden and Botany, left him no time for the management of the other garden in the University's possession. Robert Lang, with the active support of Hamilton, had been made responsible for all facets of the University's gardens. In the next chapter we explore this larger aspect of Lang's work.

Notes

1. FM, 13 February 1781: 26692, pp. 68–9.

2. A. Duncan, 1896. *Memorials of the Faculty of Physicians and Surgeons of Glasgow* (John Maclehose & Sons, Glasgow), p. 262.

3. FM, 20 February 1781: 26692, p. 72.

4. FM, 6 April 1781: 26692, p. 83.

5. FM, 9 June 1783: 26692, p. 291.

6. FM, 6 April 1781: 26692, p. 85.

7. FM, 11 June 1781: 26692, p. 119.

8. GUAA 58280.

9. FM, 10 May 1781: 26692, p. 104.

10. FM, 22 December 1783: 26692, p. 318.

11. FM, 20 May 1784: 26692, p. 358.

12. 12 January 1784: 26692, pp. 323–4.

13. GUAA 58213.

14. GUAA 58243.

15. FM, 29 November 1784: 26693, p. 21.

16. GUAA 58262.

17. FM, 22 March 1785: 26693, p. 47.

18. FM, 26 October 1786: 26693, p. 162.

19. FM, 5 June 1787: 26693, p. 241.

20. FM, 11 June 1787: 26693, p. 248.

21. GUAA 58303.

22. FM, 30 October 1787: 26693, p. 262.

23. FM, 10 December 1787: 26693, p. 269.

24. GUAA 58303.

25. FM, 11 March 1788: 26693, p. 290.

26. FM, 30 April 1788: 26693, p. 297.

27. GUAA 58303.

28. GUAA 58304.

29. FM, 6 August 1788: 26693, p. 341.

30. FM, 7 June 1788: 26693, p. 308.

31. FM, 26 December 1788: 26693, p. 365.

32. FM, 8 January 1789: 26693, p. 368.

33. Syllabus of lectures in Botany by Professor Hamilton, Glasgow (In the Archival Collection of the Department of Botany, University of Glasgow).

34. F.O. Bower, 1903. Notes on Botany in the University of Glasgow in the 18th century. *Transactions of the Natural History Society of Glasgow*, vol. 45, pp. 43–62.

35. A.G. Morton, 1981. *History of Botanical Science* (Academic Press, London), chapter 6 ('A Chart for the Future'), pp. 165–231.

36. This bound set of handwritten notes is in the Archival Collection of the Department of Botany, University of Glasgow. The booklet was presented to the Department in 1935 by John Cowan, great-grandson of Robert Cowan.

37. A.G. Morton, 1981. *History of Botanical Science*, chapter 6, pp. 165–231; chapter 7 ('Camerarius to Linnaeus'), pp. 232–86.

38. These 24 Classes in Cowan's notes are exactly as described by W.E. Stearn in 'Linnaean classification, Nomenclature and Method', in W. Blunt, 1971. *The Compleat Naturalist. A Life of Linnaeus* (Collins, London), p. 244 (appendix).

39. A.G. Morton, 1986. *John Hope 1725–1786 Scottish Botanist* (Edinburgh Botanic Garden (Sibbald) Trust), pp. 21–4.

40. FM, 10 June, 1789: 26694, p. 15.

41. GUAA 58359.

42. GUAA 58359.

43. FM, 19 March, 1790: 26694, p. 50.

44. FM, 1 May 1790: 26694, p. 58.

45. FM, 26 May 1790: 26694, p. 67.

46. FM, 10 June, 1790: 26694, p. 78.

47. FM, 22 October 1790: 26694, p. 86–7.

48. FM, 28 February 1791: 26694, pp. 121–2.

49. FM, 2 March 1791: 26694, pp. 123–4.

50. D. Murray, 1925. *Memories of the Old College of Glasgow* (Jackson, Wylie & Co., Glasgow), p. 177.

51. D. Murray, 1925. Ibid., p. 176.

52. FM, 31 May 1790: 26694, p. 69.

53. I am grateful to Mr R.G. Steele of the Glasgow College of Building and Printing for this information on eighteenth-century type-founding methods.

54. FM, 18 May 1790: 26694, p. 65.

55. FM, 18 May 1790: 26694, p. 66.

'A COMMITTEE TO ENQUIRE INTO THE STATE OF THE GARDEN ...'

John Stirling, Principal from 1701 to 1727, has been described as 'masterful'; Archibald Davidson, who followed William Leechman as Principal in 1785, might well be called the 'committee man'. Faculty meetings under his chairmanship were characterised by the prodigious formation of committees to deal with almost all Faculty business, no matter how trivial. Of the Professors it might be said that when two or three were gathered together they formed a committee. Any committee formation regarding the gardens is recorded in the Faculty minutes in terms similar to the title of this chapter. Whilst the gardener Robert Lang's name appears as frequently in the Faculty records as that of his predecessor Alexander Adams, almost every aspect of Lang's work in the gardens (with the exception of the Physic Garden) came under the scrutiny of a specially appointed committee, usually of three or four Professors. William Hamilton was rarely a member and the difference with Adams's time is that there were then longer-serving Gardens Committees which generally supervised his (Adams's) management, enabling a more effective continuity of control. Through the 1780s there were changes in the names of the various gardens which gradually became standard in official records. The Great Garden became known as the College Garden. The Dovehill title gradually fell into disuse, to be replaced by Observatory Garden and Observatory Park. The Observatory Garden was an area of the Dovehill immediately to the east of the Molendinar Burn and facing the College Garden. The initial stages of its development had been supervised by Alexander Adams. Three aspects of Lang's work are considered in this chapter: his role in maintaining the College and Observatory Gardens; his collaboration with James Jeffray in cultivating the Physic Garden; and his activities as tacksman in the College grounds.

One of the conditions of employment laid down for Lang in January 1784 was that he was to be responsible for the upkeep of the College

Garden, for which he could not make any extra charge to Faculty, as well as being responsible for the Physic Garden. Any work carried out by him, or done under his supervision, in either the Observatory Garden or the Park, could be charged. In the summer of 1785 Lang submitted a bill for two years of such work,[1] and his accounts follow much the same pattern as those of Alexander Adams, with claims for the costs of 'clipping, digging, howing the Hedge around the Observatory House' (March 1784); 'cleaning the gravel about the house two times', 'clipping and digging the Hedge on the South side of the Observatory Ground', '4 Carts dung for said Hedge and Cartage' (all in August 1784). In December of the same year, and again in April 1785, these same hedges needed clipping and digging. Also in December 1784, the 'Hedge on the Burnside oppsite the Tanwork' needed clipping and the trees there required 'prunning'. This is the same Tanwork whose dam caused serious flooding of the gardens in the winter of 1772, and whose proprietors came into legal conflict with Faculty in February and March 1772. The trees and the hedge formed part of the angle-foot plantation developed by Alexander Adams. The care of the hedges around the Observatory, and the weeding of the gravel around the Observatory and of the walk leading to it from the bridge over the Molendinar Burn, became regular annual chores; accounts and precepts are available for the years 1784-90. In August 1786, £4 was paid to workmen supervised by Lang for 'Cleaning the Burn of rubbish left by the flood'.[2] The flooding had taken place at the beginning of the previous May and was discussed at the 3 May meeting of Faculty.[3] A wall had been 'recently thrown down by the flood at the foot of the College Garden'. An earlier meeting in April had received a report that the flooding of the garden and the destruction of the wall was 'by the bursting of the Monkland Canal'.[4] The canal, opened in 1790, lay north of the town and must have had some connection with the Molendinar Burn. The report to Faculty suggests that some breakage of its banks had occurred during construction. The inevitable committee formed to inspect the damage and reported back that it would not be worthwhile to rebuild the existing old wall owing to the 'ruinous state of part of it still standing'.[5] Better to remove it and build a new wall, for which the mason Matthew Cleland presented an estimate of £75/15/-. The same meeting decided that an iron gate should be placed on the bridge over the burn.

The rubbish-clearing supervised by Lang followed the rebuilding of the wall in the early summer months, and included some of the old wall 'thrown down'. Lang then had to supervise men 'putting the turf on the top of the wall'. In early July 1786 a trench was dug 'on the top of the Observatory bridge to plant stobs in and filling it up again'. Hence the bridge was surfaced with earth and clay and required fencing. On 15 August 1786 a workman was paid £2 for 'Cutting the Walks in the Observatory Park'; an identical operation in October 1787 cost the same.[6] In November 1786, a 'committee for garden improvement' advised that the banks of the burn should be strengthened;[7] Lang supervised this work (costing £12) in the spring of 1787. A Faculty decision of early May 1787 stated that 'Many of the walls belonging to the College thereof are in great disrepair' and John McLachland, Master of Work, was to employ tradesmen to 'repair properly and particularly to see that they are all pointed and capped'.[8] This necessary repair work cost £20 and was completed by the beginning of June,[9] after which men were paid for 'cleaning the walks and Borders of Rubidge left by the Masons after Casting the Garden wall'.[10] The walks and borders were in the College garden. Advantage was taken of a 'windfall' left by the masons when workmen were paid for 'Wheeling in lime left at the outsides of the Garden wall and putting the same in a heep in the Garden'. At the same time, work was carried out 'laying a stone in the threshold of the Grass door of the College Garden to prevent the watter from getting in thereat, also Removing the stibs placed at the Loe end of the Garden Walk to prevent people treading on the new Soan Walk'. The burn required cleaning out again in August 1787.

It will be remembered that in 1757 there was a proposal to create a gravel walk in the College Garden, a proposal fiercely opposed by Professor Robert Simson (p. 149). On 26 October 1786, the Faculty instituted a committee of four 'to consider the Propriety of Gravelling a part of the Upper Walk in the College Garden of about fifteen feet in breadth and to report the Estimate of Expence — and likewise the propriety of planting some small parts of the College Garden'.[11] In early November this committee reported back and '... considered the gravel walk to be highly convenient'.[12] Lang's estimate of £25/12/- was ordered to 'lie upon the Table to be considered at some future date'. One month later the estimate was accepted and the gravelling of the Upper Walk was 'immediately to be carried out'[13] (the Upper Walk = New Vennel Walk of p. 107). The details of the project are recorded in a precept of Lang's of 12 December 1786:[14]

College 12 Dec. 1786

The College Dr

To Robert Lang

For digging a walk 286 yds long & 15 feet wide, carting gravel, laying it on 6 inches thick & finishing the whole agreeable to his estimate £25/12/-

Lang's receipt is dated 14 December and the whole operation had occupied about four days. Whilst this gravel walk was popular with the Professors, Lang may well have had reservations. On 28 June 1785,[15] he reported the costs of 'Picking the Grass off the Gravel Walk in the College Green', an operation which was also necessary on 20 July, 12 August and 2 October. 'Cleaning the burn' was again listed in his accounts for 28 August, and 'Cutting the walks in the Observatory Park four times all round and up the middle and Rolling them' on 2 October. On 2 May 1788[16] this round of jobs started again, viz. 'To Cutting the Edges and Picking the weeds of the Gravel walk in the College Garden', and was repeated on 15 June, 5 July, 3 August, 25 August and 3 October. The cost ranged from 2/- to 3/6d for each weeding and probably involved three to four days' work for one man on each occasion. Weeding and tidying up this gravel path was to become a regular annual maintenance exercise.

The purchases of replacement trees were a regular feature of the accounts of Alexander Adams. Lang had to put in an order for tree replacements in the College Garden in the spring following his appointment:[17]

Glasgow 12 Apr 1784

Robt. Lang Bot of William Cowan for the Coleg garden

1784		
April 12	12 Larg Lime 6 feet high @ 5d	£"-5- "
	1 Larg Larch for /1d 10 Larg Spruce	"-"-11
	30 Ash, Plain & Elms	"-1-"2
1785		
March 26	12 Lime trees @ /4 Each	"-4- "
Apr 12	12 More Lime Trees @ /4	"-4- "

Comparison of the prices rather suggests that Lang was buying older trees than those bought by Adams. There are no indications as to where these trees were placed, but the limes and elms were usually required for lining the walks.

In early December 1785, a Faculty committee of five was instituted 'to consider the best methods for improving and disposing of the College Garden, the park around the Observatory, and to lay their views before Faculty as soon as possible'.[18] Usually such an overall review would have included the gardener, although Lang is not mentioned in the minute. The committee duly reported their recommendations on 22 December.[19] They proposed that '½ of sd Park should be immediately laboured and kept in grain for 3 years and in the course of the 3rd year should be sown with grass seeds. After this the other ½ should be managed in the same manner'. With the College Garden the proposal was that a quarter of it 'after another, should be successively treated in the same manner with the Park above'. (To be 'laboured' meant ploughing, harrowing, etc.) Alternatively, it should be 'well trenched and dunged for a year and laid down with barley and grass seeds'. The decision was to follow the second alternative, and a week later the committee informed Faculty that this would require '50 carts of Dung, 6 Carts of lime shells £6 to manure ¼ of garden with trenching three feet and shovelling'.[20] These estimates of the work involved give an impression that someone with the necessary practical experience was consulted; this was probably Lang. The same committee was charged with overseeing the proposed improvements, and on 7 February authorisation was given for the southern half of the Observatory Park to be ploughed and 20 carts of dung to be applied per acre, '. . . and it shall continue in culture for two years longer, in order to be laid down with grass in the third crop'.

The overall rotation plan was clearly intended to improve the quality of the soil. The use of barley for this purpose (which carried the additional bonus that the grain could be sold for making whisky) followed agricultural procedure of the time. Edward Lisle's *Observations on Husbandry* (1757)[21] includes a pertinent descriptive account:

> Farmer Biggs of Hampshire tells me, he sows much of the rath-ripe ['rath' = rathe, or fast] barley, that he sows it on clay-ground, because the fault of that land is that its corn will be late ripe, which is mended by the barley . . .

Growing barley was regarded as a means of improving a clay soil and it is by now well known that the College land was clayey.

Despite the recommendations and their approval by Faculty, it is uncertain whether all the proposed work was carried out at the time. A precept in Lang's name for 18 April 1786 covers a sizeable order for manure:[22]

Glasgow 5th April 1786

Dr. The College of Glasgow
To the following persons viz.

Archibald M'Queen for 6 carts Dung @ ½ per cart		£—. 7.—
John Wotherspoon	25 Do.	1. 9. 2
John Blair	6 Do.	—. 7.—
William Robertson	7 Do.	—. 8. 2
Andrew Wotherspoon	8 Do.	—. 8. 0
James Russell	21 Do.	1. 4. 8
William Rusell	18 Do.	1. 1.—
To driving 96 carts 5d per cart		2.—.—
To wheeling		—.9.—
To 3 men and 2 horses driving the dung on the park		1.—.—
To 1 day of one man and a horse		-. 4. 6

Whilst allowing for some imbalance in the accounting (e.g. eight cartloads at 1/2d priced at 8/- and 91 cartloads in total becoming 96 in the summing), this represents a sizeable dressing for part of the Observatory Park. It is also unusual to see all the individual suppliers listed, and the labour of spreading is not mentioned. There are no further available records of 'labouring' the Observatory Park in preparation for sowing with barley. In April 1788, Lang presented an account which included the entry 'To Plowing and Harrowing 3 Rood of Ground in the Observatory Park £-.12.-; To Levelling and Reaking the furrows thereof -.4.-'.[23]. In old Scots measure 3 roods = 108 square ells, or about 115 square yards, which was unlikely to represent 'half of the park' that was to be 'laboured' as advised by the committee. If the College Garden had been trenched, dunged and sown with barley, then Lang's salary would have been affected; the grass of the garden was to be regarded as part of his annual emoluments (p. 187). Had any of this allowance been lost owing to labouring the College garden, then Lang would have claimed compensation from the Faculty. It seems likely that the committee's recommendations were not put fully into practice immediately. In June 1787, Lang made a claim for compensation of part of the rent due to loss of land in the College Garden, viz., 'the Rood at the north end of the foot of the Garden' and 'all that ground by the Molendinar Burn which is now planted with young trees'. The origin of this claim lies in a Faculty minute of 7 November 1786:[24]

> The Committee appointed at the last meeting to consider the Propriety of planting some parts of the College Garden reported that they had looked at the ground proper to be planted: and the meeting empower the Committee to carry out the said planting at an expence not exceeding ten pounds

This move was carried further on 13 February 1787,[25] when consideration was given to an estimate by Lang '... for enclosing with stobs about 236 yards in length of ground at the foot of the garden for planting some amounts to £17/6/6d'. The estimate was ordered to 'lie on the table' and was then accepted on 7 March 1787.[26] Lang's estimate is dated 13 February 1787:[27]

> The Estimation and Representation of Robert Lang Sheweth
> That there is about Two Hundred and Thirty Six Yards of Length of Ground that may be inclosed Two Hundred yards of which must be enclosed to preserve the intended young Planting from being destroyed the Expence thereof as under viz.
> Each yard will require at least Six stobs to make it so close that the Students etc. may not get through to hurt the planting, each stob to be at least Six foot long, which will take One hundred dozen of Stobs at 1/10d per dozen is £9.3.4 to plant the thickest end of the Stobs into the Ground & the sharp point uppermost will make it more fencable & durable which must also be raftered on both sides on the top and will take 12½ dozen Rafters which will cost 2/- per dozen Amounting to 1.5.0
> Each stob will require two nails which will take about Twenty Six Hundred which at 7d per hundred comes to 0.15.2

The Cartage from the Broomalaw of ten draught at 1/- per draught is 0.10.0

To Workmanship 1.5.0

The enclosure will take about Eight Hundred Plants which he thinks should be of the following kinds viz

Ash, Elm, Laburnum, Limes, Roan trees, Oaks, Weeping birch, Poplars, Tamahauk trees, Birch, Larach Fir, Plane trees or any other kinds that may be thought proper good Plants will cost at 12/- per hundred

which amounts to	4.16.0
To Planting ditto	0.12.0
	£17. 6.6

The tree plantings envisaged in Lang's estimate are mainly decorative. Whilst the 'Larach Fir' is the Larch, 'Tamahauk trees' probably mean the Tamarack or American Larch (*Larix lacinia*). These proposed plantings and the dense wood fencing to keep out the students suggest that this enclosure at the foot of the College Garden would have been on the burnside opposite the Observatory Garden and was a further development of the 'private walks' laid out by Alexander Adams in the 1770s. Lang's claim for compensation in June 1787 was for ground lost alongside the burn 'now planted with young trees'. In October of the same year, the Faculty permitted some more tree-planting 'to the sum of nine pounds additional to that already paid out'.[28] A bill for trees supplied by a John Wilson was presented by Lang in March 1788:[29]

200 Ellm Trees	3/-	£—.	6.—
100 Ash do.			2. 6
60 Larix do.			1. 6
60 Beeleh do.			1. 6
60 Horse Chestnut do.			2. 6
30 Rawn do.			2. 6
30 Laburnum do.			2. 6
90 Plain do.			3. 4
60 Lime do.			10. 0
15 Weeping Birch do.			1. 3
45 Poplar do.			3. 9
40 Oak do.			1. 0
20 Spruce fir do.			1. 0
20 Silver firr do.			1. 8
40 Scotts firr do.			6
30 Walnuts & Sweet Chestnut do.			5. 0
		£2.	6. 6

In the above, 'Beeleh' probably means 'Beeles' — young tree stocks used for grafting purposes; 'Rawn' is the Rowan. Whilst the above account was presented in March 1788, it probably describes the tree purchases made for the new plantings in the previous year (accounts from merchants were frequently sent in at the end of the year and even later). The list shows some notable departures from previous tree purchases by the University, when the emphasis tended to be on limes, elms and beeches. A number of the trees listed are relatively fast-growing, a feature much valued in landscaping at that time.[30] The list totals 900 trees, as against the 800 suggested in Lang's estimate.

Lang's conditions of employment came under regular scrutiny by the relevant committee, as shown in the preceding chapter. In December 1787, whilst a committee was deliberating on an account submitted by him for work 'about the Molendinar Burn and in the Observatory Park amounting to £5/0/-', the Faculty 'called in the Gardener and signified to him that in consideration of his work in the Old College Garden being now much diminished they required that the walks around the Observatory Park be cut and rolled four times a year without the Gardener making any charge against the College for the same to which proposal the Gardener agreed in praesentia'.[31] The reduction in the workload in the College Garden is not explained. Six months later Lang's salary was increased (p. 191), and after a further twelve months the Faculty decided to increase his salary significantly once more owing to his work in the College Garden being 'much increased' (p. 192).

With Lang's workload in the College Garden being regarded as diminished, it is surprising to find his account submitted in March 1788 for 'planting, dunging and liming parts of the College Garden under the Direction of the Committee formerly appointed to superintend that business'.[32] Lang's account shows the extent of the operation:[33]

1788
February To 39 Carts Dung including Cartage

Wheeling &c 1/9	£3. 8. 3
17 carts Lime Shells from Cathcart @ 5/-	4. 5.—
197 dozen Stobs per Acctt @ 1/- p. doz.	9.17.—
20 Rood Rafters per do. 1/8 p. rood	1.13. 4
14 Cart Load of Stobs and Rafters @ 1/- pr load	—.14.—
Spreading the Dung viz 39 Carts	—. 3.—
Cutting a Trench and Planting the Stobs putting the earth about them and removing part of the old pyling	
Double rafting and Nailing ditto	2.—.—
Slackning the 17 Carts Lime Shells Wheeling it out to the Ground and spreading ditto	—.12.—

Digging the ground deep & pointing
it again   3.10.—
Making pits and Planting trees therein   1.—.—
4000 Nails @ 5/-p.   1.—.—
1035 Trees of various kinds per Wm Cowans
Account   3. 6. 3
932 Trees of various kinds per McAslams &
Austin's Account   2.13. 9
a small Gate to go into the planting   —. 4.—

£34. 6. 7

There are no clear indications as to the part of the College grounds involved, although a clue lies in the reference to 'removing part of the old pyling' (= paling). This suggests refencing and replanting an area already enclosed but with now deteriorating 'stobs and rafters'. If so, it would probably refer to the area first laid out by Adams in the 1770s — the angle-foot plantation and the burnside private walks on the southeast side of the College Garden and on the burnside. Without the individual accounts of the suppliers the tree plantings remain unknown, but the quantities and prices do suggest replacements and new plantings consisting of very young trees.

In October 1789, Lang made representation to the Faculty regarding the unsatisfactory state of part of the College Garden. As reported in the minutes: '... about 1½ acres lying in a very bad state and can never be made more useful or beautiful until it is trenched or levelled so that water may be carried off. And so also that it would be proper to plant a belt of trees along the side of the wall of the Observatory Garden'.[34] The overall costing was estimated at £13 and the relevant committee agreed to the proposal on 5 November. In February 1790 another committee was formed to consider further improvements in the Observatory Garden,[35] and on 25 February reported to Faculty that 'digging, dunging and planting' was necessary to the sum of £28.[36] This recommendation was additional to the earlier one and permission to proceed with the work was given in March. Lang meantime was already engaged on some improvements as agreed by Faculty the previous November, and in February 1790 was forced to state that 'some advance of money was immediately necessary for purchasing materials for Improvements at present carrying on in the Observatory Park', for which £9 was granted. With two sets of committee proposals to deal with, it was decided in April that the Principal should be able to issue precepts for Lang 'from time to time regarding improvements in the Observatory Park, not to exceed £28'.[37]

Lang's estimates and representation give some idea of the extent of the work:[38]

To additional Digging Etc	£2.—.—
To 150 Carts Dung for manuring upwards of three acres of ground in said Park at 2/-p. cart	15.—.—
To refreshments to the men at different times	—.5.—
As the Dung must be laid down in a heap from the Big Carts and Carried on the ground with smaller carts the ground being soft	1. 5.—
To Spreading the Same	—.5.—
To 4 Carts of Lime already got	1.—.—
The Arable ground and walks will require 22 lbs White Clover seed at 1/- pr lb to beautifie the feild and 1½ Boles Rye grass seed at 8/- pr Bole	1.14.—
To Harrowing and Rolling the same	—.8.—
To Digging the Dung down	3.—.—
The ground to be planted will take about 1000 and to fill up the vacancies amongst the Old planting about 200 in all about 1200 Plants About	2. 8.—
To an Assistant planting the same	—. 5.—
To the grass walk to be made along the sides of the said planting	—.10.—
	£28.—.—

The rye-grass seed at 8/- per boll compares with 9/- (sterling equivalent) in 1776 and 10/- (sterling equivalent) in 1728. The 1728 price of the dwarf-clover seed was 1/3½d per lb, and 10d per lb in 1776 (both sterling equivalents).

The practicalities of the operation were such that, since the preceding rainfall had so softened the ground, two cartings of manure were necessary, smaller and lighter carts (hurlies?) being used within the confines of the garden area. A total of 150 cartloads to 3 Scots acres represented one cartload per 123 square yards of ground. The timing of the manure-spreading cannot be estimated as the number of men involved is not mentioned. Since this would have required unskilled labour at about 1/- per day, some five working days were involved. 'Digging down the dung' would have cost the equivalent of 60 working days, and the number of workmen would have depended on how quickly the job was to be done. The quantity of rye-grass seed (1½ bolls = 24 pecks = 168 lb = 2688 oz) allows 1 oz of seed per 5.4 square yards, a thinner sowing than that used in the College Green in 1728 (1 oz per 3.6 square yards), although these earlier sowings were mixtures of rye grass and red clover. Dwarf white clover was still used for the walks in the Observatory Park, as in the College Garden. Rye grass was favoured for two reasons, both explained by Edward Lisle from his experience in southern England in the early years of the eighteenth century:[39] first, because it 'will bear the winter'; and second, because it 'propagates itself by sending forth fibres from its joints', e.g. tiller formation — lateral shoots formed from the basal region of the stem. Lisle also reported that, when grown for hay, rye grass was sown at '3 bushels on an acre'. Exact comparisons are difficult because of the local variations in weights and measures existing at that time. If Lisle's 3 bushels was equivalent to 12 pecks per Imperial acre, and Lang's sowings would have been of 8 pecks per Scots acre, then Lisle's application of seed per Scots acre would have been 9 pecks.

Settlement of Lang's accounts for the work in the Observatory Garden was somewhat complicated, as explained in a minute of 18 May 1790.[40] Lang had been allowed £8/5/- for trenching ground in the Observatory Park, of which he had received £6. An additional outlay of £28 had then been allowed for the improvements proposed in Lang's estimate, which he had exceeded by 10/9d. Lang had already been paid £21 and was owed £7/10/9d, plus £2/5/- from the previous allowances. All this was meticulously explained in Principal Davidson's precept of 19 May.[41] In the following June, Lang claimed 15/6d for 'dunging hedge around Observatory Park 2 springs past — carting and wheeling dung' and 'sowing plott of ground within moat of Observatory with clover seeds'.[42]

Lang's extensive replanting of the angle-foot region and other parts of the garden in 1788 was followed four years later by his representation to Faculty that the plants, trees etc. in the same locality were 'in great need of fresh manure'.[43] Having received permission to carry out these improvements,[44] Lang also bought trees and plants to replace those dead. His account was submitted in November 1792:[45]

Glasgow 6th November 1792

To Robert Lang

To 17 Carts Dung for the planting in the College Garden at 1/6 per Cart	£1.15. 6
To wheeling same to the Street @ 2d	0. 2.10
To Cartage of d0 at 6d p. Cart	0. 8. 6
2 Carts Lime shells @ 7/- Each	14. 0
To 10 days of a man assistance @ 1/6	0.15. 0
	£3.15.10

Robert Lang

Begs leave to represent that it would Require about 300 Good plants of different kinds to fill up vacancies in the College Garden and Observatory Park which will cost 4/6 p. Cent £0.13.6

On the precept written at the bottom of the account in Principal Davidson's hand, the sum of 13/6d was added on with the note 'To 300 young trees or plants to fill up the vacancies in the planting'. The Faculty minute of early February 1793 which authorised the above precept also referred to the 'Pailing around the young planting being in a ruinous condition' that would have to be renewed.[46] Lang was ordered to carry out the necessary repairs at a cost not exceeding £3.[47] He duly presented his account.[48]

Glasgow 26 February 1793

To 14 dozen stobs for mending the palling in the College Garden @ 1/1 per dozen	£—.15. 2
To 3 dozen Rafters @ 2/- p. dozen	—. 6.—
1000 Nails	—. 6.—
Cartage from Broomlielaw	— .1.—
March 16th To 12 dozen stobs @ 1/1	—.13.—
3 dozen Rafters 2/-	—. 6.—
Cartage from Broomlielaw	—. 1.—
	£2. 8. 2

When the Faculty revised Lang's conditions of employment in January 1789, his salary was increased on the condition that he was to bring no extra labour charges without the express permission of the relevant committee. The one exception was 'for nails, pailing and other materials bought by him'. This replacement and repair of the 'ruinous' wood fencing became almost an annual event in the College Garden. At the end of January 1794, Lang reported that the 'Pailing which was intended to defend the young plantations in the Garden is in much need of repair'[49] and he was allowed £3. In the autumn of the same year, the paling fence 'that defends the young plantation' being again in 'great disrepair', a sum of £2/10/- was authorised.[50] In late December 1795, the 'pailing around the young plantations' was yet again in need of repair in 'sundry places'; the sum was allocated as before, plus 6/- for 'nursery trees' to replace those that had died.[51] In 1796 the wood fences seem not to have received any attention, which is perhaps why Lang had to report in February 1797 that 'a great part of the pailing in the College Garden is ruinous and in need of repair'.[52] Again £2/10/- was allowed — by now something of a standard rate — and again in December 1797. In this latter month, 'the said Robert Lang at the sight of Mr Wilson is desired to bring an Estimate for the complete Repair of the Door and Railing at the foot of the College Garden, which is at present quite ruinous'.[53] Andrew Macfarlane, a wright, submitted an estimate of £2/10/- and the repairs were ordered to be carried out 'in sight of Mr Wilson'.[54]

This repetitive repair and replacement of the wood fencing around the angle-foot plantation and the burnside private walks was somewhat costly. In the accounts for stobs and rafters, no mention is made of any attempt to protect the bases of the stobs against rotting. The damp clay soil may have played a significant role in the deterioration of the wood. Since, however, the paling was there to 'defend' the enclosed plantings from students, this human factor may well have accounted for the constant need of repairs. Students were given the freedom of the

College Garden (but not the Observatory Garden and Park, being kept out by a locked door on the bridge over the Molendinar Burn). The temptation to climb over the fences into the forbidden territory was probably too strong for many of the students. They were expected to take walks in the garden only for their exercise; no running, jumping or playing of ball games was permitted.

Tree replacements were a constant feature of Lang's management, as with his predecessor. In June 1800, a Faculty committee of five, including the Principal and James Jeffray — the latter making one of his rare appearances on such a committee — was formed 'to inspect the old trees in the College Garden which are decayed and to cut down and sell such as they judge to be in that state, and to order the planting of young trees in such places as they shall think proper'.[55] The processes of measuring and public auction would probably have been carried out, as described by Alexander Adams (p. 162). Also in Adams's time there were frequent references to the work involved in cleaning up the Molendinar Burn. This operation appears much less frequently in Lang's accounts of work done over the years. In May 1785, a new brander (= iron grating) was fixed at the northern New Vennel opening of the burn to reduce the amount of rubbish being carried into the College grounds.[56] This does not seem to have been very successful and five years later the Faculty moved that the 'arch over the Molendinar Burn adjacent to the New Vennel' was to be enlarged and heightened. The responsible committee was also to ensure that a 'good and sufficient Brander' be fitted to the arch, '. . . the present one being insufficient'.[57] There would seem to have been a combination of problems of flow rates and rubbish transportation with the water entering the garden from the New Vennel region. Whilst a 'variety of work about the burn' had been included in an account presented by Lang in December 1787,[58] at the beginning of the same year he had been paid £1 'to defray the expence of cleaning the Molendinar Burn, now greatly banked up with sediment'.[59] The arch over the burn at the New Vennel again came up for repair in the late summer of 1795, when £4/15/- was allowed for its reconstruction.[60]

The bridge over the burn became a matter for concern in January 1800, when the Faculty decreed:[61]

> John Millar, Mr Cumin, Mr Jardine, Mr Young and Dr Meikleham are constituted a Committee to examine the state of the Stone Bridge at the bottom of the Garden and to report as to the most advisable method of repairing or altering the passage to the Observatory Park

The committee eventually reported back in the following June that the bridge was 'out of repair' and that its materials should be 'sold to the best advantage'. A temporary bridge was immediately to be put in position before the dismantling of the stonework of the existing one. A special meeting of Faculty was called for 29 August at which the committee would provide plans and an estimate of the expenditure. The cost of the new bridge was placed at £20/8/6d, and the Faculty recommended that the work be 'executed with all convenient speed'.[62] Removal of the old stonework 'as soon as possible' was recommended in the following October,[63] and was completed by the end of November 1800[64] under William Lang's supervision.

Reference to a 'Laboratory Garden' is to be found in a Faculty minute of 4 April 1795[65] — its first mention in any of the University's records. Its location can be determined from a minute of 10 June 1783, when it was decided that the 'Elaboratory or Tenement on the west side of the present Botanical Garden' should be insured for £250.[66] The Laboratory Garden would therefore have been a plot of ground on the west side of the Physic Garden. There are no records of any plantings in this Laboratory Garden. It seems to have been beset with drainage problems, as was general, and in June 1787 it was recommended that an 'open shewer' be built for £2 'to carry the rain water away in a commodious manner'.[67] In April 1785, it was recommended that part of the wall bounding the Laboratory Garden towards the head of the Old Castle Pens Close be rebuilt.[68] Then, in October 1786, it was decreed that part of the wall of the Physic Garden in the same region should be raised to a height of 10 feet along part of its length.[69] The reasons become more apparent from the records of the 5 June Faculty meeting, which brought to light some problems with neighbours in houses on the west side of the Physic Garden and facing onto the Laboratory Garden. The ground by the Laboratory was 'greatly incommoded by the throwing out of Rubbish and Filth from the back windows of the new house lately built by Mr Simson next to the College property: for the immediate prevention of such nuisance the Committee suggest that either a new wall should be built up before the back windows or that the Proprietor should fix close stenchers in all those windows and execute an obligation that nothing whatever shall be thrown out of the said windows upon the College Ground in time coming'. The 'close stenchers' were iron bars to be affixed so close together that presumably no hands or containers could be pushed through. The Faculty decided that to erect a new wall would be too expensive, and whilst the old wall could be repaired it was preferable that the proprietor of the new house should fit the close stenchers. There are no records of any wall-building, so it is likely that the proprietor of the new house fitted the metal grids over the offending windows. The raised height of the Physic Garden wall ordered in October 1786 was probably associated with this same neighbourhood problem.

In 1785 some problems seem to have arisen with householders on the south side of the Observatory Park, but not of the kind experienced in the Laboratory Garden. The burden of the Faculty complaint was that the houses, which fronted onto the Gallowgate (Figure 7.1), had

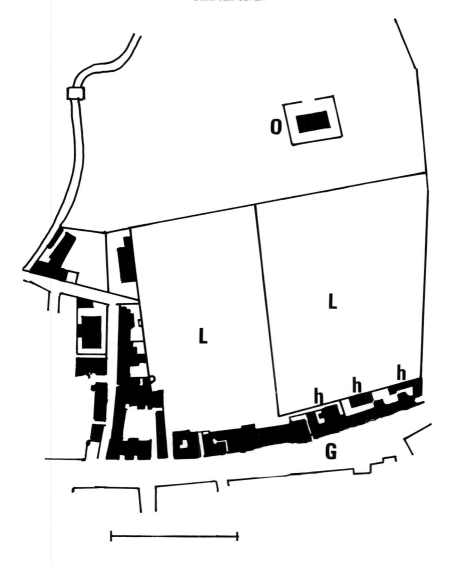

Figure 7.1. The houses (**h**) on the Gallowgate (**G**) overlooking College land (**L**). The Faculty objected to the open windows

0 = Observatory.

Scale line: 300 feet

windows which opened onto the Observatory Park. On 31 May 1785, it was decided to ensure that these windows remained closed.[70] Earlier in the same month, it had been decided that a new wall be erected on the south side of the Observatory Park from the gate leading into the Gallowgate.[71] On 24 May, the relevant committee reported that a new wall '3 yards in height 20 inches thick with a good stone coping' would cost £55/6/8d.[72] Consultations then took place between the College and the householders, on completion of which the committee was able to report that the householders 'contiguous to the ground' had agreed both to meet half the cost of the new wall and not to open their windows facing onto College land. In early June 1788, it was agreed that this new wall be raised along its length by 2 feet.[73] Privacy in the Observatory Park was still a highly valued asset.

James Jeffray, on his appointment to the joint chair of Botany and Anatomy in May 1790, assumed responsibility for the Physic Garden and the supervision of Robert Lang's labours. The last traceable order for the garden in William Hamilton's name had been dated June 1789. On 21 December 1791, Jeffray represented to Faculty that no financial allowance had been made for the Physic Garden for two years. He claimed £15 (his personal outlay) for manure, earth and plants,[74] and after the claim had lain 'on the Table' the precept was authorised on 10 February 1792. As the original bills of sale are unavailable, the plant purchases remain unknown. From 1792 onwards, it was agreed that £5 annually was to be allowed for plants and manure for the garden, with payments made either in arrears or for the current year, as shown in the precept of 13 June 1793:[75]

Pay to Dr Jeffray five pounds sterling ordered for him for manure and plants brought into the Physic Garden last year and also the like sum ordered for him for manure and plants brought into the said Garden for the ensuing year both by minute of the Faculty of 17 May last in all ten pounds sterl.

Arch Davidson Principal

Two years later, in June 1795, Jeffray again reminded Faculty that no allowance had been made for the garden since May 1793, whilst he himself had 'expended considerable sums for manure and plants since that date', and he added that it was usual to indemnify the Professor of Botany 'in part' for the annual expenses with £5 yearly.[76] The £10 precept was granted, and the sequence of events was repeated two years later after Jeffray had again reminded Faculty of the 'considerable sum for plants and manure' that he had laid out.[77] This system of repayments continued on into the early 1800s, on each occasion Jeffray not being slow to remind Faculty that he was really being repaid only part of the outlay he had made.

Jeffray's lectures on Botany were given in the summer months, as was usual, but no records of his lectures are available. His class register for the first ten years of his tenure of the Chair shows that the numbers of students attending his Botany lectures were always on the small side compared with those attending Anatomy (Table 7.1).[78] The steady decline in attendance at the Botany lectures compared with Anatomy may be a reflection of Jeffray's respective enthusiasm for the two subjects of his joint Chair, a feature which may have some bearing on events from the summer of 1799 onwards. On 1 April 1799, Faculty granted Jeffray leave of absence until the following June. He then left for London on business.[79] On 16 May, he wrote to the Principal explaining that the business he was engaged on would not allow him to return to Glasgow in time for the summer's lectures on Botany due to commence in June.[80] He was at pains to point out that it was 'not amusement but business that detained him'. Jeffray then proposed that Dr Thomas Brown, whom he regarded as being the one man in Glasgow capable of teaching Botany at such short notice, should take the class that summer. Outlining Brown's experience, Jeffray pointed out that he had studied Botany at Edinburgh University under Daniel Rutherford (Professor of Medicine and Botany during 1786–1819) and had been a great favourite of the Professor. Jeffray's letter concluded 'But I know of none so well acquainted with the Business and he is prepared to teach'. To some extent the Faculty was faced with a *fait accompli*, as implied in the tone of the minute of 21 May 1799, when Jeffray's letter was discussed.[81] The Principal and Robert Findlay, Professor of Divinity, were delegated to converse with Brown on the subject and 'to place an advertisement on the class opening in the Glasgow newspapers'. The Clerk of Faculty was further ordered to enquire of Jeffray by how much his leave of absence was to be extended, and to settle 'the consideration that Dr Jeffray is to pay to Dr Brown for teaching that Class'.

Table 7.1. Numbers of students attending the classes of James Jeffray (1790–99)[78]

	Anatomy	Botany
1790	54	—
1791	60	22
1792	70	28
1793	63	22
1794	66	14
1795	82	10
1796	96	30
1797	85	9
1798	110	8
1799	115	—[a]

Note: a. Lectures given by Thomas Brown: see text

Jeffray, having succeeded in installing Brown as his substitute in 1799, was determined to keep him in that position. He again approached Faculty in May 1800 with the same request regarding Brown's employment as lecturer for the summer course.[82] Some members of Faculty raised objections to this arrangement for a second year, and in reply Jeffray wrote a letter to the Principal stressing that it would be of great inconvenience to him if the request was not granted. He further embellished Brown's qualifications, viz.: '... Dr Thos. Brown is the fittest person I know in this part of the country for teaching Botany. I am persuaded that it would be advantageous for the College in general and for the Medical Department of the College in particular were it understood that he shall lecture in Botany in future. And I state this more confidently because I know that he is an Enthusiast in Botany and proposes to enrich the Course of Lectures in Botany by the intermixture and addition of a sett of Lectures in Agriculture on the plan recently instituted in Edinburgh by Sir M. Pulteney and so credibly given by Dr Coventry. I therefore beg leave to request that the faculty would take the business under their serious consideration'. This letter, including its suggestion of a 'Freudian slip' in laying great stress on Brown's enthusiasm for the subject, found favour with the majority of the Professors and on 7 May 1800 it was agreed that Brown should be employed by Jeffray 'to teach Botany in this University so long as it shall be expedient', with the proviso that Brown was to have no claim on College funds.[83] In consequence, his payment would have come from the class fees paid by the students. Jeffray's astute moves over a two-year period constituted the first separation of the teaching of Anatomy and Botany under a joint Chair, a separation which culminated in 1818 in the institution of a separate Chair of Botany.

Brown's stewardship of the teaching of Botany and his association with the Physic Garden will be subjects for discussion in the next chapter. Jeffray's management of affairs regarding the garden is seen only in his biennial claims for plants and manure; no real indication of the state of the garden is available. Robert Lang continued to receive part of his salary for work in the garden. The official records give no further information on the state of affairs following William Hamilton's legacy of £200 (which was never forthcoming, but which underlined his dissatisfaction with the state of the garden). One small clue which shows that the Faculty realised all was not well is to be found in a minute of the meeting of 27 February 1799.[84] This minute was principally a statement regarding the disposal of the tack for some College land 'between the Barracks and Duke street'. The Barracks lay to the east of the Observatory Park (the Muir Butts) and Duke Street was north of the College lands. The conditions of tack contain the following clause:

The faculty agree to accept the said offer upon Condition that the

Tackman must be bound to relinquish possession of the whole or such parts of the said Land as they shall think proper to feu during the currency of the said Tack, or take for the purpose of a Botanical Garden ...

Hence it would seem that some moves were afoot (possibly orchestrated by Jeffray), though not of a very forceful nature, to move the Physic Garden to a site on the northeast side of the College grounds. The plan did not materialise and remains a brief mention in a tack condition.

Whilst Thomas Brown was now installed as Lecturer in Botany, Jeffray as occupant of the joint Chair was still to be responsible for the annual purchases of manure and plants. Although Jeffray may not have been over-enthusiastic regarding his own Botany lectures, he did maintain the high standards of those in Anatomy as set by his predecessor in office. After the creation of the separate Botany Chair in 1818, he was to remain Professor of Anatomy until his death in 1848. In December 1805, he offered to Faculty for £40 the greenhouse and plants he had purchased from the trustees of William Hamilton's estate in 1791, but the Faculty 'did not find it expedient to make the purchase' and advised Jeffray to dispose of the articles as he saw fit.[85] In 1790 Hamilton's greenhouse had been valued at £15, so that if, as he claimed, Jeffray had paid £40 for the greenhouse and plants the latter must have been of an expensive nature. On the other hand he may have been trying to raise the price somewhat, since evidence suggests that he was of an impecunious nature. At some time he converted a small building fronting onto the High Street at the side of his University house into a shop. This evoked some ribald comment in the newspapers and a rhyme:[86]

This once was Dr Jeffray's shop
The famous saw-bone cutter
But now it is let to Peter Cook
For selling Bread and butter

The shop also met with the disapproval of the other Professors and he was forced to close it, the closure being fully reported in Faculty minutes. Reference to him as the 'saw-bone' cutter probably commemorates his fame as inventor of the chain-saw. Besides being a sound anatomist, he was also an adventurous scientist. On 4 November 1818 Matthew Clydesdale, a miner, was hanged for murder. The Judge had decreed that his body was to be delivered to Jeffray for public dissection. In the crowded Anatomy Hall of the College, the body was placed in a sitting position in a chair (the latter still in the possession of the University today) and Jeffray, with the help of Andrew Ure, Lecturer in Chemistry, placed two tubes attached to bellows and electrified with a galvanic battery into the corpse's nostrils; whereupon (according to a reliable contemporary account) Clydesdale's chest heaved and he stood upright, with accompanying movements of hands and legs.[87] The resulting consternation was followed by the cheers and handclaps of the hardier members of the audience and by fainting of those of weaker dispositions. Jeffray then despatched the unfortunate Clydesdale for the second time with a lancet. It is perhaps regrettable that his advanced scientific outlook did not extend to Botany.

As with his predecessor, Robert Lang sought to increase his income by leasing College land for the production of grass and other crops. Grass sales were the mainstay of this investment, the fruit sales from the College Garden being less mentioned in the later years of the century. In the first few years of Lang's employment the grass-sales profits did not come to him, as indicated in a Faculty minute of 10 June 1784:[88]

> The College Gardener having as yet entered into no agreement with the College for the Observatory Park lately possessed by Alexr. Adams he is ordered in the meantime to cut and dispose the grass to the best advantage for the ensuing season and to give an exact accompt of all his intromissions with regard to this matter and the Clerk is appointed to give him more particular instructions about the management.

The accounting later presented by Lang came up for review in May 1786,[89] when the committee appointed for disposing of the grass reported in his sales:

1784	Grass receipt	£10/15/2
	balanced by accompt of work done	
1785	Grass receipt	£9/16/0
	work done	9/15/10
	(only 2d due to the College)	

There was no advantage to Lang in the above arrangement — only that the grass sales just covered the expenditure of labour in both years. A side issue which eventually involved Lang was initiated at a Faculty meeting in early June 1784.[90] Francis Oliphant, a tenant of the College in the Butts ground, was given permission to dig clay 'in lands belonging to the College adjoining the Iron Foundry'. Oliphant promised to fill in the land 'so digged' and to 'put it in a better state than formerly'. This liberty was given until the following Martinmas, with a charge of £2/10/- for an area of 40 square yards 'since otherwise he may be thrown out of livelihood'. Oliphant was a potter and the clayey nature of the ground would have been appreciated by him, although perhaps less well favoured by the gardeners. On 29 October 1784, Oliphant presented a petition in which he proposed that he be allowed the tack of 2½ acres of ground in the region of the Butts, then in possession of William Findlay, at £10 per annum, and that from this land he be allowed to dig clay for his pottery.[91] The Faculty's response was immediate: Oliphant's petition was refused out of hand and William Findlay was to be advised that his tack of the Butts ground would cease from Candlemas 1786; the College would then advertise for a new tackholder, for which Findlay could not apply. Oliphant had evidently overstepped the mark so far as Faculty was concerned. Whilst he had been given permission to dig clay from June to November 1784, this was a special favour. On previous occasions the Clerk had had to take legal steps to prevent Oliphant digging clay without permission on College land. By dispossessing Findlay, although allowing a reasonable interval — actually to the advantage of the College in guaranteeing that cultivation of the ground would continue — the Faculty appeared to suspect that he was acting in collusion with Oliphant. In passing, it is worth noting that some 14 years later the Faculty was again discussing the disposal of clay from ground lying to the north of the College.[92] A Mr Mure had offered £10 per acre for the liberty to remove clay. The value of the clay strata, however, was now realised, and a committee was appointed to negotiate a higher rent, with Mure's petition 'lying on the table'.

The outcome of the dismissal of Oliphant's petition and the proposed dispossession of Findlay came up for discussion in December 1785,[93] when it was decided that the land should be let at £4 per acre, with the fences, inevitably, 'badly in need of repair'. To hasten matters, the responsible committee was asked 'to commune with the College Gardener and any other interested persons who may be willing to take said Park and other Ground' and to find out the terms they were prepared to offer. In consequence the ground was let to Lang, who on 23 February 1786 asked for £5 to pay for necessary fencing,[94] a precept being granted on 1 March. Later, in June 1786, Lang made an offer of £2 per acre for the grass on the Observatory Park and £6/6/- per acre for that already sown in corn.[95] This offer was accepted subject to Lang obtaining proper security.

Lang's determination to take maximum advantage of the available land is seen in a memorial he presented to the Faculty which came up for discussion on 19 March 1787.[96] This memorial contains a precise account of his proposed management of land in the Observatory Park. He sought the lease on the understanding that he 'be allowed to labour the same for the first three years, on purpose to raise proper grass thereon, as the sward or surface thereof will not dissolve sooner, so as to have right or proper grass' ('dissolve' is used here in the sense of loosening a heavy soil). After this he proposed that the ground should remain in grass for four years 'by which time the manure will be exhausted, and the grass become very poor and therefore will be required to be tilled up for other two years, and again get proper manure which must alternatively take place during the whole space of the intended lease (say two years plowing and four years grass successively) upon which condition he is willing to give three pounds sterling per Acre. But if allowed to labour it every year and put what grain thereon to him seems proper, he will give three pounds ten shillings Sterl. per Acre yearly. At same time he obliges himself to keep the ground of the Park in proper order, and as the ground is at present very foul he hopes you will allow one crop of Potatoes for cleaning the same'. The sequence proposed was a long-term one, of 'labouring' the land for the first three years and growing a grain crop, probably barley, and thereafter to keep the land in grass for four years, then in grain for two years, and again in grass for four, with the necessary manuring taking place during the 'labouring' phase with the grain crops. The alternative plan was to till the ground annually for cereal crops, for which a higher rental was proposed.

Faculty's response to the memorial was to lease the Observatory Park to Lang for 13 years at a rent of £3 per acre payable at the term of Whitsunday after separation of each crop from the ground. The conditions laid down were in agreement with Lang's first proposal, viz., 'First of all that the South Part of the said Park, which was ploughed last year, is again to be ploughed for this and the succeeding crop, and that the other half of the said Park is to be ploughed for three successive crops: that in said course of ploughing each half is to be laid down with grass seeds at the last ploughing, and properly manured, and then to continue four years in grass and then ploughed for two other successive crops: after which it is to be laid down with grass seeds for four successive years as formerly'. The remaining conditions covered rights of holding. The College could take back the land, in whole or part, on giving twelve months' notice; Lang could not 'subset' any part of the ground; in the event of Lang's death, his heirs would have no rights to the land; if Lang was given notice of dispossession, he was to be compensated for 'any manure laid upon said grounds, of which he shall not have reaped the benefit'. Such compensation would be determined 'at the sight of proper Judges, mutually chosen', and this compensation for previous manuring would be the only competent claim any of his heirs would have against the College.

Both Lang and the Faculty had the advantage of knowing the precise position of the ground to be leased. No plans are available which enable us to decide the location of the ground leased by Lang in the Observatory Park. Difficulties in interpretation also arises through the casual use in the minutes, memorials and precepts of the terms Observatory Garden and Observatory Park. In some instances the former can be recognised as an area of trees, shrubs and walks immediately east of the burn on the raised ground facing the College Garden. On occasions this area is called the Observatory Park, or the whole ground to the east of the burn called the Garden. If the measurements on the copy of McArthur's 1778 map are reliable,[97] the ground east of the burn, and which constituted the original Dovehill land, was about 8.8 Imperial acres. In addition there were some 6.2

acres of land which extended down to the houses fronting on to the Gallowgate (Figure 7.1). Any present-day attempts to determine the size of Lang's holding must take into account previous rulings by Faculty. In December 1785 (p. 214) Faculty decided that half the ground of the Observatory Park was to be 'laboured' and kept in grain for three years, then in grass for the following three years; after this the other half was to be similarly treated. Then, in February 1786, it had been decreed that the southern half of the Park was to be ploughed and dressed with 20 carts of dung per acre (p. 215) and tillage was to proceed for two years before the ground was grassed. This 1786 ploughing and manuring is that referred to in the conditions of lease laid down at the Faculty meeting of 19 March 1787: namely 'that the South Part of the said Park, which was ploughed last year ...' There is on record the result of a survey carried out by William McIlguhan in April 1790:[98]

The Content of the Arable Ground in the Observatory Park after deducing the Observatory and Planting etc. etc. is Three Acres and one rood nearly

Assuming that Lang was adhering to the conditions laid down, by 1790 the southern half of the land under tack would be in grass whilst the northern half would have been ploughed and sown with grain, and this may well be the 'arable ground' (that under tillage) surveyed. If so, the area of the Observatory Park leased by Lang would have been about 6 acres (£18 rent per annum), probably on the south side of the Observatory itself (Figure 7.1). This siting is borne out by a Faculty minute of 8 June 1788,[99] which mentions the 'ground lying to the south and east of the Observatory, presently in tack to William Buchanan and Robert Lang, might tend considerably to the improvement of the College Revenue by being fenced'. Whilst the rent was placed at £3 per acre in the 1787 agreement, some ten years later (21 December 1797) Lang obtained from Faculty an agreement for the rent to be reduced to £2 per acre. In June 1794, Lang was allowed to 'possess a piece of Ground lying between the Observatory Garden and the Gallowgate' for one year from Candlemas 1795, at a rent of £18.[100]

This renting of land by Lang carried with it an element of risk. His salary from the University was still £18, £1 of this being for tools for the gardens. A further £8 was quoted as part of his salary, but this depended on grass sales from the College Garden crop; his house was rent-free. The extra land he leased from the College was a potential source of additional income, so long as the grass and grain crops proved to be profitable over and above the expenses he would have in 'labouring' the ground — ploughing, harrowing, seeding, manuring, etc. He would have had little reserve to fall back on if the crops had failed or if the prices for grass and grain had fallen dramatically.

As with his predecessor Alexander Adams, Lang's name suddenly disappears from the Faculty records. His signature is appended to a receipt dated 25 October 1800 for £2/5/- from the College Factor in payment of five days' cartage of rubbish and gravel 'for making walks in the College Garden'.[101] A receipt from one Daniel Chrystie dated 18 December 1800 is for 3/3d for three carts of gravel for walks in the College Garden 'Received from Glasgow College by the hand of Robert Lang Gardener'. The Faculty records for 29 November 1800, however, include reference to an account submitted by W. Lang for work done on the walks in the garden,[102] and for taking down the stone bridge over the Molendinar Burn, altogether costing £12/10/-. The dismantling of the stone bridge had been advised by a committee in January 1800, and Robert Lang was to have supervised the work. W. Lang was his eldest son William, and it can be assumed that Robert Lang died early in November 1800. On 14 January 1801, the Faculty minuted that William Lang was to be appointed College Gardener for one year from the next Candlemas, and to have the house and land rented by his late father and to receive the same wages.[103] In late January 1801, William Lang presented the Faculty with two bills: one from W. McKechny for 12/- for 16 carts of gravel 'for a new walk in the Observatory Park', and the other for £2 from William Alcorn for 4½ days' cartage of rubbish and gravel for the same walk.[104] A precept of £18 issued in February was for William Lang 'as the sum due to his deceased Father Robert Lang from the College at the term of Candlemas for his wages as College Gardener for a year on his filling the Rents due to the College by his said Father'.[105] This precept and the mention in the 14 January minute are the only traceable announcements of Robert Lang's death. His son William having succeeded him meant that the family (quite numerous) was able to remain in the gardener's house.

With Robert Lang's death at the end of 1800 there is a natural break in the chronicle of events and, with Thomas Brown installed as Lecturer in Botany at the instigation of James Jeffray, we have entered on another phase in the history of the Physic Garden. This is more suitably discussed in the next chapter.

Notes

1. GUAA 58243.
2. GUAA 58302.
3. FM, 10 May 1786: 26693, p. 143.
4. FM, 10 April 1786: 26693, p. 134.
5. FM, 10 June 1786: 26693, p. 158.
6. GUAA 58303.
7. FM, 7 November 1786: 26693, p. 168.
8. FM, 5 May 1787, 26693, pp. 223–4.
9. FM, 11 June 1787: 26693, p. 248.
10. GUAA 58304.
11. FM, 26 October 1786: 26693, p. 163.
12. FM, 7 November 1786: 26693, p. 169.
13. FM, 8 December 1786: 26693, p. 179.

14. GUAA 58302.

15. GUAA 58303.

16. GUAA 58304.

17. GUAA 58243.

18. FM, 2 December 1785: 26693, p. 100.

19. FM, 22 December 1785: 26693, p. 105.

20. FM, 29 December 1785: 26693, pp. 107–8.

21. E. Lisle, 1757. *Observations on Husbandry* (J. Hughes, London), vol. 1, p. 271 (reprinted in Offset by Gregg International Publishers Ltd, Farnborough, Hants, 1970).

22. GUAA 58263.

23. GUAA 58304.

24. FM, 7 November 1786: 26693, p. 169.

25. FM, 13 February 1787: 26693, p. 203.

26. FM, 7 March 1787: 26693, p. 207.

27. GUAA 58440.

28. FM, 30 October 1787: 26693, p. 262.

29. GUAA 58304.

30. K. Thomas, 1983. *Man and the Natural World* (Allen Lane, London), pp. 210–11.

31. FM, 22 December 1787: 26693, p. 272.

32. FM, 24 March 1788: 26693, p. 291.

33. GUAA 58303.

34. FM, 23 October 1789: 26694, p. 22.

35. FM, 8 February 1790: 26694, p. 42.

36. FM, 25 February 1790: 26694, p. 46.

37. FM, 5 April 1790: 26694, p. 55.

38. GUAA 58440.

39. E. Lisle, 1757. *Observations on Husbandry*, vol. 2, pp. 57–9.

40. FM, 18 May 1790: 26694, pp. 64–5.

41. GUAA 58305.

42. FM, 7 June 1790: 26694, p. 72.

43. FM, 23 October 1792: 26694, p. 262.

44. FM, 7 December 1792: 26694, p. 268.

45. GUAA 58313.

46. FM, 1 February 1793: 26694, p. 277.

47. FM, 17 February 1793: 26694, p. 280.

48. GUAA 58313.

49. FM, 30 January 1794: 26694, p. 327.

50. FM, 21 October 1794: 26694, p. 381.

51. FM, 21 December 1795: 26695, p. 66.

52. FM, 6 February 1797: 26695, p. 144.

53. FM, 28 December 1797: 26695, p. 215.

54. FM, 19 January 1798: 26695, p. 216.

55. FM, 3 June 1800: 26695, p. 384.

56. FM, 5 May 1785: 26693, p. 56.

57. FM, 11 October 1790: 26694, p. 80.

58. FM, 22 December 1787: 26693, p. 272.

59. FM, 6 February 1797: 26695, p. 144.

60. FM, 27 August 1795: 26695, p. 44.

61. FM, 23 January 1800: 26695, p. 359.

62. FM, 29 August 1800: 26696, p. 3.

63. FM, 10 October 1800: 26696, p. 9.

64. FM, 29 November 1800: 26696, p. 16.

65. FM, 4 April 1785: 26693, p. 30.

66. FM, 10 June 1783: 26692, p. 291.

67. FM, 5 June 1787: 26693, pp. 241–2.

68. FM, 4 April 1785: 26693, p. 50.

69. FM, 26 October 1786: 26693, p. 162.

70. FM, 31 May 1785: 26693, p. 70.

71. FM, 5 May 1785: 26693, p. 56.

72. FM, 24 May 1785: 26693, p. 64.

73. FM, 8 June 1788: 26694, p. 8.

74. FM, 21 December 1791: 26694, p. 187.

75. GUAA 58311.

76. FM, 9 June 1795: 26695, p. 38.

77. FM, 24 May 1797: 26695, p. 176.

78. GUAA 19057, (J. Jeffray's Class Register).

79. FM, 1 April 1799: 26695, p. 291.

80. GUAA 58434.

81. FM, 21 May 1799: 26695, p. 312.

82. GUAA 58434.

83. FM, 7 May 1800: 26695,p. 375.

84. FM, 27 February 1799: 26695, p. 281.

85. FM, 26 December 1805: 26696, p. 379.

86. D. Murray, 1925. *Memories of the Old College of Glasgow* (Jackson, Wylie & Co., Glasgow), pp. 398–9.

87. J. Lenihan, 1979. *Science in Action* (Institute of Physics, London and Bristol), pp. 186–7.

88. FM, 10 June 1784: 26693, pp. 14–15.

89. FM, 15 May 1786: 26693, p. 145.

90. FM, 9 June 1784: 26693, p. 6.

91. FM, 29 October 1784: 26693, p. 17.

92. FM, 20 November 1798: 26695, p. 269.

93. FM, 2 December 1785: 26693, p. 100.

94. FM, 23 February 1786: 26693, p. 123.

95. FM, 9 June 1786: 26693, pp. 153–4.

96. FM, 19 March 1787: 26693, pp. 210–12.

97. GUAA 13471.

98. GUAA 58306.

99. FM, 8 June 1788: 26694, p. 9.

100. FM, 10 June 1794: 26694, p. 378.

101. GUAA 58429.

102. FM, 29 November 1800: 26696, p. 16.

103. FM, 14 January 1801: 26696, p. 21.

104. GUAA 58429.

105. GUAA 58429.

8 'THAT PLOT OF GROUND WHICH IS DIGNIFIED WITH THE NAME OF BOTANIC GARDEN ...'

William Lang's appointment as gardener commenced at Candlemas 1801. Before this date he stepped in to supervise work set in hand by his father and in so doing ensured that the full sum of his late father's salary came to him as heir. William Lang also took over the tenancy of the College land previously held by his father, although the original conditions of let of the Observatory Park in 1787 specifically stated that such a transition could not be guaranteed. The rapidity of the change rather suggests that Robert Lang's death was sudden. His son's management of the work in hand in the late autumn of 1800 may well have convinced the relevant committee of his suitability as successor to his father. The account submitted for these late-autumn labours show the extent of the innovations:[1]

To William Lang

Cutting down the ascent of the walk that runs South from the New Bridge in Observatory Park and wheeling earth to make up the end of do. as pr agreement	£1. 5.—
Forming part of a walk that runs East from the New Bridge in Observatory Park	.10.—
Cleaning the Molendinar Burn	1.—.—
Throwing out of the Burn the earth and rubbish that was dug out as a foundation for building a wall for the support of New Bridge in Observatory side as pr agreement	—. 5.—
Forming, Covering with Rubbish and breaking the large stones of do. wheeling part of do. from the Old Bridge and laying with gravel the walks in the College Garden	4.16.—
Taking down the Old Stone Bridge as pr agreement	3.10.—
Levelling and making ready for planting the Bank in the Observatory side of the Old Bridge	—.17.—
Removing the stones of the Old Bridge and piling them up	

in a Corner of one of the plots in College Garden also
Banking up the earth to the wall now built where the
Old Bridge stood in the College Gardenside   —. 7.—

                                                £12.10.—

The account is dated 22 November 1800, tending to confirm the likely date of his father's death. The new bridge, over which there had been much discussion earlier in the year, was placed in a different position from the old one, and removal of the latter called for some rebuilding and replanting of the banks of the burn. William Lang's supervision was mainly of the dismantling of the 'landstools' of the old bridge, as well as replanting in the Observatory Garden.

A second account in William Lang's name was submitted on 13 February 1801:[2]

                                          To William Lang

Making a new Gravel Walk with drains from New Bridge
to Observatory House   £2.—.—
Stobbing a piece of Ground at foot of College
Garden   1.—.—
Planting the same with trees   —.15.—
Stobbing round the Mount Planting do. and filling up
several vacancies in Observatory Park and College
Garden   —. 8.—

The Mount on the west side of the Middle Walk was still regarded as a decorative feature of the College Garden.

In early January 1801, William Lang placed a large order for trees and flowering shrubs with the firm McAslan and Austin.[3] This included some 1,450 trees of various sizes (Table 8.1). What is most noticeable is the variety of trees obtained, other than the usual limes, beeches, elms, poplars and thorns so often ordered in the past. In many ways this represents a more adventurous investment in trees by the College than heretofore, with numbers of horse chestnuts, sweet chestnuts, laburnums, weeping willows, birch, larch, spruce and flowering cherries. Many of these are fairly quick-growing, a point much favoured in garden-planning at the time. Some particular purchases are worthy of comment. These include the North American Wayfarer Tree or Hobble-Bush (*Viburnum lantanoides*), the Sugar Maple (*Acer saccharum*) and the Cockspur Thorn (*Craetagurus crus-galli*), all of these illustrating the interest at that time in tree importations from North America. Further examples of novel tree orders were the Dogwood (possibly *Cornus flavida*), the Service Tree (*Sorbus domestica*), the Turkey Oak (*Quercus cervis*) and the Western Red Cedar (*Thuja plicata*). Large numbers of unnamed shrubs were also purchased, with only lilacs and spiraeas being specifically mentioned. Whilst many of

Table 8.1. Trees and shrubs ordered by William Lang from McAslan and Austin, January and February 1801[3]

1801							
Jany 23							
300	Elms	6/-	190	Birch	5/3	£- .11. 3	
100	Plains	2/-	10	Sugar Maple	3/4	- . 5. 4	
100	Laburnum	5/-	30	Beech	1/- q- . 6. 4		
20	Oaks	6d	30	Larch	9d	- . 1. 3	
160	Ash	3/-	20	Thorns	3d	- . 3. 3	
6	Double Flowering Thorns	3/-	12	Weeping Willows	3/-	- . 6. -	
40	Huntington Willows	1/-	10	Limes	20/-	1 . 1. -	
20	Horse Chestnuts	1/-	20	Large Roans	1/-	- . 2. -	
26	Poplars	1/-	2	Guilderose	6d	- . 1. 6	
1	Wayfarer Tree	6d	2	Double flowering Cherries	1/8	- . 2. 2	
2	English Maple	6d	2	Sweet Chestnuts	6d	- . 1. -	
2	Evergreen Thorn	6d	2	Service	4d	- . -.10	
6	Silver Firs	4d	6	Spruce	2d	- . -. 6	
12	Cockspur Thorn	6/-	12	Lilac	3/-	-. 9- -	
6	Dogwoods	1/6	4	Spireas	1/-	- . 2. 6	
Jany 24							
4	Double flowering Cherries	3/4	60	Limes	10/-	- .13. 4	
60	Ash	1/-	60	Large Elms	1/6	- . 2. 6	
Jany 31							
108	Shrubs of Sorts			@ 3d		1 . 7. -	
6	Sweet Chestnuts	1/-	6	Horse Chestnuts	6d	. 1. 6	
4	Red Cedars	2/-	40	Birch	1/-	- . 3. -	
10	Hollies						
Feb 3							
10	Laburnums	6d	2	Turkey Oak	1/-	- . 1. 6	
6	Grafted Elms	3/-	41	Shrubs of sorts	10/3	- .13. 3	
5	Cockspur Thorns	2/-	4	Yews	2/-	- . 4. -	
10	Sweet Briars	2d	4	Double flourg Thorns	2/-	- . 2. 2	
Feb 24							
6	Large Limes	3/-	3	Large Horse Chestnuts	1/6	- . 4. 6	
8	" Poplars	8d	3	" Elms	3d	- . -.11	

the trees were probably replacements for those lining the walks (elms and limes), for the most part the purchases were more of a decorative nature, destined for the angle-foot region, the burnside, the Observatory Garden and the borders of the College Garden. The size of the order is all the more impressive when it is remembered that William Lang was not at the time officially on the staff of the University. The disposal of some of the replacements is recorded in an account he submitted later in the year:[4]

Making several alterations on the Gravel Walk, New Vennal Side College Garden	£1.10.—
Covering the whole of said walk with fine gravel	—.10.—
Digging up and sowing with Grass Seed the Old Tracks	—.4.—
Paid seed for do.	—. 2. 6
Spreading eight carts of gravel Old Vennal side in Coll. Garden	—. 3.—
Planting a row of Trees along the Molendinar Burn Observatory side, Replanting of Mount, Making up several deficiencies in College Green	—. 7. 6
	£2.17.—

Lang's work in the Physic Garden goes virtually unrecorded, though Jeffray was repaid £15 for plants and manure for the year ending in June 1801.[5] The continuing use of the type foundry was now proving a greater hindrance to the proper functioning of the garden, a state of affairs which eventually received official note in the Faculty minutes for 14 March 1803:[6]

It having been stated that the smoke of the Foundery was very prejudicial to the Botany Garden the Faculty hereby express the intention of getting a new Botanic Garden in a suitable place as soon as convenient

What had on occasions been hinted at in the past now became recognised. Dissatisfaction with the long-standing site south of the Blackfriars Kirkyard had been apparent for a number of years. Continuing attempts to improve its productivity, which were evident throughout the 1780s under William Hamilton, were also continued by James Jeffray. The uncertainty about the future of the Physic Garden was seen in another item of Faculty business discussed in the spring of 1803. In 1781 William Hunter left to the University his magnificent collection of anatomical preparations, medals, coins, minerals, archaeological relics, paintings, books and manuscripts (then valued at £60,000), together with £8000 to build a museum in the University grounds with lecture facilities for both the students and the general public.[7] According to his Will, the collection was to remain in London for 30 years after Hunter's death, at the disposal of William Cruikshank, his partner, and Matthew Baillie, his nephew. Cruikshank died in 1800 and Baillie retired from teaching anatomy, so that the removal of the collection could then take place before the expiry of the 30 years. The College meantime had to decide on a suitable site for the proposed museum. One of the first proposals was to build it 'in the Garden opposite the Lyceum'.[8] In May 1803,[9] however, the members of Faculty were in some disagreement regarding the nature of the building itself. Some favoured the inclusion of lecture rooms etc. suitable for the students of anatomy and midwifery, as well as housing the extensive collection. Others were of the opinion that the inclusion of teaching facilities for anatomy would not be satisfactory and that the collection should be kept entirely separate from the anatomy and midwifery classrooms, since the 'addition of an anatomical theatre would hurt the external Elegance of the Museum as well as the Structure, form and light of the Apartments destined to receive those parts of the Collection which are unconnected with Anatomy'. There was also concern, in the light of more recent events, 'That if the Mob should be excited in consequence of the teaching of Anatomy, which has happened more than once this winter, there might be from their breaking into the Museum great danger to the Medals, paintings etc.'. A letter was sent from the Faculty to Baillie explaining the differing views and asking his advice on the matter.

The letter also explained that to include an anatomical theatre would call for additional land in the College Garden having to be used, and that most of the Faculty members would oppose this as it would 'destroy both its beauty and its retirement'. If, however, Baillie advised that the anatomical theatre was to be added, the Faculty would be 'very willing to place the Museum in the Botanic Garden which contains nearly three roods of ground, and you may probably recollect, is close by the College Green, and they will further find another Botanic Garden for the Professor of Botany at their own expense. If the Museum is placed in the Botanic Garden it might be made with a most beautiful front looking into the College Garden, and as the Botanic Garden's almost entirely surrounded with buildings belonging to the College it would be in perfect safety'.

The Faculty (now headed by William Taylor as Principal) expressed concern about the siting of an enlarged museum building. The possible loss of more of the College Garden amenity and the fears of 'the Mob', which could be quickly inflamed by associations of anatomy-teaching with grave-robbing, lay behind their offer of the Physic Garden — a walled site (although more than the 'three roods' quoted, which presumably referred to only a part of its area). The effect on the collections of fumes from the type foundry was not taken into account. In the event Baillie's advice seems to have favoured only the museum being built, and between 1804 and 1807 it was erected to the design of a young architect, William Stark, in the College Garden behind the main block of the College buildings (Figure 8.1). The Physic Garden was to continue under the management of William Lang, the annual allowances for plants and manure often now being made to Thomas Brown.[10] Repairs to the garden wall were allowed in April 1804.[11]

In 1801 Lang had taken over the tacks held by his father. In June 1802 he received £9/9/- as compensation for the loss of plants when the College sold to the Government some land on the east side of the Butts.[12] A more formal personal arrangement was introduced in March 1804, when a Faculty committee was formed to 'transact with the Gardener regarding the lease of the College Garden'.[13] Lang presented an obligation to the Faculty on 31 March 1804[14] in which he agreed to allow the College to repossess any land rented by him, with either a

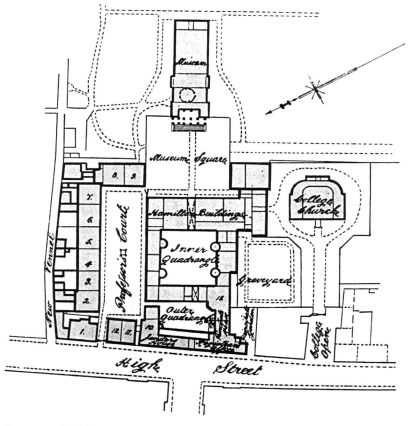

Figure 8.1. Position of the Hunterian Museum in the College Garden. The Mound or Bank was removed during its construction

proportional reduction in his rent or payment of a sum in compensation. In May 1804, a missive of lease for 'two crops of the Dovehill Garden Ground and old house thereon as presently possessed by you' was drawn up between the College and Lang, the annual rent being set at £18 until Candlemas 1806.[15] Noticeably, this is one of the rare occasions when the name Dovehill is once again used. The 'old house' mentioned was not Lang's residence. Over the years there were occasional references to the gardener's 'laigh' house in the Dovehill, so it was probably a small building for storage of tools, seeds, vegetables, etc. These several lettings, together with land near the Gallowgate also leased by him, gave Lang[16] the opportunity to supplement his income with crop sales, with all the attendant risks, as with his father. The foundation stone of the Hunterian Museum was held with due ceremony on 2 August 1804, and in the following January the ground around the construction site was well 'stobbed', presumably to keep out the students. The scribe noting down the Faculty minutes suffered a lapse of memory here, attributing the 18/- for the stobs in the account to *Robert* Lang.[17] Whilst the annual repayments for plants and manure were now usually in Brown's name, in 1806 there was a change, with £5 being allowed for 'plants for the Botanical class'. On 10 June 1806, a committee was formed with James Jeffray as convenor 'to see that the garden be properly kept'.[18] There is a hint of criticism here and, as if in response to this move, Brown wrote a lengthy letter to Jeffray on 12 June 1806 dealing with a number of matters and including the following (Figure 8.2):[19]

I am very sorry to learn that the College is disatisfied with William Lang's behaviour & I am much afraid that is has been improper in many respects, but I can only say that as far as the Botanical Department is concerned I have no fault to find, but every reason to be compleatly pleased with it. That plot of ground which is dignified with the name of Botanic Garden is so very barren, that its produce can scarcely be of any advantage to a lecturer on Botany. He is therefore under the necessity, during the greatest part of the course, both of collecting plants himself in the fields & in neighbouring gardens, & of trusting to the exertions of the gardner. William has always been active & intelligent in this part of his duty, & you must be sensible that a common gardner, ignorant of the names & places of growth of the wild plants in this country, would be entirely unqualified for the office of assistant to the Botanical Lecturship on its present foundation. William unfortunately engaged in the business of an apothecary, but this imprudence is now over & I know that he has lost so considerably by the speculation that he will not again engage in a similar one. The College however ought to calculate whether the emoluments at present derived from the office of College Gardner be sufficient or not to maintain a man with his family in this city, where the expence

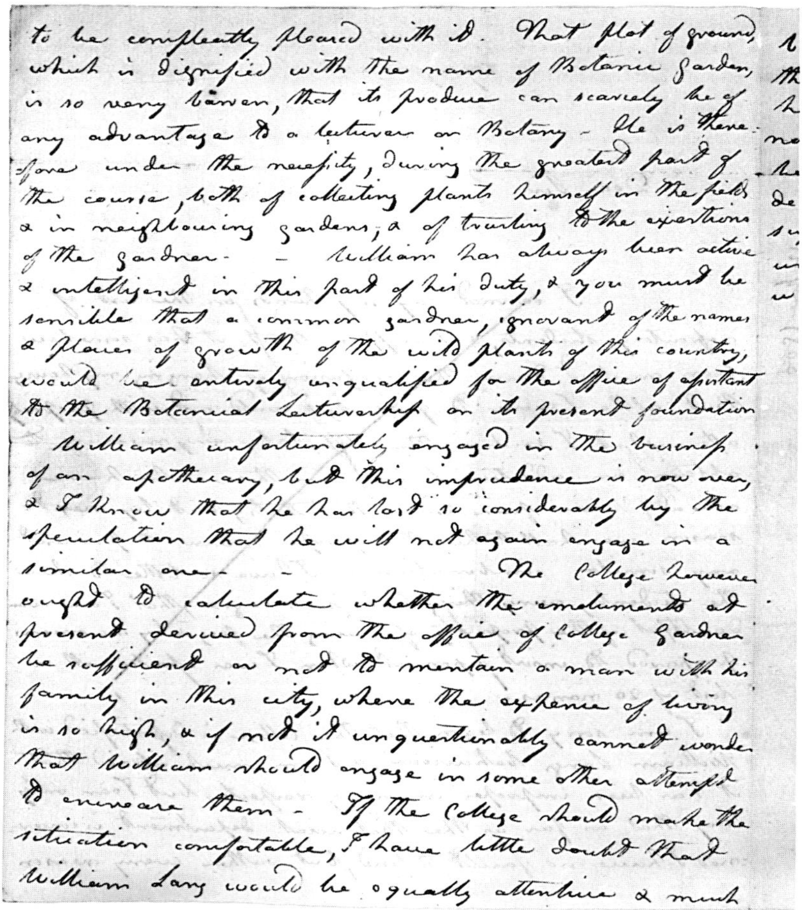

Figure 8.2. Part of Thomas Brown's letter to James Jeffray including comments on the Physic (Botanic) Garden

of living is so high, & if not it unquestionably cannot wonder that William should engage in some other attempt to increase them. If the College should make the situation comfortable, I have little doubt that William Lang would be equally attentive & much better qualified for it than any common gardener that it could employ. His health unfortunately has been bad for some time past & it will probably be soon completely restored. Since his father's death he has maintained a mother, & educated or supported four or five brothers and sisters, which unquestionably ought to have some influence on the College in his favour.

Brown's strong appeal in defence of Lang was aimed at smoothing over matters with the Faculty. Since the Physic Garden was in such poor shape, the complaint levelled against Lang concerned mainly the state of the College Garden and probably the Observatory Garden. From the tenor of Brown's letter, it is evident that Lang had acquired an extensive knowledge of field botany and of plant distribution in the area, important attributes in supporting the Botany classes. Lang had been appointed gardener when 19 years of age, so his knowledge of the local flora and of gardening would presumably have come from his father. Brown's final appeal was to ask that the gardener's job be made financially worthwhile, the cost of living being then, as now, a point of debate regarding emoluments.

Despite Brown's letter, the Faculty seems to have been unconvinced and on 25 January 1807 Lang found it necessary to make a detailed representation of his case to the College:[20]

To the Revd Principal & other Members of the Faculty of Glasgow College

Gentlemen

I have thought it necessary to lay before you a fair statement of facts respecting my conduct and circumstances, since my appointment as Gardener to the University, which was commenced (as You all know) immediately upon my father's decease. Gentlemen, when my father was appointed Gardener it was then observed to him, by several members of Faculty, that the wages allowed were in their opinion equivalent for the work he had to do as their Gardener, but not sufficient for supporting himself and family, and therefore granted him the liberty of occupying his vacant time in that way he thought best for the advantage of his family.

The hard labours and struggles my father had to encounter are well known; his salary being small and having an inclination for educating his children he found himself in circumstances somewhat straightened, even with all his exertions: so that he was not able to make any provision for his wife and family — At the age of Nineteen I was left the guardian and protector of a mother and seven infant children, the youngest only a few weeks old; and the sole provision for them being the salary you allowed me. Gentlemen, as of late much blame has been attached to me for not keeping the College Garden in proper order, it becomes necessary that I should state the cause. During the summer when the Botanical lectures are going on the garden allotted for that Department furnishing but a very few specimens for illustrating the Science of Botany. It is required of me to collect elsewhere whatever plants may be necessary for carrying forward the lectures. For which purpose I have to traverse the country round in search of plants: and that, Gentlemen, not on a particular occasion but almost every day during the course. A great part of my time, therefore, which should be devoted for dressing the

Gardens is occupied in this manner. Because a certain number of different plants, all in flower, must be had for each lecture, And oftentimes after, I have travelled to a wood or waterside two or three miles from Town. I have been disappointed in finding the individual plants wanted — and must again set out to some other quarter to find them. And, Gentlemen, as the number of students last season was upwards of thirty, it became necessary for me to provide upwards of thirty specimens of each individual plant demonstrated. And as several hundred Genera and Species were examined last season, the Botany Garden not furnishing near one hundred in perfect condition. A great proportion of my time must be occupied in this manner. For the truth of the above statement I beg leave to refer you to Dr Brown. And, Gentlemen, during the winter season, when the students are permitted to amuse themselves in the College Garden (having greatly encreased in number of late years) it really becomes very difficult to keep them from doing mischief of one kind or another. Which tends much to hurt the appearance of the Gardens, So, Gentlemen, during the spring season a considerable part of my time is taken up dressing the Botany Garden: the College Garden is in some measure neglected, and injury done to it by the students, in my absence, as it is impossible I can be in both Gardens at once. However, Gentlemen, having already begun my operations for this season, in the Botanic Garden, I shall for the future, so far as I am able, endeavour to do all which either your interest or my station may require.

I am
Gentlemen
Your Most Obedient & Humble
Servant
William Lang

College Land

Blackfriar's Wynd
Jan 25 1807

Lang's representation, explicit in itself, is also a source of valuable information on several aspects of the Physic Garden and the teaching of Botany. It seems likely that his father Robert died suddenly in early middle-age, leaving a young family, and William's appointment was probably an attempt on the part of the College to obviate the immediate distress of Robert Lang's widow and family. At the same time, the committee responsible must have been satisfied of William Lang's capabilities; Jeffray in particular would probably have advised on the appointment. The salary was regarded as being equivalent to the amount of work involved and remained the same in the later years of the century as in the earlier times, an example of eighteenth-century work study. The opportunity for extra earnings was usually offered by the College in the form of tacks for its ground, but the financial risks involved were always borne by the tacksman. It would seem from William Lang's letter·that his father found it difficult to make ends meet, despite the extra crops that he cultivated over the years. William Lang may well have realised the same problem, hence his attempt at setting up business as an apothecary, though with no financial success. Despite the excuses in his letter, it is more likely that the Faculty disapproved of his extra-mural work. When he was given compensation in June 1802 for land sold by the College to the Government, mention was made in the precept of the loss of some herbs, which would rather suggest the source of some of his stock for the ill-fated apothecary's business. Thomas Brown's lectures evidently required large numbers of flowering plants, both for demonstration and for examination (each student was issued with a specimen of all the plants under discussion), and there is some suggestion that practical work went on after the lectures. With the Physic Garden in such poor condition (and how much this was due to the pollution problems and how much to Lang's seemingly inefficient use of his time is unknown), the 'several hundred' plants mentioned in the letter would have required extensive field work. In 1806 there were 39 students in attendance at Brown's Botany lectures (Table 8.2),[21] and this multiple of the several hundred plants required gives some idea of the amount of systematic botany involved. Lang's field-botany knowledge must have been of a high order to cope with the quantities of material required, and this was certainly one of the points in his favour underlined by Brown in his letter to Jeffray. Lang's letter also refers to student damage to the garden. He implies that their freedom to use the garden was restricted to the winter, i.e. the winter session, which extended from October to the following spring. It is also clear from Lang's letter that the gardener's house was still that in Blackfriars Wynd and which had been rebuilt in 1705–6.

Both Brown's letter and Lang's representation seem to have fallen

Table 8.2. Numbers of students attending the Botany classes of Thomas Brown (1799–1810)[21]

1799	15
1800	22
1801	26
1802	20
1803	34
1804	26
1805	20
1806	39
1807	16
1808	33
1809	44
1810	55

on deaf ears so far as the Faculty was concerned. Whilst Lang was not immediately dismissed, it is clear that his appointment was to be terminated, as shown in the minute of 13 February 1807:[22] 'let to Lang the Gardener till Candlemas next the ground presently possessed by him for flowers and herbs etc. for three pounds ten shillings sterl. and he is to remove without any warning at that date'. Candlemas was 2 February, so Lang was being allowed an extra year in possession of the land, but at the end of 1807 it was reported that 'with the resignation of W. Lang the office of College Gardner was vacant from Martinmas last'.[23] Lang's last letter to the Faculty was written on 30 November 1807[24] and was 'for behoof of my eldest sister and those now entrusted to her care', which rather suggests that his mother had died, leaving his sister to care for the younger members of the family. His letter took the form of a request to forward to his sister any moneys owed to him by the College after deduction of his rents. At the same time he claimed a reduction in rent for the land taken over for the building of the Hunterian Museum for the three years from 1804. A Faculty minute of 12 December 1807 includes reference to the amounts of money involved, declaring a balance of £16/10/- being due to Lang, and including an additional award:[25]

> The Faculty agree to order a precept of £3/10/- to be paid to Wm. Lang's Eldest Sister for behoof of the Family under a declaration that nothing further is to be expected from the College and with intimation that she is to leave the house at Whitsunday next.

A note addressed to the Factor outlines the moneys involved:[26]

William Lang Dr. to the College of Glasgow

To Rent of Garden crop	1805		18
	1806		18
	1807		3.10
			39.10
Wages due at Ms	1805	10	
	1806	20	
	1807	20	
		50	50.—
			10.10

To this £10/10/- there was added £6 in compensation for the three years' loss of ground due to the building of the Hunterian Museum and the £3/10/- special award to Janet Lang, who was paid £20 on 14 December 1807. As with Alexander Adams' widow, the Lang family were allowed to retain use of the gardener's house until the following Whitsunday 1808. William Lang meantime passes into oblivion in terms of the garden's history.

The resignation of William Lang sees the end of the Physic Garden as a source of plants for teaching. A Faculty minute of 17 March 1808 states: 'a sum not exceeding Twenty Pounds is agreed this year for finding plants for the Botanic Class, but not to be continued'.[27] This was the allowance for plants to be purchased for handing out to the students, and henceforth this £20 allotment was to be an annual event paid either to Jeffray or Brown, despite the statement in the minute that it was 'not to be continued'. There are no records of an appointment of a gardener in succession to Lang. A committee formed on 22 March 1808 was given the brief 'to consider the state of the College Garden and what improvements may be made', proving that work went on, presumably with hired labour.[28] In April 1808,[29] another committee was set up 'to examine and report on the state of the Gardener's house' with a view to obtaining an estimate of the repairs necessary to make it ready as official residence for the Under Keeper of the Hunterian Museum. The house in the Blackfriars Wynd had been a definite additional asset to the job of College Gardener for just over 100 years, and now became linked with another University official. The repairs were estimated as £3/16/4d and were agreed to on 14 April 1808.[30] The committee formed in early April to consider the state of the garden informed Faculty on 12 May[31] that plans had been made immediately to 'dress' the ground around the Hunterian Museum, and that future work was being planned, particularly to oversee the 'forming of the College Garden during the summer'.[32] On 10 June, the committee was authorised to pay a William Mercer £25 for 'work in the College garden and they are empowered to advance whatever sum may be necessary for compleating it'.[33] Mercer's payment was then made on a precept dated 23 June 1808[34] 'for work now carrying out in the College Garden around the Museum', and on 17 February 1809 he received a total of £117/5/10d, again for work carried out around the museum and other parts of the garden. William Mercer was a man of many parts, being described on one of the precepts as an undertaker, and then in December 1809 being paid a small sum for 'casewing the Garden gate' ('casewing' = causaying).

A second item of Faculty business was dealt with at the 10 June 1808 meeting:

A Disposition from James Burns to the Principal and Professors of the ground intended for a Botanic Garden was given in, and the Faculty authorize the Principal to pay the purchase.

The precept was made out on the next day:[35]

Pay to Mr James Burns One Hundred pounds str as the purchase money of four acres of Land on Blythswoods grounds contiguous to Mr Towers property which he has conveyed to the Faculty of the College

With the College Physic Garden now in a moribund state (it was never formally closed but seems to have faded away into insignificance), the Faculty was making a positive move to establish a new and larger garden at some distance westwards from the College but away from pollutant effects.[36] No immediate use was made of the land, and on 1 March 1809 it was decided it should be let for summer pasture at a rent of £15.[37] On 10 December 1810 a further 12 months' letting was agreed;[38] there seems not to have been much urgency about laying out the new garden. As already mentioned, Brown's summer courses of lectures on Botany were dependent on the £20 allotment for plant material. According to one historian of the Old College, Brown gave his lectures in a house separate from the College, with a collection of plants being available from the neighbouring garden.[39] According to the Faculty records, however, the £20 annual allotment for plants was given every year until 1815, Brown's last year as Lecturer. The available records of attendance at Brown's lectures (Table 8.2), when compared with those of Jeffray for the preceding ten years (Table 7.1), certainly imply that Jeffray's enthusiastic support of Brown's appointment as Lecturer was well justified. Brown was succeeded by Robert Graham, who was appointed Lecturer in Botany under the same conditions as his predecessor in May 1816.[40]

Other routine matters of maintenance and use of the College lands continued. John McLachlan was paid £10 in August 1808[41] for cleaning out the Molendinar Burn, and in October 1811 received £5/8/8d for supplying and spreading gravel on some of the walks.[42] William Lang's resignation left free the land he had held in tack. Much of the Observatory Park was henceforth laid down as pasture, and let for grazing each year between May and November. In 1809 the annual rent for this was £16/10/-. In 1811 John Hannah, a local butcher, offered £20 for the annual grazing rights, and was to become a tenant each year until 1822. The conditions of his holding were clearly defined.[43]

1. The land was to be pastured wholly by sheep 'of the same number as last year and no more'.
2. Entry was to be on 1 May and removal on 1 November.
3. One pound additional rent would be charged for every day that the sheep were kept on the ground after the six months.
4. The fences were to be taken over 'as they are' and Hannah would have to make them thoroughly 'sheep proof' at his own expense.

Henceforth, in place of the annual grass crop, the Park was to be kept in a trim condition through the summer by the grazing action of sheep, with the additional benefits of a continuing supply of manure evenly spread on the surface.

In William Lang's representation of December 1807, the complaint was made that the students caused damage in the gardens which he was unable either to control or to rectify. In November 1811 it was reported to Faculty that there had been a 'disagreeable interference between the students and the military in the Observatory Park'.[44] The soldiers had come from the Barracks on the east side of the Butts. A decision was taken to lock the garden door 'until the matter could be sorted out', the garden door being the one on the bridge over the Molendinar Burn and intended to prevent students going into the Observatory Park. The Professors were 'loath to deprive the students of the Liberty of taking Exercise in the College Garden bounded in the east by the Molendinar Burn'. It was then decided that the garden would be open to the students between 10 a.m. and 4 p.m. daily, but with the 'express condition That no student shall upon any account pass over the said ground into the Observatory Park which shall be intimated by the Professors in their lectures'. Any student found disobeying would be fined half-a-crown for each infringement. A similar incident, said to have taken place in November 1810, is described in Murray's *Memories of the Old College of Glasgow* (p. 492), when there was a fracas between soldiers of the 71st Foot who had entered the Observatory Park and students who challenged them and who themselves were excluded from the Observatory Park. The fighting was said to have spread into the College Garden and up to the walls of the Hunterian Museum and to have been brought to an end only when the Officers of the Regiment ordered the men back to barracks. Whether this is the same incident as that of 1811 but with the year given incorrectly is not known. The attitude of the Faculty to student use of the College Garden had changed appreciably since the early 1700s, when their exclusion (except for the sons of noblemen) was firmly upheld. A proposal to shut the gardens for some time was made in March 1813,[45] but the reasons were not stated.

The final phase of the history of the Physic Garden was heralded in November 1813, when the Principal was authorised to accept an offer from a William King, a plumber, for the purchase of a 'lot of ground in the Old Botanic Garden'.[46] The sale was formally recorded on 26 November [47]

1. The Lot of ground shall be laid off from the West boundary, at least sixty feet along the North side of the Blackfriars Wynd, & running at right angles from the said Wynd northward, till it joins the backwall of the burying ground, & where the Type foundry comes in, to be lined off according as the College shall direct, and that you shall get the ground lined off on the West boundary between you & the contiguous Proprietors

2. That when the boundaries are ascertained the Lot shall be measured off by Mr Kyle by whose measurement both parties shall abide it being declared that he is to measure all beyond a line drawn parallel to the south side of said Wynd at the distance of twenty feet, and that no building shall be erected nearer to the said line than

other twenty feet — the meaning being that if ever a public Street shall be carried eastwards, that room may be left opposite the said old Garden for a street of forty feet wide

3. That any building along the front of the ground to the said Wynd shall be ashlar and covered with slates, and that no thack shall be used on any buildings on the background

4. That nothing deemed a nuisance shall be erected on the ground — Cotton milnes & similar public work, which throw out great volumes of Smoke are particularly to be excluded

5. That within three years you shall erect buildings sufficient to secure the feu duty

6. That the price of the ground with the Materials thereon shall be twenty two shillings & six pence per square yard, to be converted into a perpetual feu of five per cent per an. free of deductions — and that at the end of every nineteen years there shall be a double feu in place of entry money

7. As a street may possibly be opened hereafter to run eastwards through the College Garden towards the Barracks & to communicate with the Gallowgate. It is hereby provided that, as soon as said street shall be opened, there shall be a rise of six shillings additional on the square yard of the said lot to be converted into a feu rent upon the same terms as in the preceding article

8. That your entry shall commence immediately on the satisfaction of this agreement by the Faculty: but that you shall possess the same till Whitsunday without paying any feu duty shall only begin to run at Whitsunday next, the first half of the feu being payable at Martinmas 1814 & so on half yearly in all time coming.

Jeffray formally entered a protest against these arrangements, but nothing further was heard of his intervention. The 'lot' of ground to be sold is shown in Figure 8.3 (again assuming that the scale measurements on McArthur's plan of the University are accurate).[48] The surface area involved was 1200 square yards, so that its purchase price would have been £1350. The Faculty was not to be faulted on its forward planning, leaving room for any future road-widening of the Blackfriars Wynd (which did take place later on) so that they would have land to sell for this purpose. Some degree of planning permission is implied in the nature of the houses to be built and the exclusion of any industrial buildings. Disposal of the remainder of the Physic Garden ground came up for discussion at successive Faculty meetings; the offer eventually accepted was that of James Taylor.[49,50] This offer was again for £1/2/6d per square yard,[51] and since Taylor had the larger 'lot' of 1800 square yards he paid the College £2050. The combined price was converted into a joint ground annual of about £181, representing an actual price of near £3620. The University retained possession of the east wall of the garden and declared that Taylor should 'have no servitude for lights upon the College Garden',

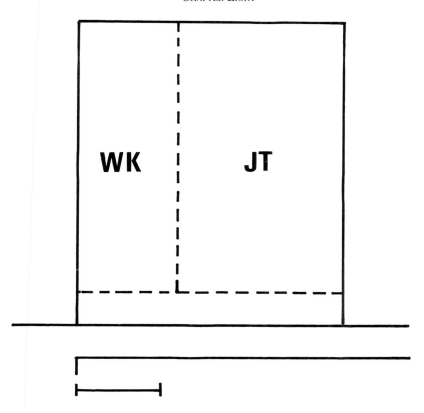

Figure 8.3. Division of the Physic Garden at time of sale

WK = William King's purchase **JT** = James Taylor's purchase

Scale line: 50 feet

i.e. the College could still plant trees in the College Garden without Taylor being able to make any claim for obstruction from the east side of the house he was to build.

With the sale of the ground to Taylor, the Physic Garden ceased to exist. From its initiation in 1704 it had just under 100 years of existence, since by 1803 it was in a very poor condition. Indeed, it was probably in a state of decline over the 1780–1800 period. The site of the new Botanic Garden came up for discussion at the end of March 1814, when a committee was asked to supervise the fencing of the ground at Blythswood.[52] But this new garden was not to be. Moves were afoot in 1817 to establish a Botanic Garden in the town and involved some leading citizens from Glasgow and its neighbourhood, the Crown and the University. These deliberations were to receive Royal acknowledgement in the Charter issued on 20 September 1818 for the creation of the Royal Botanic Institution of Glasgow. The part to be played in this affair by the University came up for discussion at the end of April 1817, when the views of a committee set up to investigate and report back came before Faculty. These views were summarised in a letter to the committee of local citizens involved in the project. The letter was entered in full in the minutes:[53]

> The College propose to contribute to the Institution and maintainance of the New Botanic Garden what is equivalent to a capital of Two Thousand Pounds Stg consisting of the following items
>
> 1st. To Pay the annual feu of Sixty Pounds for the Six Acres of ground to be purchased
>
> 2ndly. To advance at a term to be specified Two Hundred Pounds in cash
>
> 3rdly. As the College have four acres of ground acquired with a view to a Botanic Garden but which will now fall to be sold, which cost the College at least three hundred pounds, they will assign to the new Garden whatever the said Ground shall produce which they will guarantee at three hundred pounds, but whatever more can be got for it shall Accrue to the funds of the new Garden
>
> In consideration of which the College will expect to be secured in a Patrimonial right in said Garden proportional to the amount of said subscription, and that no other demands shall be made on their funds, either now or in future on account of said Garden, its Buildings, the salary of the Gardner, or any other annual expence otherwise. And that the privilege of teaching, and of using the plants for teaching Botany should be secured to the College for which purpose it will be necessary that the Gardner, at least during the season for teaching be especially under the direction and orders of the Professor of Botany or Lecturer for the time being in the University
>
> The College are willing to waive all claim to the right of having votes at meetings of subscribers in proportion to the number of shares they may hold, but will expect one third of the Committee of Management shall consist of Members of Faculty and of which the Professor of Botany shall always be one
>
> It is understood that any other Corporate Body shall have equal privileges as the College upon equal terms
>
> That members of the Faculty and their Families shall have equal privileges in walking in the garden and otherwise as shall be given to the most favoured class of subscribers
>
> That the Committee shall draw up regulations to carry into effect the teaching of Botany by the Professor of Botany agreeably to the spirit of this report
>
> That the resolution shall not be binding on the College unless at

least Four Thousand Pounds Stg shall be raised otherwise by those interested in promoting the scheme.

The University's prime interest in the proposed new Botanic Garden was to replace the lost teaching facilities, for which the Faculty was prepared to outlay the equivalent of £2000. This investment underlines the importance the Faculty placed on the practical facilities for teaching the subject, no doubt pressurised by Jeffray following the sale of the Physic Garden land. It is not known why so little progress was made on the Blythswood land. The letter from the group of citizens, led by Thomas Hopkirk who formed the local pressure group, and written in direct reply to the letter from Faculty quoted above, is dated 8 May 1817. The group letter is more explicit regarding the University's financial commitments than that sent to them by Faculty; perhaps the scribe writing the Faculty minutes made an incomplete record of the contents of its letter. The signatories (Thomas Hopkirk, James Hardie jnr, T. Brown, Thos. McGill, Robert Austin and William Cumin) were in general agreement with the proposals put forward by Faculty for the joint management of the garden. Their letter, however, also described in more detail the financial promises of the University: that it would pay the annual feu of £60 to Mr Campbell of Blythswood, or to his heirs, but if the feu could be bought the University would pay the £1200 capital outlay required. This mention of the larger capital outlay was missed in the copy of the Faculty's letter. (At a later date, 3 December 1818, it was agreed that the 'superiorities in place of the annual feu' for the garden would be paid for by the University.)[54] The letter from Hopkirk and his colleagues also mentions the proceeds of the sale 'of the Ground near Woodside belonging to the College, originally intended for a Botanic Garden'. This was the land purchased for £300, and reference to it in the letter from Hopkirk and the others appears to be the only record of the University having bought land at Woodside, a locality northwest of Blythswood. It would seem that over the years the University had three sites in mind for a new Physic Garden: that on the northeast side of the College ground as envisaged in 1799; the Blythswood land bought in 1809; and the Woodside ground of unknown purchase date. Later on, the Blythswood land was sold to Mr Towers, who owned property nearby. All told, the group of interested citizens seemed well satisfied with the financial outlay proposed by the University, and through them the £4000 demanded by the University in support of its outlay was to be forthcoming.

The University had called for full facilities for the teaching of botany to be available once the garden was opened. Hopkirk and his associates proposed that the Professor of Botany or College Lecturer should deliver at least one course of lectures each season in the Lecture Room to be erected in the garden, and to have the exclusive right of lecturing there. The gardener employed by the Institution would be required to attend the Professor's lectures and would have to supply all the plants required for demonstration purposes.

Thomas Hopkirk of Dalbeth, Paisley, the principal instigator of the scheme, was a keen gardener and field botanist. In 1813 he published his *Flora Glottiana*, a list of plants from Glasgow and the banks of the River Clyde; a catalogue of the plants in his garden at Dalbeth also appeared in print in the same year.[55] A collection of some 3,000 plants from Dalbeth was to form the basis of the new garden, which was laid out on a site of about 8 acres at Sandyford, an estate lying to the west of the city, and which in time was to become a select residential area for wealthier citizens.[56] In addition to the £6000 investment from the University and citizenry, the Crown also paid £2000 towards the foundation of the garden at the time that the Royal Charter was issued. The £2000 from the University was covered by a legacy of a Mr Hamilton, which was to come to the University on the death of his wife.[57] The garden was opened to the public in 1819. The University obtained a teaching facility far superior to that which had existed before, and the disadvantage of distance from the main College building was far outweighed by the accommodation and range of plant material available.

The preparations for the new Botanic Garden had commenced after Brown had resigned from the lectureship. His contributions to the teaching of Botany over some 16 years were major ones, although given largely without benefit of a supporting garden. Brown was the son and grandson of prosperous surgeons in the town, and he inherited the property of Langside and later an estate at Lanfine in Ayrshire. He bequeathed a large collection of minerals and fossils in equal quantities to the two Universities at Glasgow and Edinburgh; in due course his daughter, who inherited the Lanfine estate, was to leave £5000 to Glasgow University for bursaries in Arts.[58] Robert Graham, who followed Brown as Lecturer, was to receive the £20 allowance for plants in 1816 and 1817.

James Jeffray, having convinced the Faculty in 1800 of the desirability of having a separate Lecturer in Botany, was to be responsible for the salaries of Brown and Graham via the class fees. The separation of the two subjects of his joint Chair became permanent on 16 December 1817 when a Royal Commission was issued establishing a Regius Chair of Botany in the University and naming Robert Graham as its first occupant.[59] Graham is said to have played some part in the institution of the Chair through his influence with the Duke of Montrose, Chancellor of the University, of whose family he was a cadet.[60] Graham's conditions of appointment followed the pattern of all such commissions but with the following additional clause:

Doctor Robert Graham to be Regius Professor of Botany in the said University during all the days of his life and to have and enjoy all the powers and privileges which belong to any other Professor and Teacher in the said University with the exceptions after specified, viz., Excepting the right and power of taking any share of the examinations of Candidates for degrees in Medicine or participating in the emoluments arising therefrom and excepting any right to share or to participate in any of the Funds or Emoluments belonging to the College or University of Glasgow, or to interfere with the patrimonial rights of other Professors already established in said College or University, or to Act and interfere in the Management of Funds vested in the said College or University for Literary or other purposes and declaring that the said Regius Professor shall have no right to vote or Act in Elections of Professors, or to exercise in virtue of this appointment Privileges as a member of this College of Glasgow not otherwise appertaining to him but shall in virtue hereof have power to Vote in the Election of Dean of Faculty and to act as a member of the University of Glasgow in all cases not especially excepted ...

The burden of this clause is linked with the long-standing rivalry between the Faculty, the principal governing body of the University composed of the Principal and the occupants of Chairs established prior to 1761, and the Senate or 'University Meeting', which by 1817 would have included professorships of later establishment.[61] Graham presented his Commission to the Senate on 5 March 1818,[62] and was duly required to present his 'trial exercise' on 17 March on the subject *De vita plantarum et analogia sua ad vitam animentum* ('On the life of plants and its resemblance to the life of living things').[63] With the acceptance of this trial exercise, and having completed the necessary formalities as described for William Hamilton (p. 185), Graham was duly admitted to office. He arrived at an opportune time, with the arrangements for the new Botanic Garden being well in hand. Yet despite the understanding that the Professor of Botany was to be one of the three Managers (later Directors) of the Sandyford garden available to the University, in December 1818 the Faculty appointed the Principal, James Jeffray and William McTurk (Professor of Ecclesiastical History)[64] as the representatives for the ensuing year — although Jeffray had dropped the title of Botany from his Professorship in April of the same year. Again, in December 1819, Jeffray, McTurk and Robert Freer (Professor of Practice of Medicine) were appointed the College's representatives on the Committee of Management.[65] Graham, who was closely involved with the organisation of the new garden from the time of his appointment, was not to become a Manager. Whether this was a further manifestation of the Faculty versus Senate imbroglio is not known. In December 1819, Graham was appointed Professor of Medicine and Botany at Edinburgh University in succession to Daniel Rutherford, and once in post there he was to become deeply involved in the planning of the new botanic garden then being laid out at Inverleith.[66]

Whilst the Faculty was deliberating on the possible sites for the Botanic Garden and the arrangements for the Sandyford development, the other garden and park areas in the College ground had still to be maintained, although without a resident gardener. John Hannah, who in 1813 had obtained the right to graze sheep in the summer months in the Observatory Park and was to continue annually to obtain the same facility until 1822, had to cope with a steadily increasing rental which by 1818 had risen to £28. In 1821 (and again in 1822) he was let the Observatory Park and the College Garden for a combined rental of £43 'to be pastured by sheep only';[67] the convenience of using sheep to crop the grass and manure the ground was extended to the College Garden. The Butts Park was let for £40 in March 1816.[68] Two years later, the clay strata in the Butts Park became a source of income when the tacksman Charles McKid proposed setting up 'two additional tables for making clay' and offered £130 per annum for this facility.[69] Committees for supervising work in the gardens continued to be appointed, as in February 1817 when the Principal headed a committee 'to superintend some small projected improvements in the College Garden'.[70] In the summer of 1818, another committee was formed to attend to the sale of lots in the College Garden with power 'to act in the business for the interest of the College agreeably to the articles of sale'.[71] The lots were not defined, nor are any further deliberations of this committee available.

A Faculty decision of 24 April 1818 indicated further changes in the state of the College Garden:[72]

> The Faculty resolve that the stob railing along the north side of the intended street through the College Garden shall be put up immediately and a Parapet wall and Iron Railing and that the Ground shall be Advertised without delay

The line of the new road becomes clear with the resolution passed in February 1819, when a committee was formed to 'consider building a parapet wall with an iron rail from the East end of the Blackfriars Wynd to the Molendinar Burn and report'.[73] An estimate for the new wall was accepted the following April and payment (£413/5/6d) on its completion made in March 1820.[74] The new road (Blackfriars Street) replaced the narrow Wynd and ran along the southern border of the College Garden. The Faculty's holding on to 20 feet of land at the front of the old Physic Garden — for just this eventuality — seems like well-planned foresight, or possibly fore-knowledge. On the same day in March 1819, when the final bill for the new wall was passed, another committee was formed to obtain estimates for a new bridge over the Molendinar Burn 'in line with the new street'. The estimate accepted was that of James Dick, who for £700 (to be paid in instalments) guaranteed completion of the new bridge by the following 31 August.[75] In April 1821 another committee met to consider 'the proper mode of arching over the Molendinar Burn',[76] but the covering-over of the Burn along its length was not effected until the 1850s. As in previous years, the Burn remained something of a problem. On 15 May 1823, it was decided 'to get all dams removed that impede the running of the Burn and to get the Nuisances erected about the Burn without any title, removed'. Whether a verse from an 'Ode to the Molendinar' published in the College Album of 1832 is truly descriptive has been questioned:[77]

> With weariness and pallor fraught
> Upon the clay-built banks I'd lie
> And gaze upon the smoke-veiled sky,
> Or watch thine ever-changing hues
> And breathe the scents thy waves diffuse
> Roll on, with murky billows roll
> Juice of the mud-cart and the coal

Another bridge over the burn in line with the New Vennel on the northern boundary of the garden was discussed by a committee set up on 1 November 1822, presumably to accompany road-widening.[78] Concern was also expressed about the need for a new wall to enclose the Observatory grounds following the development of the new roads around the area. On 5 May 1823, the relevant committee was required 'to speedily ensure the building of said wall'.[79] In June 1821 plans were drawn up for a new walk in the Observatory Park, and this was eventually completed two years later at a cost of £72/4/6d.[80] Occasional references to the hired labour used for garden maintenance are to be found in the Faculty records. William McNair was paid a total of £4/6/4d 'for work in the College gardens' in June 1821.[81] In November 1822, John Walker was appointed 'Gardener, Bell Ringer and Scavenger' and was to receive the total emoluments for the three offices.[82] At some time the gardener's house in Blackfriars Wynd, which had been made available to the Under Keeper of the Hunterian Museum, became vacant again when the Under Keeper moved into the Keeper's residence in the Museum. The house may then have become available to the appointed gardener. John Walker's appointment as gardener is the first recorded since William Lang's resignation in 1807.

In March 1813 it was decided to close the garden to the students for an unspecified time, and no reasons were given. The students presented a petition to the Principal in December 1819 asking that the garden be re-opened. The Faculty agreed on condition that the open hours should be limited (to 10 a.m. — 4 p.m.), that no ball games should be played and that no damage be done to the plants.

Robert Graham's appointment to the Professorship of Medicine and Botany at Edinburgh in December 1819 left the Chair of Botany at Glasgow vacant — just two years after the issue of the Royal Commission for its establishment. His successor was William Jackson

Hooker, who was to occupy the Chair until 1841 when he became Director of Kew Gardens. Hooker differed from his predecessor in lacking any medical background, but he had undoubted botanical qualifications, though mainly self-taught. His botanical field work (1806–14) had extended from Britain to the Continent and his correspondence with European botanists was extensive. His appointment to the Glasgow Chair followed advice from Sir Joseph Banks, still a highly influential figure. Hooker's Commission was dated 10 February 1820 and followed similar lines to that of Graham.[83] The exceptions listed in Graham's Commission were not entered in full in Hooker's, but were covered by the words: 'with all rights, immunities and privileges which belong to any other Professor within the said University that he or his predecessor in office hitherto enjoyed'. There was a further inclusion in Hooker's Commission, viz., 'giving and granting to the said William Jackson Hooker the oversight, care and direction of the Royal Botanic Garden established at Glasgow and to be our Botanist within that part of the aforesaid United Kingdom ...'. This rather implies a more overall Directorship of the Sandyford Botanic Garden, as well as the Regius Chair — more than was proposed in the original heads of agreement drawn up between the Faculty and the other proprietors of the garden. The result, however, was that Hooker became one of the three Directors appointed by the University, and continued to serve as such during the time of his tenure of the Chair. A unique feature of Hooker's appointment was that his Commission was read and he gave his trial Latin discourse (*De Laudibus Botanices* — 'On the praises of botany') at the same Senate meeting, 27 April 1820.[84] As stated in the relevant minute: 'From the speciality of the circumstances in which Mr Hooker is placed, being just on the eve of beginning his Lectures, the Senate agreed to proceed to his admission immediately, at the same time resolving that this departure from the usual forms shall not be drawn into a precedent'.

Hooker was to make Glasgow a major centre for botany through his prowess as a lecturer, author, field botanist and taxonomist. Whilst his salary from the Crown as Regius Professor was at first £50, this was raised to £100 by Royal Warrant in 1827. In addition he received the class fees from his students, and these rose from £60 to £700 with the increasing popularity of his lectures —[85] regarded with some jealousy by other Professors, especially some of the Faculty members. Hooker was knighted in 1839, and became the leading botanist in Britain. This is not the place to review his life's work, since this has already been done expertly.[86] Hooker arrived in Glasgow after the essential spadework had been literally and metaphorically completed under the direction of Graham, Hopkirk and associates. Whilst he inherited an established garden, he undoubtedly made major contributions to the management of the garden over the years and took full advantage of the facilities it offered. He was able to attract to his lectures townspeople and some officers from the Foot Regiments stationed in

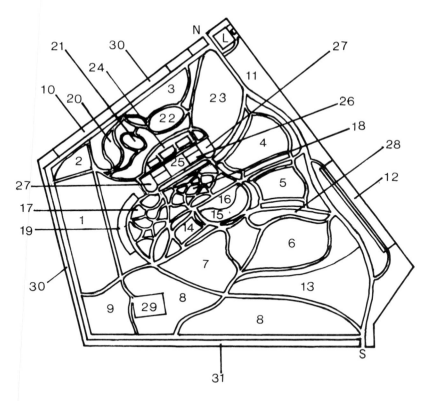

Figure 8.4. 1825 plan of the Botanic Garden of the Royal Botanic Institution of Glasgow

1 Herbaceous plants
2 Grasses
3 Linnaean system collection
4 Jussieu's Natural Method collection
5 British collection
6 Medicinal plants
7 Plants of agriculture and commerce
8 Forest trees
9 Willows
10 Borders for annuals
11 Biennial collection
12 Esculent vegetables
13 Grass and shrubberies
14 American plants
15 Aquarium
16 Rockery with alpine plants

17 Rose collection
18 Flower borders
19 Carnations, auriculas, anemones
20 Variegated plants
21 General alpine collection
22 Summer station for greenhouse collection
23 Shrubs
24 Forcing Beds, Frames etc.
25 Greenhouse
26 Stoves
27 Stoves
28 Medicinal plants (smaller collection)
29 Rare and North American plants
30 { Borders for duplicates to
31 { keep up collection

N = North entrance from Sandyford Road (now Sauchiehall St.) **L** = Lodge house

and lecture Room **S** = South entrance on Dumbarton Road (now Argyle St.)

the town. It is from Hooker's pen, in association with the Superintendent of the garden, Stewart Murray, that a catalogue of the plants and a plan of the Botanic Garden was supplied in 1825.[87]

The garden, some 8 acres in area, was irregularly pentagonal in shape (Figure 8.4). Buildings included a lodge house, lecture room and greenhouses. The divisions within the garden included a general collection of herbaceous plants; a collection of grasses; a collection illustrating the Linnaean system; a collection illustrating the Natural Classification of Jussieu; a British collection; two collections of medicinal plants; plants used in agriculture and commerce; forest trees; willows; borders for annuals; a collection of biennials; esculent vegetables; shrubberies and lawns; a collection of American plants; an aquarium (pond and aquatic plants); a rockery with alpines; a rose collection; flower borders; beds of carnations, auriculas and anemones; a collection of variegated plants; and a general collection of alpines. In addition there were special enclosures for the cultivation of rare plants, borders for maintaining duplicates, and a summer display 'station' for the greenhouse plants. The garden also contained 'Queen Mary's Yew', propagated from a tree said to have been planted in the grounds of Crookston Castle, Renfrewshire, by Mary Queen of Scots. Sandyford was a well-organised garden with a southerly aspect and on good soil. It was not strictly a University garden, despite the patrimonial rights held by the Principal and members of Faculty.

Hooker's time at Glasgow coincided with the period of existence of the Sandyford garden. By the late 1830s there were numerous buildings around its perimeter which prevented expansion, and the garden was becoming too small for the growing collection. Because of the need for expansion, the Royal Botanic Institution purchased some 22 acres of land in the northwest of the city, actually outside the city boundary, and there a new garden was initiated in 1840; this is the site of the present-day Glasgow Botanic Garden.

The title of this chapter, taken from Thomas Brown's letter of 12 June 1806, was in its context a derogatory statement on the impoverished state of the Physic Garden. After the sale of the Physic Garden land in 1817, Brown's sarcastic comment remains the sole epitaph for a small garden over which much care had been lavished in the eighteenth century. With the success of Sandyford garden and the teaching facilities then available, Brown's comment may be looked at in an entirely different light: as a favourable description of the new botanic garden — which formed an essential and valuable working background to Hooker's distinguished professorship at Glasgow.

Notes

1. GUAA 58429.
2. GUAA 58429.
3. GUAA 58416.
4. GUAA 58416.

5. FM, 15 May 1801: 26696, p. 43.

6. FM, 14 March 1803: 26696, p. 170.

7. J.D. Mackie, 1954. *The University of Glasgow 1451–1957* (Jackson, Son & Co., Glasgow), p. 241.

8. FM, 26 December 1800: 26692, p. 20.

9. FM, 9 May 1803: 26696, pp. 190–3.

10. FM, 15 May 1804: 26696, p. 296.

11. FM, 8 April 1804: 26696, p. 288.

12. FM, 10 June 1802: 26696, p. 116.

13. FM, 30 March 1804: 26696, p. 285.

14. GUAA 1959.

15. GUAA 1960.

16. FM, 30 April 1804: 26696, p. 389.

17. FM, 29 January 1805: 26696, p. 344.

18. FM, 10 June 1806: 26697, p. 9.

19. GUAA 1961.

20. GUAA 1961.

21. GUAA 25032.

22. FM, 13 February 1807: 26697, p. 31.

23. FM, 12 December 1807: 26697, p. 160.

24. GUAA 58389.

25. FM, 12 December 1807: 26697, p. 161.

26. GUAA 58389.

27. FM, 17 March 1808: 26697, p. 192.

28. FM, 21 March 1808: 26697, p. 192.

29. FM, 11 April 1808: 26697, p. 196.

30. FM, 14 April 1808: 26697, p. 200.

31. FM, 12 May 1808: 26697, p. 208.

32. FM, 8 June 1808: 26697, p. 220.

33. FM, 10 June 1808: 26697, p. 220.

34. GUAA 58422.

35. GUAA 58422.

36. A. Gibb, 1983. *Glasgow: the making of a City* (Croom Helm, London), pp. 95–6.

37. FM, 1 March 1809: 26697, p. 251.

38. FM, 10 December 1810: 26697, p. 325.

39. D. Murray, 1925. *Memories of the Old College of Glasgow* (Jackson, Wylie & Co.), p. 249.

40. FM, 8 May 1816: 26698, p. 97.

41. GUAA 58422.

42. FM, 16 October 1811: 26697, p. 362.

43. FM, 11 March 1811: 26697, p. 344.

44. FM, 5 November 1811: 26697, p. 364.

45. FM, 18 March 1813: 26697, p. 423.

46. FM, 12 November 1813: 26698, p. 11.

47. FM, 26 November 1813: 26698, pp. 12–14.

48. GUAA 13471.

49. FM, 15 December 1813: 26698, p. 15.

50. FM, 20 December 1813: 26698, p. 15.

51. FM, 14 January 1813: 26698, p. 16.

52. FM, 31 March 1814: 26698, p. 20.

53. FM, 29 April 1817: 26698, p. 127.

54. FM, 3 December 1818: 26698, p. 165.

55. H.R. Fletcher and W.H. Brown, 1970. *The Royal Botanic Garden Edinburgh 1670–1970* (HMSO, Edinburgh), p. 96.

56. A. Gibb, 1983. *Glasgow,* pp. 121, 126.

57. FM, 28 April 1817: 26698, p. 127.

58. J. Coutts, 1909. *A History of the*

University of Glasgow (James Maclehose & Sons, Glasgow), p. 503.

59. Scottish Record Office, Ref. P 53/14.

60. H.R. Fletcher & W.H. Brown, 1970. *The Royal Botanic Garden*, p. 103.

61. J.D. Mackie, 1904. *The University of Glasgow*, pp. 196–7.

62. SM, 5 March 1818: 26698, p. 339.

63. SM, 17 March 1818: 26698, p. 342.

64. FM, 3 December 1818: 26698, p. 165.

65. FM, 9 December 1819: 26698, p. 204.

66. H.R. Fletcher and W.H. Brown, 1970. *The Royal Botanic Garden*, p. 102.

67. FM, 17 April 1821: 26698, p. 262.

68. FM, 29 March 1816: 26698, p. 98.

69. FM, 26 November 1818: 26698, p. 164.

70. FM, 11 February 1817: 26698, p. 118.

71. FM, 29 June 1818: 26698, p. 158.

72. FM, 24 April 1818: 26698, p. 151.

73. FM, 24 February 1819: 26698, p. 176.

74. FM, 8 March 1820: 26698, p. 213.

75. FM, 16 May 1820: 26698, p. 232.

76. FM, 17 April 1821: 26698, p. 262.

77. D. Murray, 1925. *Memories of the Old College of Glasgow*, p. 51.

78. FM, 1 November 1822: 26698, p. 319.

79. FM, 15 May 1823: 26698, p. 357.

80. FM, 10 June 1824: 26698, p. 386.

81. FM, 15 June 1821: 26698, p. 286.

82. FM, 13 November 1822: 26698, p. 322.

83. Scottish Record Office, Ref. P 53/14

84. SM, 27 April 1820: 26689, pp. 44–5.

Biography (Compact Edition), p. 1001.

86. M. Allen, 1967. *The Hookers of Kew 1785–1911* (Michael Joseph, London).

87. F.O. Bower, 1903. Notes on Botany in the University of Glasgow in the Eighteenth Century. *Transactions of the Natural History Society of Glasgow*, vol. 7, pp. 121–36.

'What is the Memory of the Old College of Glasgow?'

This question was posed by Edmund Law Lushington, Professor of Greek (and brother-in-law of Alfred Lord Tennyson), in an address on 7 November 1870 at the first general congregation of the University in its new home at Gilmorehill. Lushington's theme was essentially one of continuity — that the new buildings and location represented a staging post in the long life of the University. We may paraphrase this question as a form of enquiry regarding the state of the gardens in the years leading up to the University's migration. For this purpose we can draw on the memories of observers who lived into the present century. A recent historian has summarised the state of the gardens at the time: '... the famous gardens at the back of the College resembled a blackened waste, on which the playing of cricket was fraught with the greatest danger'.[1] The Molendinar Burn had been covered over in the 1850s; perhaps its state at that time had been graphically described by an unknown medical-student poet:[2]

> It must have been in this same stream
> That Achilles' mother held him,
> That scathless he 'mong foes might be,
> For they'd all cut and run when they smelled him.

In part our purpose in this last chapter is to assess the extent to which a deteriorating environment affected the garden and its management. Once again we meet a change of name. The Great Yard or Garden of the early 1700s, which in time became known as the College Garden, becomes the College Green in the 1850s. This still refers to the area west of the Molendinar Burn as originally enclosed by James Fall in the later years of the seventeenth century. It should be remembered that the Faculty (the Principal and those Professors in post before 1761) was to remain the main governing body until a new constitution came into being as a result of the Royal Commission (with the brief to reform the Scottish Universities) of 1858.[3] Hence, for a large part of the time with which we are concerned the main deliberations regarding the gardens were those of Faculty committees.

In the preceding chapter there are references to the College Garden being closed to the students on occasions. On 22 November 1822 the Faculty expressed its disapproval of the playing of football in the garden, and a committee was formed 'to draw up an intimation to be read out to the students at lectures.'[4] Within a few weeks there was more trouble, and it was decided that the garden should again be closed since 'disturbances have happened by a Fray between the Students and Children and Apprentices of some Townspeople in the neighbourhood. Any students found in the garden during the period of closure would not then be allowed to attend further classes during the session'.[5] Seemingly this was rather a harsh penalty for disobedience, but suggests that the 'Fray' may have been a serious one. The need for proper enclosure of the College land was voiced at the Faculty meeting of 5 May 1823 (now chaired by Duncan McFarlane, after the death of William Taylor on 1 March). A committee was formed to receive estimates for 'building a proper fence around the Observatory Grounds, and to have it executed with all speed'.[6] The new wall cost £252 and seems to have been built almost within days of the decision having been taken.[7] New roads were in the process of formation in the neighbourhood, and in time certain of these were to cross College ground, so that by 1836 the College Garden and Observatory Park almost formed an island surrounded by roads (Figure 9.1).

A link with past Garden history came up for consideration on 29 April 1825, when offers were considered for the ground 'upon which the Old Houses stand usually called the Gardener's Houses', with an offer of 35/- per square yard (to be converted into a ground annual) being accepted. Built about 1708, these 'old Gardeners houses' were the tenement and laigh houses of which part of the tenement was made available to the tackholder of the Great Garden. The stones from the old houses were to be made available to the purchaser.[8] In November 1825, £10 was approved 'for a house for the gardeners tools' and the gardener was ordered to see that it was properly built.[9] At the same time, a committee was formed to oversee improvements in the College Garden and Observatory Park. The name of the gardener is not given, nor is the date of his appointment known, or whether he was full- or part-time. These events in Faculty rather suggest a re-awakening of interest in the gardens. In October 1826, £1/6/3d was allowed for the purchase of manure,[10] and in November 1827 an account from the merchants Austin & McAslan for plants costing £3/15/6d was presented by the gardens committee.[11] In October 1828, the gardener was allowed to buy '12 carts of dung for the College Garden and a wagon of coals to be used in the house for keeping the gardeners tools'.[12] It seems unlikely that the coal was for keeping the tools warm

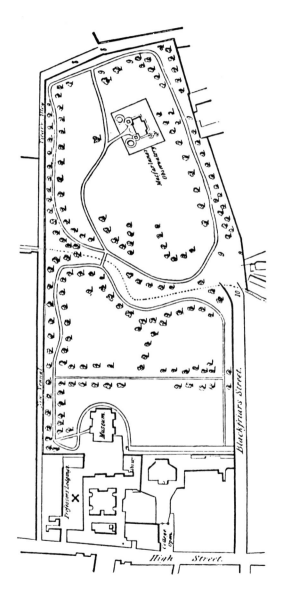

Figure 9.1. Roads surrounding the College lands in 1832

and dry. The so-called house was probably more of a small bothy, allowing some daytime creature comforts for the gardener in the winter months.

Few records of plant purchases are available for the period, but an 1830 account, again from Austin & McAslan, lists tools and plants:[13]

	s.	d.
1 Draw hoe 8 in	1	4
1 Scythe	5	0
1 Scythe Sned	4	6
2 Hand shovels	8	6
1 Scythe Stone	0	6
1 Garden Line	1	6
1 Pair Hedge Shears	5	0
1 Hand Saw	5	3
1 Hammer	2	3
1 Spade	5	0
12 Large Beech	2	0
24 Large Willows	2	0
50 Strong Thorns	1	0
74 Indian Cress		
60 Hardy Annuals	5	2
Wallflowers	3	0
4 Mignonette	2	8
Sweet Williams	1	0
25 Strong Crabs	1	0
2 Standard Plums	1	6
4 Lilac	1	0
Cowslip	0	11
Convolvulus	0	11
White Clover Seed	2	3

An account from John Walker, dated 17 May 1831, contains a mixture of domestic and garden requirements, the latter being 120 poplar trees (£1/14/-) and birch besoms (£1/10/-). The lengthy list of plants from Austin & McAslan suggests that planting of borders and of some walks was taking place — either in spite of or because of the environmental changes in the immediate neighbourhood. It is unfortunate that the nature of the hardy annuals is not disclosed. There does seem to be some emphasis on herbaceous border plants, of which the Indian Cress (*Tropaeolum polyphyllum*) is perhaps the most unusual. Hedge-plant replacements were still being sought, as shown above by the order for 'thorns' and 'crabs'. An account from Cowan & Co of the 'Clydehuagh Nursery, one mile on Paisley Road', dated 21 April 1826 was for '20 strong Elms, 5/6d; 2 Flowering Thorns, 2/6d'.[14] Elms, beeches and willows seem to have been the principal tree purchases. Limes are not mentioned.

The precise status of the gardener remains uncertain in the official records of the time. On 1 May 1832, the Faculty directed that the Principal was 'to appoint a fit person to act as Gardener in the College Garden during the ensuing summer and generally manage the garden according to his directions'.[15] From a minute of a November meeting in the same year we know that this gardener's weekly wage was 11/- in the summer, and that he was to be retained over the winter at 9/- per week.[16] These were temporary appointments and are not recorded in detail every year. A Faculty decree of 4 April 1837 required that 'a proper person as Gardener [be] appointed from the 1st May'.[17] Occasional purchases of surrounding land to increase the area of the gardens are recorded. On 2 November 1832, a purchase price of £555 for some 'subjects' — houses and ground at the foot of the College Garden and in the Dovehill (this last an old name long since discarded) — was approved by Faculty.[18] The 'subjects' included the old tanwork opposite the angle-foot region on the southeast side of the College Garden — the same tanwork whose effects on the Molendinar Burn became the subject of litigation in February 1772 (p. 168). The general state of the gardens came up for discussion again in March 1838, and another committee was formed 'to consider the state of the College garden and that the planting of a few trees would improve its appearance'.[19] The committee was instructed to inspect the garden and report back in due course — but, according to the Faculty records, it never did so.

With the year 1840 we enter a decade in which a number of significant changes were set afoot. The first of these concerns the Botanic Garden in the Sandyford area. It was earlier shown that the opening of this garden in 1819 just preceded the 1820 appointment of William Jackson Hooker to the Regius Chair of Botany in the University, and that the garden became the perfect setting for his activities. The 20-year period saw Glasgow emerge as a major botanical centre, for which Hooker's energy and drive were to be mainly responsible. His life in the University was not an easy one; he was subject to some petty and irritating restrictions and manoeuvrings on occasions, and there was some envy on the part of a few colleagues over the popularity of his lectures. His leaving the University was to some extent as controversial as his arrival and inauguration. On leaving to take up his Kew directorship in 1841, Hooker informed the Secretary of State for Scotland of his resignation, but did not inform the Senate or Faculty. His successor, John Hutton Balfour, had his commission of appointment read on 11 October 1841, at which Senate meeting it was minuted 'that the Senate should, previous to receiving the Commission, have received a formal resignation from Sir William Jackson Hooker'. Hutton Balfour was not to have the facilities of the Sandyford Botanic Garden. As already mentioned, the Directors of the Royal Botanic Institute, looking to the future, had decided that the 8-acre site would in time be too small, and expansion would be difficult in an area already proving popular for residential development. They purchased, in 1840, some 22 acres of ground lying on the northwest of the city, at that time outside the city boundary, the cost of the land being £200 per acre. The Sandyford site was sold for £1500 per acre.

Hutton Balfour became deeply involved in the planning and layout of this new garden, which was opened in 1842. Joseph Paxton, engaged as architect, was knighted in later years and was architect for the Crystal Palace. What the new garden lacked was a lecture room — the facility which had proved so valuable at the Sandyford garden. The supply of plants for Balfour's classes was continued, as was also the opportunity for students to visit the gardens and inspect plants, but from the time of the closure of the Sandyford garden the Professor of Botany had to use a room in the College for his lectures, and this room seems not to have been entirely satisfactory. A Faculty minute of 20 December 1844 advised that 'a fire [be] kept in the Room granted to the Professor of Botany for the preservation of the herbarium in consequence of its dampness'.[20] Hutton Balfour resigned from the Chair on 10 December 1845, following his appointment to the Chair of Botany at Edinburgh in succession to Robert Graham. George Arnott Walker Arnott's Commission of appointment to the Glasgow Chair was read on 11 December 1845, and he was to remain in office until his death in May 1868. During Balfour's last year the Faculty drew attention to the lack of teaching facilities in the new 22-acre garden, with the decision to 'instruct their representatives at the Botanic Garden to take the proper steps for maintaining the Claim of the College to a Classroom in the Gardens'.[21] The steps taken were ineffective. A lecture room for the University in the new garden was not to be forthcoming. The state of affairs is well expressed in the Glasgow University Calendars over the years. That for the 1829-30 session (in Hooker's time), outlining the Botany course and briefly describing the Sandyford garden and lecture room, concludes: '... the collection of plants, from the zeal and ability of the Superintendent, and the favourable situation of Glasgow, has become one of the richest and most valuable in the island'.[22] The Calendar for the 1845-6 session contains the identical account of the course and the description of the Sandyford garden as above, continuing '... most valuable in the island. Unfortunately however, the extension of the town again compelled the removal of the garden to a greater distance from the College, so that the Professor, whilst he visits it frequently with his students, finds it more convenient for all purposes, that his lectures should be delivered in the College'.[23] Evidently Arnott was quite happy to lecture in the College, despite the Faculty recommendations of 1 May 1845.

Andrew Dickson was appointed Professor of Botany in 1868 and was in office when the University removed to the new site at Gilmorehill. He preferred to lecture in the new University buildings, as can be seen in the 1872-3 Session Calendar entry:[24]

... as the extension of the town again compelled the removal of the Garden to a greater distance from the College, so that the Professor, whilst he continued to give in it the practical portions of the course (demonstrations) of late years has found it more convenient to deliver his *lectures* in the College, and even now, although the College has moved westward, so as to be comparatively near the Ground, yet the greatly superior Class-room accommodation in the College and the convenience of students who have other classes to attend, shall render it desirable, if not absolutely necessary, that the lectures be delivered there.

From these two entries we may conclude that from 1845-79, in which latter year Dickson resigned on his appointment to the Edinburgh Chair (the third such move since 1820!), there was no real desire on the part of the two Professors to have teaching facilities in the new garden, which with the removal of the University in 1870 would have been 15 minutes' walking distance from Gilmorehill.

Isaac Bayley Balfour, son of John Hutton Balfour, succeeded Alexander Dickson in the Glasgow Chair in 1879. His views on the role of the Botanic Garden are expressed in the Calendar entry for the 1880-1 sessions. Whilst quoting the history of the garden as in all previous entries, he concludes: 'It would be desirable, if the accommodation in the Botanic Garden permitted it, that the systematic lectures as well as the practical demonstrations should be given in the Garden, that the Botanical Laboratory should be established there also, and that the Herbarium and Museum should be lodged alongside the classroom'.[25] Bayley Balfour pursued his intentions with zeal, but ultimately to no effect. With his plans well formulated in his mind, he drew up a scheme for a lecture room, museum, herbarium and laboratory to be built in the new garden at a cost of £8000. It is unfortunate that these plans are no longer available; they would constitute a valuable commentary on the teaching requirements of one who at the time was a progressive and inspiring teacher of botany. When the scheme for the lecture room etc. in the garden fell into abeyance, he turned to a large house close to the garden as the seat of his proposed teaching and research activities, again without success. The house was to become the home of Queen Margaret College, the first women's teaching institution in the University, and at the present day is the headquarters of BBC Scotland.

A reminder is necessary here that the University, besides its concern for adequate teaching facilities, had also entered into a business contract with the Royal Institution. The Directors of the Botanic Garden had seemingly from the beginning been faced with financial problems. Whilst the sale of the Sandyford garden had been with a good profit, this was swallowed up in the laying out of the new 22-acre site. The University was naturally concerned that these financial problems should not prove too much of a drain on its own resources.

The draft of a memorial from the Faculty to the Lords Commissioners of Her Majesty's Treasury, written at some time in 1846, is available.[26] In this the memorialists first review briefly the history of the Royal Institution and the gardens, carefully stressing the Crown support (as defined in the Royal Charter of 20 September 1818).[27] The memorial continues: '... That the garden is an essential appendage to the Chair of Botany, inasmuch without it the Professor is unable to impart that instruction which his Commission requires him to give to the Students attending the University of Glasgow and which is demanded by the Army and Navy to the Medical Boards. That the annual revenue has not been sufficient to pay the necessary expense of keeping up the garden in a state of efficiency and that unless some additional source of revenue is provided, the establishment must become totally unfit for the purpose of Science'.

The stress laid on the requirements of Government departments regarding medical education reads like mild psychological pressure. The main thrust of the memorial follows, however, when attention is drawn to the fact that the two botanic gardens in Scotland are both linked with Regius Professorships; but, whilst that at Edinburgh received £1000 per annum from the Government, and the garden at Glasnevin in Dublin also received £1000 yearly from the Government via the Royal Dublin Society, there was no annual grant for the Glasgow garden. The request was for an annual grant of £800-900 to help defray the yearly expenses of running the garden, which was described as 'well stocked with valuable plants from all parts of the world and admirably suited for instruction in botanical science: with extensive conservatories for the protection of the more rare and delicate specimens'. Lack of support from the citizens of Glasgow meant that the Directors had 'come under personal pecuniary obligations with one of the Banks in Glasgow'. Such an obligation would have included the University. It was then pointed out that without adequate financial support from outside sources the garden might have to be abandoned. The further extension of the city was likely to be westwards, and the 22 acres of open ground would be of the 'utmost consequence to the health and comfort of the inhabitants'. It was proposed that the garden might be made open to the public on certain days, but the concluding appeal was for 'a grant for keeping up the garden in such a state as will render it useful for the purposes of Science and enable the Professor of Botany to continue his practical demonstrating to the students of the University of Glasgow'.

The outcome of this memorial is not recorded. In fact the garden's debts steadily increased. The Senate minutes for 14 December 1860[28] record a discussion regarding a letter from the Directors of the Botanic Garden asking for help to pay off their debts. This letter also offers some explanation of why a lecture room was not part of the new garden from the beginning. At the time of the sale at Sandyford the Royal Institution was already £6000 in debt, and, despite the profits on the sale of the Sandyford garden, after the laying out of the new garden they were then £7000 in debt. The lecture room was not built simply through lack of money; the annual balance of income and expenditure was insufficient to pay the interest on the accrued debts. Whilst the Senate was sympathetic to the plight of the Directors, it was felt that the financial position of the University did not favour any assistance being given, but the suggestion was made that the Directors themselves write to the University Commissioners.[29] In March 1863, however, the Senate agreed to lend the Directors £8000.[30]

Bayley Balfour's motives in seeking to lecture, hold practical classes, and carry out his own research in the Botanic Garden were straightforward enough. He wanted to have at Glasgow the counterpart of what was already established at Edinburgh. He also wanted the Botanic Garden, whilst not owned by the University, to become a more integral part of its scientific activity. He was not helped by the seeming lack of real interest in these directions over some 34 years by his two predecessors. Balfour left Glasgow in 1884 on his appointment to the Chair of Botany at Oxford. His successor was Frederick Orpen Bower, who came to Glasgow (to his own great surprise) in April 1885;[31] he was to occupy the Regius Chair until 1925. Bower's views on the role of the Botanic Garden in the life of the University were identical with those of Balfour. Within weeks of his appointment Bower was to find himself embroiled in Botany Garden problems. The Royal Botanic Institution was now in debt to the Town Council of Glasgow to the sum of £43,000. In July 1885 Bower received intimation that the Council were to 'call up' their loan the following Martinmas. He was faced with the possibility of the demise of the Garden, there being no guarantee that the Council would take over its running. Bower publicly stated his position in an inaugural lecture to the Faculty of Medicine on 27 October 1885.[32] His main theme was that 'The City of Glasgow now has the fate of the Botanic Garden on its hands' and were the Council to take over the garden it could 'raise from the ruins of the old Botanic Institution an establishment worthy of a great city and an ancient seat of learning'. He went on to stress that any future development of botany in the University would be linked inextricably with the continued survival of the Botanic Garden.

Whilst Bower's address was received with boisterous approval by the assembled medical students, its reception outside the University was not entirely one of approval. The address was fully reported in the local press, and some editorial comments questioned the need of the University for the Garden when only some occasional visits by a few medical students were all that was required. A few shareholders of the Institution also viewed the address with suspicion, seeing it as a covert move by the University to have a much greater say in the running of the Garden after its takeover. The city eventually took over the Garden on 31 March 1887, with Bower still holding hard to his plans and working behind the scenes in attempts to obtain closer physical links with the University. In fact he seems to have held on to his hopes that the scheme as originally envisaged by Bayley Balfour in 1879 would materialise, hopes which were finally dashed in February 1894. Then the Botanic Garden Committee of the City Council informed the University that it could not guarantee the permanency of the Botanic Garden on its site, and hence no buildings or teaching facilities could be considered. The Botanic Garden remains today on its 1841 site, and, whilst the physical linkage sought by Bayley Balfour and Bower has never come about, a close and happy association exists between it and the Botany Department of the University.

This lengthy account and review of the early association of the University with the two Botanic Gardens of the Royal Institution commenced with the removal of the Garden to the new site in 1841-2. We return to this time in a further examination of events concerned with the College gardens. A last link with the old Physic Garden came in November 1848,[33] when Faculty discussed the condition of the old type foundry and formed a committee to examine it and to report back, but no further report is available. As already described, in August of that year the Royal Assent was given to an Act under which the College was to exchange its buildings and land for 'a new College upon an improved scale on a site in the property of Woodlands',[34] to be built by the Glasgow, Airdrie and Monklands Railway Company. The company also undertook to make a major contribution to the building of a new hospital on the south side of the new College. The decisions leading up to the granting of the Royal Assent were entirely those of the Faculty — not of the entire professoriate. The proposed changes were to fall through because of a national 'slump,' although the University received £12,700 in compensation from the company's wish to clear itself of any obligations. The University had to resell the site chosen for the new hospital, but by careful investment was able to make a fair profit overall from the affair. The proposed removal of 1846, however, met with the combined resistance of the medical professors, including in their number Walker Arnott. In a letter addressed to the two judges who, at the direction of the House of Lords, were examining the Faculty's proposition, the medical professors pointed out that the decisions taken were not those of all the professoriate. The reasons put forward by the Faculty for the proposed removal were the insalubrious and disagreeable nature of the College's situation; that the habits of those residing around the College were potentially injurious to the morals of the students; and that the site would not allow for further adequate extension, and that the old buildings were now in need of extensive repairs, far more than could be afforded.

Regarding the first of the above reasons, the medical professors (stressing their professional expertise in the matter) pointed out that the rate of student mortality did not exceed the 'standard' and that disease was no more prevalent among them than was usual. They also referred to the remarkable longevity of the professors who were members of

Faculty, and who resided and taught in the College for most of the year. The signatories considered that student morals did not present a problem, since Glasgow students were so well disciplined and showed at all times correct conduct — and in any case any immoral influences which did exist would not disappear with the College being removed 2 miles westward. The view that the site did not allow of further extension was countered by the argument that such venerable buildings should be treasured, and not converted into a railway station (which did happen after the removal of 1870). Reference was also made to the 27 acres of ground available at the High Street, which formed a background to the venerable buildings. A further medical reason for opposing the move, and the building of a new hospital, was the proximity of the College to the Royal Infirmary, a few hundred yards to the north. This was a hospital with 400 beds and 'holding the very first rank in reference to the number of severe injuries and diseases of every description that are treated within its walls': a situation entirely suited to the training of physicians. A further 'dig' at the members of Faculty was made with reference to the apparent desire of some of its members to 'exchange their present accommodation in the College buildings for more elegant residences near the most fashionable quarters of Glasgow'. Whilst the removal proposed for 1846 did not materialise, the arrangements over the affair set the scene for later deliberations in the 1860s which led to the migration to Gilmorehill. By this time the decisions were those of the Senate, which included all the professors, some of whom had been among those responsible for the negotiations of 1846.

Public access to the gardens had always been limited. According to a personal memorial in a history of the University, the Faculty opened the College grounds to the public in the summer of 1850, offering, according to a contemporary advertisement, 'fourteen acres of undulating and beautifully wooded ground ... for the innocent recreation and amusement of citizens'.[35] The opening ceremony was on 1 June in that year, and took place before some 20,000 spectators. Some 2,000 juvenile teetotallers marched with bands from the Gorbals to the grounds, and the band of the 21st Regiment of Foot provided music within. There was a firework display in the evening. The Principal and assembled Faculty members welcomed the people and were thanked by a Baillie representing the Corporation. As a boy, the memorialist himself had been taken to the gardens on one evening that summer by his parents. Much seems to have been made of the liberality of the Faculty in opening the grounds in this way, which was allowed only that one summer. The Faculty minutes tell a somewhat different story. In March 1850 consideration was given to an application by a Mr MacLaws, merchant in Glasgow, to lease the College grounds for the five months from May to September 'as a place of exercise and amusement for the working classes and engaging to take such precautionary measures as to prevent damage to the College property and Grounds'.[36] A committee was then formed to discuss the proposal, and two weeks later its members reported to Faculty their satisfaction with MacLaws's arrangements regarding prevention of damage.[37] The Faculty, whilst reserving the right to put a stop to all proceedings should anything untoward occur, expressed willingness 'to give Mr MacLaws philanthropic scheme a trial'. From the earlier personal account, we know that a small entrance fee was charged. On 1 November 1850, the Faculty was read another letter from MacLaws.[38] In this he explained that his summer project had not proved profitable and he suggested that the College should meet, in part or in whole, half of the rent charged. The Faculty refused to give consideration to such an arrangement — the idea for the opening had come from MacLaws and the negotiating committee had warned him of the uncertainty of the whole undertaking. There were no grounds for any rent remission, but MacLaws was given twelve months to pay off his debts. The financial realities somewhat belie the apparent liberality of the opening ceremony, and it is all too apparent why the summer opening of the grounds of 1850 was not repeated.

That boy mentioned above who was taken to the College grounds on an evening in the summer of 1850 became a student in 1857.[39] His memories were of the two parts of the College grounds being in grass, the western section, the College Garden or Green, with many 'excellent walks', and with the eastern section, called the Observatory Park in previous years, being reached by a bridge over the covered Molendinar Burn. Football could now be played on the College Green, and cricket on a levelled area on the top of the Observatory Park. The Observatory itself had been moved from the Park to a new site in the west of the city in 1845, but the empty building remained. The young student noticed also that the numerous trees on both parts of the ground were suffering badly from the deposition of Glasgow's soot. These trees of the 1850s would have been an inheritance of the extensive plantings towards the end of the previous century under the supervisions of Alexander Adams and Robert Lang.

Student access to the Observatory Park in the 1850s came as a result of the last major operation undertaken by the Faculty with regard to the College Garden. In the earlier chapters there have been frequent references to cleaning out the Molendinar Burn and rebuilding its banks. The College Garden on its east side tended to slope down towards the burn, and suffered occasional flooding as a result. In November 1850 there came before Faculty a proposal from a contractor, who was to be engaged in dredging in the River Clyde above the Stockwell Street Bridge, and who offered the dredged soil to the College with a view to raising the level of the garden where it bordered the burn.[40] A committee to oversee this relevelling was formed in April 1851.[41] One result of these operations was that the College Green was no longer in a suitable condition for student recreation during the following session, and it was decided in October

1851 that the 'Old Observatory Park' would be opened for that purpose.[42] Once opened to the students in this way, the Old Observatory Park was to remain available to them. The whole operation of ground-raising during the summer and autumn of 1851 was reported in detail to the Faculty in November 1853.[43] The ground was first surveyed by Mr John Thomson CE, and from this survey it was found that the channel of the Molendinar Burn was no more than 1–1½ feet below ground level for some distance along its length, particularly in the southern part. A hollow in the neighbouring ground existed at one point which prevented the escape of water from the Green into the burn after heavy rain (the annual problems of drainage in the garden are frequently referred to in earlier chapters). This hollow was in that part used for playing football and on occasions contained 'a considerable accumulation of stagnant water of dangerous quality due to reflux from the Molendinar'. The nature of this standing water can be visualised from the discrete comment, and would seem to re-echo the views of the poetic medical student quoted on an earlier page. This inundation of sewage-laden water probably represents the danger reported by a University historian (p. 265), although he seems to have confused the cricket pitch with the football field.

The ground-raising operations were supervised by Mr J. Thomson, and the intention was to raise the ground level in the lowest regions to not less than 5 feet above the channel of the Molendinar and to produce a declivity over the whole surface from west to east and north to south 'sufficient to allow of its being properly surface drained'. It was a sizeable reconstruction. A total of 17,050 cartloads of soil and ashes was brought into the garden between 15 May and 1 November at an average rate of 109 carts per day. The College Green was serving as a repository for dredged soil from the river bed and ashes from various sources, and the several contractors *paid the University* 1½d per cartload for bringing it to the grounds, so raising £106/5/8d. Outgoings included £58/10/6d for labourers from May to November, £10 for soil and ashes, £5/10/7d for masons working on the banks of the burn, £2 for tools and £15 for surveying and superintendence. The balance remaining came to £10/2/7d. Some trees in the lower part of the garden suffered some damage from partial burial. Some unequal subsidence was seen in the spring of 1852, so that further importations of soil were necessary. With advice from a local seedsman, a Mr Lawson, the new ground was sown with barley seed and dressed with guano, from which treatment a 'sufficient crop' was obtained in the first year; and, despite some bare patches, the supervising committee were satisfied that a good solid turf would be obtained on the 'playground'. The seed cost £10/15/-, so that overall receipts and outgoings just about balanced. A further approach to the Faculty from without came in March 1852 requesting again the opening of the grounds to the public in the summer, but it was decided that this proposal 'cannot be considered with the present state of the garden'.[44]

The individuals interested in promoting the lease of the grounds made a second application a few weeks later, but the Faculty was more concerned about getting the Green into a suitable condition for student recreation in the following season, and the application was refused.[45]

The value of clay strata in the grounds and the varied responses of the Faculty to applications by potential users have been commented on in earlier pages. In July 1852 Messrs Allen & Mann, brickmakers, offered Faculty £300 per annum for the lease of the 'upper green of the Observatory Park for working out the clay contained in it for a limited number of years'.[46] This proposal evoked some interest, but it was decided that expert advice and valuation of the clay would be obtained first and then the field would be publicly advertised. Later on in the year, presumably following the 'expert' advice, it was decided that 'it would be inexpedient to enter into any agreement at the present time'.[47] Since the Observatory Park was now available for student recreation it is possible that this usage was given first consideration, although the 'upper green' may refer to land called 'Clayfields'. In February 1853 it was decided to dismantle and remove the old Observatory building, which had stood empty since 1845.[48] Over the remaining five years of the Faculty's rule, the gardens are scarcely mentioned. A seedsman's bill for 17/4d was authorised in November 1855,[49] and in October 1856 a committee was formed to employ a 'competent person' to inspect the gardener's house and report, which implies that a gardener was still employed.[50]

From contemporary accounts we are left with a sad picture of the once attractive grounds in the 1860s. The 'bird's-eye view' of 1864 (Figure 9.2) shows the College buildings and grounds and the dense housing around its perimeter. Whilst some walks and a few trees are visible in the College Garden, a denser tree cover is to be seen on the east side where it joins the Observatory Park. This tree cover probably represents the remains of the planting programmes of Alexander Adams and Robert Lang in the later years of the previous century, in what was the angle-foot and burnside walks region. The Molendinar Burn had been covered over at some time between 1852 and 1857. We are left with the eye-witness's description of soot-laden trees to go with the bird's-eye view. A Highland Games was held in the College Garden in 1867.[51] It is rather sad that the last official reference to the work of a gardener in the Old College Garden should be one stressing the inefficiency of an unnamed individual. At the meeting on 26 September 1861 of the now ruling Senate, a number of professors voiced their dissatisfaction with the neglected state of the garden. Thomas Barclay was now Principal, having been appointed in 1858, and was to be in post at the time of the removal of the University in 1870. The Senate requested that Barclay should 'call the Gardener before him and warn him that he is required to devote *all* his time to keeping the College walks and grounds in proper order and that any neglect of duty in future shall be visited with instant dismisal from

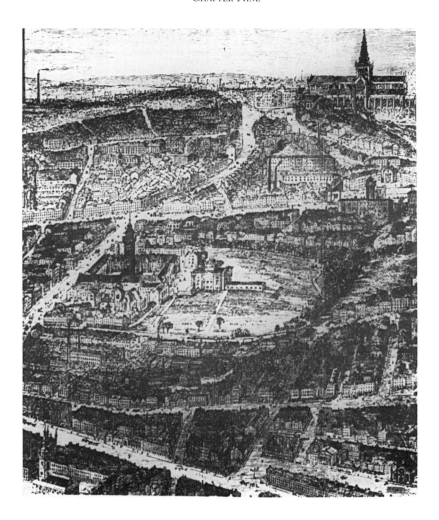

Figure 9.2. 'Bird's-eye view' of the University buildings, grounds and surroundings in 1864

office'.[52] To have been 'on the carpet' before the Principal seems to have had very little effect on this unknown gardener. On 29 October next, the Principal reported that 'the Gardener had continued to absent himself from work, and the Factor had been instructed to inform him that his services were no longer required'.[53]

In place of the sacked gardener a John Cross was temporarily appointed on the recommendation of the Clerk to the Botanic Garden, and Cross was already in post and endeavouring to 'bring the Green into proper Condition'. In December 1862 it was decided to erect a covered shed on the Green to protect the students in inclement weather.[54] The shed, open along one side, and built against the kirkyard wall on the west side of the garden, was 146 feet in length and 39 feet wide and cost £239. With a roof of corrugated iron it would scarcely have fitted in with the venerable College buildings. In November 1865 the 'Committee for the Green' decided to spend £10 on unspecified 'student's amusements'.[55] In February 1864 it was decreed by Senate that the gardener could in future have use of the cottage at the end of the Blackfriars Street where it joined the College Green. He was to have the cottage rent free from the next Whitsunday.[56] It is not known if this is the same cottage as the one erected in 1705–6.

The minor affairs of the gardens are insignificant when compared with other major events in the life of the University in the 1860s. The removal envisaged in 1846 was followed in the next decade by Senate discussions which eventually resulted in the formation of the Commission whose report on the College buildings was to be a prime factor in initiating the 1870 removal.[57] The 26½ acres of grounds at the back of the Old College came to be regarded as prime land for industrial development, and in 1863 the City of Glasgow Union Railway Company offered £100,000 for the buildings and grounds. The last garden references to be found in the minutes of Senate meetings prior to 1870 are concerned with the Botanic Garden. The 22-acre site to which the Garden had been moved in 1841 was on a clay soil. In March 1865 the Senate voted £30 to cover the cost of some drainage work in the Botanic Garden, particularly in that part 'with a general collection of herbaceous plants and the Border around it with a collection of British plants'.[58] These plants were to be grown solely for the use of the Professor of Botany. These provisions seem to have created some resentment in the Garden, and in January 1866 the Senate agreed that the grant of money for drainage work should not have any pre-conditions, expressing confidence that 'the Directors will maintain such plants as are necessary for the instruction of students'.[59] As already mentioned, Alexander Dickson succeeded to the Regius Chair of Botany in the University on the death of Walker Arnott in 1868. At Dickson's request, the Senate agreed on 30 April 1869 that they would provisionally sanction a Garden Fee of 2/6d for each student attending the Botany class should he use the Garden, in order to ensure 'harmonious action with the Garden authorities'.[60] Do we detect some provision against possible bad behaviour on the part of students, who were usually allowed free access to the gardens?

With the departure of the University in 1870, the Old College grounds were in time to be engulfed by railway works and warehouses. A warehouse for the storage and ripening of bananas was said to have been erected almost on the site of the old Physic Garden — the garden in which William Hamilton successfully grew a banana tree in the

1780s. The venerable College building fronting on to the High Street was for some time converted into a railway terminal. By 1885, the bicentenary of Principal Fall's 1685 start on the enclosure of the Great Garden with a stone wall, little sign would have been left of its former glory. Fall's decree to make the garden 'regular and profitable for the Universitie' meant exactly what it says: to be regular in form, structure and harmony and profitable in its cash returns. The late-seventeenth century Faculty members were dependent mainly on the effectiveness of the tackholders for the maintenance of the regularity of the Great Garden. To some extent they could not lose. The tackholders were committed to pay an annual rental, usually in stages. To clear this tack duty, and to make some additional profit, tackholders of necessity had to cultivate and crop the plots for their sale of grass cuttings and to foster sound fruit crops. Mowing the grassed plots and walks was a repetitive and hard labour, and among the most frequent annual purchases of implements by the College over the years were scythes (blades), sneds (handles) and 'sharping' stones. The medieval gardens were for recreation and the supply of vegetables, fruit and eggs for the Common Table of the College. By the late 1600s the fruit trees were numerous, but the fruit was for the tacksmen in exchange for their proper care of the trees, including replacements whenever necessary. The espalier and standard fruit trees (apples, pears, cherries, plums, apricots), together with other trees and shrubs, were required to add to the attractiveness of the borders and walks — to be enjoyed by Faculty members and a select few aristocratic students. By the last quarter of the eighteenth century there was student access to parts of the Great Garden, whilst the professors still retained their reserved walks. As described elsewhere, the post-Reformation University was an academic society distinct, elitist and competitive, with its own special privileges and immunities, its own rules and dress.[61] The students were completely under the authority of the masters. Even when allowed to come into the garden they could only walk, not run nor play ball games. In the spring of 1783 James Wilson, a student, was observed leaping about in the garden. This gave rise to considerable professorial dissension — inevitably involving John Anderson and two of his colleagues — an affair which seems to have been blown up out of all proportion to the original offence.[62] Only towards the end of the garden's existence in the 1850s was full student recreation allowed.

The most noticeable change in garden management and maintenance as the eighteenth century progressed was the move away from reliance on tacksmen to more direct control by Faculty through their appointed gardeners, with hired labour when necessary. The grass crop, for which they still paid a token rent, became part of the annual salary of the gardeners. The plantings in the later years were predominantly of trees and flowering shrubs. In this way the professors may well have been reflecting a national trend: in late-eighteenth-century Scotland enthusiasm for tree-planting and for gardens, large and small, was to reach its peak.[63] Their wish was to make the angle-foot region, the burnside walks and the west side of the Observatory Park attractive wooded areas.

Those enjoying the amenities of the garden in the early decades of the following century owed much to the late-eighteenth-century Faculty committees and gardeners. The latter would have been appalled at the state of their garden in the 1860 period. Contemporary accounts indicate that the eighteenth-century College Garden was especially attractive, a place in which the professors could take their leisurely strolls along the tree-lined walks with a clover greensward underfoot, and admire the fruit trees, flowering shrubs and herbaceous annuals and perennials in the borders. For the more reflective members the garden would have resembled the 'paradise yards' of monastic institutions — symbols of repose and harmony.[64] Maybe Adam Smith did find its peaceful surroundings a help in formulating his lectures and essays. Certainly the mathematician Robert Simson found the walks the ideal environment for his carefully regulated strolls, and fought a successful battle to keep the ground soft for his feet. Samuel Johnson, however, seems not to have been impressed on his visit in October 1773, although his unfavourable comments referred mainly to the buildings.[65] The business sense of the many Faculty committees who managed the College Garden and the Dowhill (Dovehill or Observatory Park) during the eighteenth-century should not go unrecognised. They never missed the chance of making a profit, or at least breaking even, in their financial management. Nor at any time was anything wasted which could either be used again or turned to good account.

The story of the small Physic or Botanic Garden occupies about 100 years in the history of the University, and is essentially a chronicle of its waxing and waning. Started with considerable zeal and enthusiasm and a sizeable financial outlay for the times, its initial success can be attributed to the conscientious management of its first overseer, John Marshall. Nor can we ignore the support and advice he received from James Sutherland. The disappearance of the letters they exchanged, and of the lists of plants sent to Marshall by Sutherland from Edinburgh, is particularly to be regretted. The Physic Garden remains the first cogent means of botanical instruction in the University (we cannot be sure that Mark Jameson's specialised garden of the mid-sixteenth century was used at all by students from the College). A Lectureship in Materia Medica was established in 1766. There is no evidence of any association between the Physic Garden and the lecturers over the years. The University Physic Garden was not the only one in the town at the time. Dr John Wodrow, son of James Wodrow (Professor of Divinity 1692–1705), had his own private garden on a site to the south of the College, now occupied by St Andrew's Square. This garden received an annual grant from the Faculty of Physicians and Surgeons. Wodrow died in 1769. His garden would then have been under cultivation at the same time as that in the College. No evidence can be found of any correspondence between Wodrow and the Professor of Botany and Anatomy at the College, nor of any exchange of plants and seeds. There was, however, some rivalry between the Faculty of Physicians and Surgeons and the emerging school of the University; the lack of communication may be a manifestation of this competition. A Mrs Balmano, druggist, had her own herb garden in the Dearside Brae, which became Balmano Street, close to what is now the City Chambers.

What are our memories of those whose profession included the management of the Physic Garden? Thomas Brisbane's reputation is forever marred by the title 'inert'. We can allow some revision of this. Whilst undoubtedly failing in his duties regarding the teaching of anatomy, we can credit him with showing an active interest in the Physic Garden and presumably in the teaching of botany, at least during the first half of his tenure of the combined Chair. During the time of the joint governance by Robert Hamilton and William Cullen, we detect the first evidence that there were environmental problems. Their concern about the deleterious effects of soot and smoke on the Physic Garden plants was echoed by a similar anxiety at about the same time on the part of David Alston, Professor of Medicine and Botany at Edinburgh University, whose garden 'in 'Auld Reekie' was similarly affected by atmospheric pollution.[66] Concern about the clay soil was also expressed by Cullen, then a leading expert in Scotland on soil chemistry.

For all the forcibly expressed concern of Hamilton and Cullen, the Physic Garden remained on the same site. In 1762 the Faculty compounded the problem of pollution by building a type foundry in close proximity. This successful venture was twice expanded and it took the members of Faculty some 20 years to realise the extent of plant damage the fumes could cause. William Hamilton's energetic and competent management, supported as he was by two of the ablest gardeners to be appointed as College servants, may well have prolonged the life of the garden despite the inhospitable nature of its surroundings. The colourful James Jeffray inherited the same pollutant problems, which came to a head during the time of his protégé and assistant Thomas Brown, whose trenchant remark in 1806 on the state of the Physic Garden is sufficient commentary in itself. The waning process of the Physic Garden was a protracted one. Certainly William Hamilton's 1790 legacy of £200 to establish a new garden, whilst never becoming available, would seem a similar reflection on the state of the garden in his own time. Although the University in due course purchased two sites a couple of miles away from the High Street with a view to establishing a new Botanic Garden, there remained a curious and inexplicable inertia about launching the project. One can almost detect a note of relief in the official writings describing the negotiations prior to the establishment of the Sandyford garden of the Royal

Botanic Institution. With its creation the University gained a teaching facility far superior to any it had previously obtained. To Robert Graham, the first Regius Professor of Botany in the University, must go the credit for his role in helping organise this new garden. Do we detect a further manifestation of Faculty members versus 'the rest' (professors of Chairs created after 1761) in Graham not being made a Director of the new garden whilst Jeffray was?

With the arrival of William Jackson Hooker we enter a golden phase of Botany at Glasgow. Hooker could not be excluded from a Directorship of the Botanic Garden; his Commission terms ensured this. With his remarkable energy, drive and dedication to botany, the Botanic Garden became the ideal setting for his teaching and research. Its flora of 9,000 species in 1821 grew to 12,000 by 1825, largely through Hooker's management, assisted by the zeal of local citizens and an able Superintendent.[67] Hutton Balfour's tenure of the Glasgow Chair in succession to Hooker coincided with the Botanic Garden's removal to a new and larger site. But neither his successor Walker Arnott nor Alexander Dickson who followed Arnott seemed especially keen on making the new garden a centre for teaching and research as in Hooker's time. Isaac Bayley Balfour and F.O. Bower, despite their undoubted dedication and enterprise, came too late to effect any recovery in the matter: by the 1870–90 period, events regarding the fate of the Botanic Garden were moving too rapidly away from control by the University.

As this history of the lost gardens of Glasgow University draws to a close, it is fitting that our last memories should be of the gardeners — those whom the clown in *Hamlet* classed with ditchers and grave-makers as 'ancient gentlemen'. These 'ancient gentlemen', servants of the University, come down to us as names on accounts and precepts, less often as entries in official records, and in some cases by their own writings. Of those named we start with Adam Wilson, left languishing in the Tolbooth in 1692. How could he have hoped to get away with chopping down four trees? John Kennedy with his elaborate seventeenth-century-style signature, who for a short time was the first gardener with responsibility for the Physic Garden, and John Hume, who for 14 years worked under the supervision of John Marshall: between them they helped lay the foundations of the slow-to-emerge Glasgow medical school. John Nichol's brief appearance is a pertinent reminder of the harsh world of the time once the breadwinner was dead. We are left wondering why William Craig's work failed to come up to expectations, although we are in no doubt about his own recalcitrance and its result. William Galbraith's long service of 28 years up to the mid-eighteenth-century probably covers one of the best periods in the history of the small Physic Garden. This was also a period of replanning and replanting of the Great or College Garden, and here the role of James Loudon should not be forgotten. Many men were employed as hired labour at various times during this period.

How rigid was the distinction between the 'bredd' gardeners and the others, to whom the description 'workmen' was more frequently applied? From the nature of the operations they were called upon to perform, the 'workmen' were gardeners in every sense of the word. Certainly there was some distinction in the skill-value of the work done by each of these categories. The University was well aware of the advantages of offering 'extras', whether as cash for 'extra-ordinar' work (or overtime), or in the supply of drink money. The regular supplies of 'morning drinks' in the form of ale during the summer months, and ale and whisky (the latter but rarely) when cold, dirty jobs were done in the winter are all carefully documented in the accounts.

We are left with the distinct impression that Archibald Graham, who followed William Galbraith, was not so efficient as his predecessor, hence the veiled comments in the memorial of Robert Hamilton and William Cullen. If this is so, the University did little better in engaging as his successor Patrick Stevenson. What more can be said of Alexander Adams? One feels that in more fortunate circumstances he would have been successful in any profession, but his dedication to the general good of the University gardens as a whole was outstanding. How he would have regretted the overall decline in the grounds as seen just under 100 years from his time, a feeling which would have been shared by his successor Robert Lang. In addition to their University employment, both men worked hard — renting land for crop-growing and sale, shouldering all the attendant risks. Was this the reason for the early death of Robert Lang? From a contemporary illustration we can visualise the appearance of the late-eighteenth-century gardeners. Figure 9.3 shows Professor John Hope in the Edinburgh Botanic Garden being greeted by his Principal Gardener, probably John Williamson.[68] The main overall was an apron, often with a large pocket — a garment commonly worn by gardeners at the present day. The outer clothes — the coat, breeches, stockings and heavy boots — would have had to be strong and resistant. The implements the gardeners used would have been similar to those of the present day, but mechanical aids were things of the future.

William Lang was probably the best educated of the gardeners mentioned. He was unfortunate in being caught up in difficult circumstances. There was the limited usefulness of the University Physic Garden, by now in a poor condition, and the demands of an active and able teacher of botany. Lang's own knowledge of field botany seems to have been extensive, with the result that he was expected to collect the class material from far and wide. His maintenance of the College Garden suffered in consequence. To help support a young family of brothers and sisters, he rented land from the University and also attempted to go into business. The failure of this last venture and the attendant difficulties of keeping up with his contractural duties met with the inevitable result: dismissal, with all the implications this would have for a family living in a tied cottage.

Figure 9.3. A gardener greeting Professor John Hope in the Edinburgh Botanic Garden

One suspects that at 19 he was too inexperienced to take on the several occupations he attempted to maintain at one and the same time.

By the 1860s, there were probably few attractions to keep an able craftsman working with enthusiasm in a declining gardens situation. It is unfortunate that in 1861 the last Senate reference to a gardener prior to the University's removal in 1870 concerned one who was not named and who was clearly inefficient. Life in all its dimensions for eighteenth-century gardeners was undoubtedly hard, but at least they had some reward in making positive contributions in attractive and well-planned surroundings.

Notes

1. J.D. Mackie, 1953. *The University of Glasgow 1451–1951* (Jackson, Son & Co., Glasgow), p. 277.

2. D. Murray, 1927. *Memories of the Old College of Glasgow* (Jackson, Wylie & Co., Glasgow), p. 574.

3. J.D. Mackie, 1953. *The University of Glasgow*, pp. 269–78.

4. FM, 22 November 1822: 26698, p. 324.

5. FM, 17 December 1822: 26698, p. 327.

6. FM, 5 May 1823: 26698, p. 357.

7. FM, 15 May 1823: 26698, p. 359.

8. FM, 29 April 1825: 26698, p. 415.

9. FM, 25 November 1825: 26699, p. 7.

10. FM, 16 October 1826: 26699, p. 37.

11. FM, 2 November 1827: 26699, p. 93.

12. FM, 10 October 1828: 26699, p. 137.

13. GUAA 9300.

14. GUAA 58440.

15. FM, 1 May 1832: 26699, p. 217.

16. FM, 25 November 1832: 26699, p. 229.

17. FM, 4 April 1837: 26699, p. 331.

18. FM, 2 November 1832: 26699, pp. 255–6.

19. FM, 26 March 1838: 26699, p. 360.

20. FM, 20 December 1844: 26700, p. 156.

21. FM, 1 May 1845: 26700, p. 188.

22. Glasgow University Calendar, Session 1829–30, pp. 32–3.

23. Glasgow University Calendar, Session 1845–6, p. 35.

24. Glasgow University Calendar, Session 1872–3, p. 74.

25. Glasgow University Calendar, Session 1880–1, p. 85.

26. GUAA 1981.

27. GUAA G14.

28. SM, 14 December 1860: 26706, p. 102.

29. SM, 18 January 1861: 26706, p. 109.

30. SM, 13 March 1863: 26706, p. 231.

31. A.D. Boney, 1985. Appointment to a 'Crown' Chair of Botany: Glasgow 1885. *The Linnean* 1, pp. 19–26.

32. F.O. Bower, 1885. *Address at the opening of the medical session in the University of Glasgow, 27 October* (Maclehose & Sons, Glasgow), 20pp.

33. FM, 17 November 1848: 26701, p. 17.

34. J.D. Mackie, 1954. *The University of Glasgow*, p. 281.

35. D. Murray, 1927. *Memories of the Old College*, p. 418.

36. FM, 15 March 1850: 26701, p. 226.

37. FM, 29 March 1850: 26701, pp. 227–8.

38. FM, 1 November 1850: 26701, p. 251.

39. D. Murray, 1927. *Memories of the Old College*, p. 419.

40. FM, 29 November 1850: 26701, p. 259.

41. FM, 11 April 1851: 26701, p. 291.

42. FM, 31 October 1851: 26701, p. 306.

43. FM, 23 November 1853: 26702, pp. 34–6.

44. FM, 5 March 1852: 26701, pp. 349–50.

45. FM, 26 March 1852: 26701, p. 352.

46. FM, 30 July 1852: 26701, p. 356.

47. FM, 5 November 1852: 26701, p. 360.

48. FM, 4 February 1853: 26702, p. 10.

49. FM, 23 November 1855: 26702, p. 219.

50. FM, 29 October 1856: 26702, p. 288.

51. D. Murray, 1927. *Memories of the Old College*, figure opposite p. 420.

52. SM, 26 September 1861: 26706, p. 143.

53. SM, 29 October 1861: 26706, p. 145.

54. SM, 22 December 1861: 26706, p. 219.

55. SM, 20 November 1865: 26707, p. 46.

56. SM, 12 February 1864: 26706, p. 292.

57. J.D. Mackie, 1953. *The University of Glasgow*, pp. 281–2.

58. SM, 9 March 1865: 26707, p. 10.

59. SM, 11 January 1866: 26707, p. 62.

60. SM, 30 April 1869: 26707, p. 356.

61. J. Durkan and J. Kirk, 1977. *The University of Glasgow 1451–1577* (University of Glasgow Press), p. 347.

62. J. Coutts, 1909. *A History of the University of Glasgow* (James Maclehose & Sons, Glasgow), pp. 284–5.

63. W. Ferguson, 1968. *Scotland, 1689 to the Present* (Oliver & Boyd, Edinburgh), p. 173.

64. K. Thomas, 1983. *Man and the Natural World* (Allen Lane, London), p. 236.

65. J. Coutts, 1909. *A History of the University of Glasgow*, pp. 305–6.

66. H.R. Fletcher and W.H. Brown, 1970. *The Royal Botanic Garden Edinburgh 1670–1970* (HMSO, Edinburgh), pp. 57–8.

67. F.O. Bower, 1891. *On the Botanic Garden of Glasgow* (Presidential Address, 28 January 1891, of the Natural History Society of Glasgow).

68. Personal communication from Professor A.G. Morton.

Appendix

Thomas Brisbane's Commission of Appointment

'28th February 1720
George &/c.   To all and Sundry whom it effects for as much as we
taking to our Royal Consideration that the office of Professor of Botany
in our University of Glasgow is vacant by the death of Mr. John
Marshall late Botanist there and that supplying the same will much
lend to the Benefit and Improvement of the Students in the said
University and more especially of such as are willing to apply
themselves to the study of medicine withall and Considering how
necessary and useful it may be and a further Encouragement to them
that the Science of Anatomy be taught and profest within the said
University And We being desirous to give all suitable encouragement
to the publick seminaries towards the advancement of all virtuous and
Commendable knowledge. And being well Informed of the Abilities
and good Qualifications of Doctor Thomas Brisbane Doctor of
Medicine for discharging such trust. Therefore Will ye us to have
nominated and presented Likeas we by these presents nominate and
present the said Doctor Thomas Brisbane to be Professor and Teacher
of Botany and Anatomy in the said University of Glasgow during all
the days of his lifetime And to have and Enjoy all the powers and
privileges of a Professor of Medicine Or which may be competent to
any other Professor or Teacher in the said University with all the
Revenues profits and Emoluments belonging to the said professions of
Botany and Anatomy and particularly the sum of Thirty Pounds
Sterling yearly granted by Us to the professor of Botany By our Gift
under the privy Seal dated at St. James's the second day of April 1719
years as part of two hundred and ten pounds thereby appointed to be
payed yearly to the said University of Glasgow to commence from the
decease of the said Mr. John Marshall who dyed in the month of

September last. Requiring hereby the Rector, Principal, Dean and aye Professors and Masters of the said University to admit and Receive the said Dr. Thomas Brisbane to the peaceable Exercise and profession of the said Office and professions in the usual form. Given at our Court of St. James's and under our privy Seal of Scotland the thirteenth day of January Seventeen hundred and twenty years in the Sixth Year of Our Reign.'

INDEX